S0-BZW-845

UNDER THE SEA

Books by GARDNER SOULE

The Maybe Monsters
Tomorrow's World of Science
Gemini and Apollo
The Mystery Monsters
Trail of the Abominable Snowman
The Ocean Adventure
UFOs and IFOs
Under the Sea
Undersea Frontiers

UNDER THE SEA

A Treasury of Great Writing About the Ocean Depths

EDITED BY GARDNER SOULE

Meredith Press New York

First Edition

Library of Congress Catalog Card Number: 68-9516
MANUFACTURED IN THE UNITED STATES OF AMERICA FOR
MEREDITH PRESS

ACKNOWLEDGMENTS

MEN EXPLORE THE DEPTHS
"Exploring the Sea," by Jacques-Yves Cousteau, in *Industrial Research,* March, 1966.

THE FIRST COLLEGE CAMPUS ON THE BOTTOM OF THE SEA"
"High Learning Underwater," in *All Florida,* 1966.

"I LIVE IN A LITTLE HOUSE ON THE BOTTOM OF THE SEA"
Reprinted by permission of Coward-McCann, Inc., from *The Deepest Days* by Robert Stenuit; © 1966 by Robert Stenuit.

THE SEA'S BIGGEST GEOLOGICAL SPECIMEN
From Stewart's *Deep Challenge,* Copyright 1966, D. Van Nostrand Company, Inc., Princeton, New Jersey.

BREAKTHROUGH UNDER THE OCEAN
From *North Sea Oil: The Great Gamble,* by Bryan Cooper and Dr. T. F. Gaskel, William Heinemann Ltd., London, 1966.

MEN REACH OVER SIX MILES DOWN
Reprinted by permission of G. P. Putnam's Sons from *Seven Miles Down* by Jacques Piccard and Robert S. Dietz. Copyright © 1961 by Jacques Piccard and Robert S. Dietz.

THE DEEPEST DIVE HAD A HAIRY MOMENT
From *Time,* February 15, 1960.

AT LAST WE KNOW WHERE BERMUDA IS
From *Bermuda Mid-Ocean News,* September 19, 1964.
DIVE EIGHTY-FOUR INTO THE "SEA SNOW"
"Dive 84," by Eugene LaFond, in *Sea Frontiers,* May, 1962.
THE PORPOISE—MAN'S BEST FRIEND?
"Porpoise Is Studied for Ocean Secrets," *The Houston Post,* April, 1967
"Navyman's Best Friend: The Porpoise—Or Is it a Dolphin?" by Jim Teague, in *All Hands,* February, 1968.
MARINE GEOLOGY: WHAT WILL IT SHOW US?
Chapter XI of *Ocean Sciences,* edited by Captain E. John Long. Reproduced by permission from *Ocean Sciences.* Copyright © 1964 U.S. Naval Institute, Annapolis, Md.
THE WHALE THAT TALKED
"Whale Talk," by Ray Thomas, in *Boeing Magazine,* February, 1966.
HOW (TO TRY) TO CATCH A SEA MONSTER
"How (to Try) To Catch a Sea Monster," by Willard Bascom, in *Geo Marine Technology,* March, 1967.
THE BIGGEST SEA BEASTS
From *Sea Secrets,* January, 1962; April, 1963; December, 1963; December, 1964; February, 1965; April, 1965; October, 1966.
LONG LOST ATLANTIS—HAVE WE FOUND IT?
"Volcanoes and History or 'Atlantis' Revisited," by J. W. Mavor, Jr., in *Oceanus,* November, 1966.
CRABS TURN DARKER AT LOW TIDE
"Some Animals Exhibit Surprising Accuracy" by Margaret Biggerstaff, in the Palm Beach *Post-Times,* November 10, 1963.
THE BARNACLES THAT HITCHHIKE and THE MOST UNUSUAL SEAFOOD CHOWDERS
From *Crustaceans,* by Waldo L. Schmitt, the University of Michigan Press, Ann Arbor, 1965.
GREAT VOYAGE: THE *CHALLENGER*
From *UNESCO Courier,* November, 1954.
THE DAY WHEN OCEANOGRAPHY BEGAN
From *New Worlds of Oceanography* by Capt. E. John Long, Pyramid Publications, New York, 1965.
THE JUNGLE BENEATH THE SEA
From *The Edge of the Sea,* by Rachel Carson, Houghton Mifflin Company, Boston, 1965.
From *The Sea and Its Mysteries* by John S. Colman, W. W. Norton & Company, New York, 1950.
From *Zaca Venture,* by William Beebe, copyright 1938, by Harcourt, Brace and World, Inc.; renewed, 1966, by Elyswyth Thane Beebe. Reprinted by permission of the publisher.
THE GREAT BARRIER REEF
David Anderson in *POSH,* Spring, 1963.
HOW DID THE SALMON DO IT?
From *Sea Secrets,* October, 1966.

CAN WE EXPLAIN THE DEEP SEA RIVERS?
From *Abyss: The Deep Sea and the Creatures That Live in It,* by C. P. Idyll, Copyright © 1964 by C. P. Idyll. Reprinted by permission of the publishers, Thomas Y. Crowell Company, New York.
From *Sea Secrets,* April, 1963.
From *Frontiers of the Sea,* by Robert C. Cowen. Copyright © 1960 by Robert C. Cowen. Reprinted by permission of Doubleday & Company, Inc.
MEN HAUL UP A STRANGE NEW ANIMAL
"Pogonophora," by L. Zenkevitch, translated from the Russian by D. B. Carlisle, in *Oceanus,* September, 1964.
A MAN IMAGINED *NEOPOLINA* BEFORE WE KNEW IT EXISTED
From *Abyss: The Deep Sea and the Creatures That Live in It,* by C. P. Idyll. Copyright © 1964 by C. P. Idyll. Reprinted by permission of the publishers, Thomas Y. Crowell Company, New York.
TWO THOUSAND SUNKEN TREASURE SHIPS
"Museum Will Blend Past, Present, Future," by Margaret Biggerstaff, in Palm Beach *Sunday Times,* October 13, 1965.
THE SUBMARINE CITY OF PORT and THE TUCKER TREASURE
From *History Under the Sea,* by Mendel Peterson, The Smithsonian Institution, Washington, D.C., 1965.
THE FIGHT WITH THE GIANT SQUID
From *Twenty Thousand Leagues Under the Sea,* by Jules Verne, Charles Scribner's Sons, New York, 1925.
MAN VERSUS OCTOPUS: OR, CHILD'S PLAY
From *We Chose the Islands* by Arthur Grimble. Reprinted by permission of William Morrow and Company, Inc. Copyright © 1952 by Sir Arthur Grimble.
THE SUBMARINE MOVES DEEPER
"A Time of Change," in *Geo Marine Technology,* March, 1967.
THE HIGHEST WAVE MEN HAVE SEEN
"Great Sea Waves," by Ross P. Whitemarsh from August 1934 *Proceedings.* Reprinted from *Proceedings* by permission; Copyright © 1934 U.S. Naval Institute.
THE HIGHEST WAVE MEASURED BY INSTRUMENTS
L. Draper in *Oceanus,* June, 1964.
MEN IN GLASS BUBBLES TO SURVEY THE DEPTHS
New York World-Telegram & Sun, November 10, 1965.
FOOD FOR ALL MANKIND
Charles Butler and John A. Holston, in *Oceanology International,* October 15, 1966.
NEXT? CITIES IN ROCK BENEATH THE SEA FLOOR
John R. McCabe, in *Rocketeer,* November 25, 1966.
WHALE FARMS AND SEABED HOTELS
Lee Edson, in *Petroleum Today,* Winter, 1967.

For Carl W. Ackerman

CONTENTS

WHAT MEN WHO KNOW SAY OF THE SEA 3

MEN EXPLORE THE DEPTHS 5

by Jacques-Yves Cousteau

SECTION I

THE OCEANAUTS: Men Live Beneath the Sea 17

MAN'S FIRST MONTH ON THE OCEAN FLOOR

from a National Geographic Society News Bulletin 18

THE FIRST COLLEGE CAMPUS ON THE BOTTOM OF THE SEA

from All Florida *magazine* 21

"I LIVE IN A LITTLE HOUSE ON THE BOTTOM OF THE SEA"—JON LINDBERGH

by Robert Stenuit 22

MEN AND A PORPOISE AT HOME ON SEA FLOOR

from a U.S. Navy News Release from Sealab II 40

NOW MEN CAN STAY IN THE OCEAN

by L. B. Melson 45

SECTION II

THE OCEAN PROSPECTORS: Men Obtain Great Wealth from the Sea 47

THE SEA'S BIGGEST GEOLOGICAL SPECIMEN

by Harris B. Stewart, Jr. 48

BREAKTHROUGH UNDER THE OCEAN
by Bryan Cooper and T. F. Gaskell 52

SECTION III
THE OCEAN ADVENTURERS: Men Cruise at Great Depths 61
NEWLY INVENTED SHIPS TRAVEL FAR BELOW
from a National Geographic Society News Bulletin 62
MEN REACH OVER SIX MILES DOWN
by Jacques Piccard 64
THE DEEPEST DIVE HAD A HAIRY MOMENT
from Time *magazine* 66

SECTION IV
THE OCEAN'S SURPRISES: Men Learn Some Amazing Things 69
WE FIND AN UNDERSEA GARDEN
by Don Seaver 70
AT SEA, JOHNS HOPKINS FINDS EARTH'S FOUR CORNERS 72
WE LOCATE A DROWNED ISLAND
from Columbia University News Office 74
WE MAP DOZENS OF UNKNOWN SEAMOUNTS
from U.S. Coast and Geodetic Survey 77
UNDERSEA SOUND HEARD ROUND THE WORLD
from Columbia University News Office 79
AT LAST WE KNOW WHERE BERMUDA IS
from the Bermuda Mid-Ocean News 82
WE MAP HATTERAS SUBMARINE CANYON
by Don Seaver 85

SECTION V
THE OCEAN'S FALSE BOTTOM: Just What Is the Deep Scattering Layer? 89
DIVE EIGHTY-FOUR: INTO THE "SEA SNOW"
by Eugene LaFond 90

SECTION VI
THE DIVERS' ASSISTANT: The Porpoise Helps Men in the Sea 97

THE PORPOISE—MAN'S BEST FRIEND?
from United Press International in The Houston Post 98
WHAT I'VE LEARNED ABOUT PORPOISES
by William B. Gray 100
NAVYMAN'S BEST FRIEND: THE PORPOISE—OR IS IT A DOLPHIN?
by Jim Teague in All Hands 102

SECTION VII
THE OCEAN'S MYSTERIES: In the Seas Are Many Riddles 113
WAS THERE AN EARTH-SHAKING ENCOUNTER?
from Columbia University News Office 114
DO TINY ANIMALS DIE WHEN EARTH'S POLARITY CHANGES?
from National Science Foundation 116
HOW DOES THE SEA CHANGE ITS LEVEL?
from the Scripps Institution of Oceanography 118
WHAT HAPPENS TO THE SEA AROUND ISLANDS?
from the Scripps Institution of Oceanography 120
CAN WE FIND TWO MISSING "MICROCONTINENTS"?
from the Department of Commerce, Environmental Science Services Administration 122
DID THE CONTINENTS DRIFT APART?
from a National Geographic Society News Bulletin 126
OR HAVE THE CONTINENTS STAYED IN THEIR PLACES?
from the Lamont Geological Observatory 127
MARINE GEOLOGY: WHAT WILL IT SHOW US?
by Maurice Ewing in Ocean Sciences 130

SECTION VIII
THE OCEAN MONSTERS: We Study Biggest Animals in the Sea 149
WE FIND OUT HOW THE SHARKS FIND US
from the National Science Foundation and the University of Miami 150

THE WHALE THAT TALKED
by Ray Thomas in Boeing Magazine 153
HOW TO (TRY TO) CATCH A SEA MONSTER
by Willard Bascom in Geo Marine Technology 156
THE BIGGEST SEA BEASTS 160

SECTION IX
THE LEGEND OF ATLANTIS: Are We Writing an End to Plato's Tale? 173
LONG-LOST ATLANTIS—HAVE WE FOUND IT?
by J. W. Mavor, Jr. 174

SECTION X
THE OCEAN'S DENIZENS: We Learn Some Amazing Things about Animals 183
EVERY FISH MAKES A NOISE
from Naval Research Reviews 184
CRABS TURN DARKER AT LOW TIDE
by Margaret Biggerstaff in the Palm Beach Post-Times 186
WHY THE TUNA NEVER STOPS SWIMMING
from the Bureau of Commercial Fisheries Biological Laboratory 188
THE BARNACLES THAT HITCHHIKE
by Waldo L. Schmitt in Crustaceans 193
THE MOST UNUSUAL SEAFOOD CHOWDERS
by Waldo L. Schmitt in Crustaceans 194

SECTION XI
THE OCEANOGRAPHERS: Men Aboard the *Challenger* Pointed the Way 195
GREAT VOYAGE: THE CHALLENGER
from the UNESCO COURIER 196
THE DAY WHEN OCEANOGRAPHY BEGAN
by E. John Long 199

SECTION XII
EYEWITNESSES IN THE DEPTHS: Men in the Sea Have Unique Experiences 203
THE JUNGLE BENEATH THE NEAREST SEA
by Rachel Carson; William Beebe; and others 204
THE GREAT BARRIER REEF
by David Anderson in Posh 208

SECTION XIII
PUZZLES OF OCEAN LIFE: There Are Fish and Monsters We Can't Catch 215
WE PREDICT THE FISHING
from the Bureau of Commercial Fisheries Biological Laboratory 216
WHERE ARE THE MISSING TUNA?
from the Bureau of Commercial Fisheries Biological Laboratory 220
THE ANTARCTIC MYSTERY OF THE FISH GRAVEYARD
from the National Science Foundation 221
SOLVED: THE MYSTERY OF THE TRACKS ON THE BOTTOM OF THE SEA
from Columbia University News Office 225
HOW DID THE SALMON DO IT?
from the Bureau of Commercial Fisheries in Sea Frontiers 227

SECTION XIV
THE RIVERS IN THE SEA: Scientists Tackle the Gulf Stream—and Others 229
CAN WE EXPLAIN THE DEEP-SEA RIVERS?
by C. P. Idyll; from Sea Secrets; *and by Robert C. Cowen* 230
DOES THE GULF STREAM HAVE A PULSE?
from a National Geographic Society News Bulletin 233
WE LEARN THE GULF STREAM ACTS "LIKE A LIVING THING"
by Raymond Wilcove, U.S. Coast and Geodetic Survey 236

SECTION XV
THE OCEAN'S NEWLY FOUND ANIMALS: We Discover Some Unknown Creatures 241
MEN HAUL UP A STRANGE NEW ANIMAL
by L. Zenkevitch in Oceanus 242
THE UNKNOWN FISH WITH THE MONOCLE
by Jane Wood 244
ON THE DEEP-SEA FLOOR WE CAPTURE OLDEST SPECIES
from Columbia University News Office; by C. P. Idyll 246

A MAN IMAGINED NEOPILINA BEFORE WE KNEW IT EXISTED
by C. P. Idyll 249

SECTION XVI
SUNKEN TREASURE: The Sea Around Us Is Full of It 251
TWO THOUSAND SUNKEN TREASURE SHIPS?
by Margaret Biggerstaff and Charles Harnett in the Palm Beach Sunday Times 252
THE SUBMARINE CITY OF PORT ROYAL
by Mendel Peterson 253
THE TUCKER TREASURE
by Mendel Peterson 260

SECTION XVII
"THINGS EAT ON YOU": Squid May Hurt—Octopuses Rarely Do 261
THE FIGHT WITH THE GIANT SQUID
by Jules Verne 262
MAN VERSUS OCTOPUS: OR, CHILD'S PLAY
by Sir Arthur Grimble 266
THE LATEST WORD FROM THE KINGDOM OF THE OCTOPUS 271

SECTION XVIII
NAVAL SUBMARINES: Some Amazing Ships and Surprising Escapades 279
THE SUBMARINE MOVES DEEPER
from Geo Marine Technology 280
"FASTEST, DEEPEST-DIVING, BEST-ARMED . . ."
by Matt McDade 281
OUR MISSILE BASES UNDER THE SEA
from General Dynamics 286

SECTION XIX
THE OCEAN WAVES: They Turn Out Even Taller than Sailor's Tales 291
THE HIGHEST WAVE MEN HAVE SEEN
by R. P. Whitemarsh in United States Naval Institute Proceedings 292

THE HIGHEST WAVE MEASURED BY INSTRUMENTS
by L. Draper in Oceanus 299
HOW A MONSTER WAVE CAN OCCUR
from Naval Research Reviews 300
NOW WE MAY MEASURE ALL THE OCEAN'S WAVES
from the Lockheed-California Company and New York University 301

SECTION XX
THE OCEAN'S FUTURE: The Sea Holds Many Possibilities for Man 303
MORE SOPHISTICATED SUBMARINES
from General Dynamics 304
WEATHER FORECASTS FROM THE OCEAN
from General Dynamics 306
MEN IN GLASS BUBBLES TO SURVEY THE DEPTHS
from the Associated Press 310
THE HYDRONAUTS: THE NEW NAVY BREED
from the Department of the Navy 311
FOOD FOR ALL MANKIND
by Charles Butler and John A. Holston in Oceanology International 313
A NUCLEAR SUBMARINE TO FOLLOW THE FISH
from the Bureau of Commercial Fisheries Biological Laboratory 321
NEXT? CITIES IN ROCK BENEATH THE SEA FLOOR
by John R. McCabe in Rocketeer 323
WHALE FARMS AND SEABED HOTELS
by Lee Edson in Petroleum Today 327

Index 335

Definition of Oceanography:
The study of the seas
and all that in them is

The depth of the sea is a new environment for man's exploration and development, just as crossing the West was a challenge to centuries past.

We shall encounter that environment with the same conviction and pioneering spirit that propelled ships from the Old to the New World.

—Lyndon B. Johnson in "Marine Science Affairs—A Year of Transition" (February, 1967), the first report in history of the President to the Congress on Marine Resources and Engineering Development.

UNDER THE SEA

WHAT MEN WHO KNOW SAY OF THE SEA

What men who know about the sea say about the sea—that is what this book is all about. Here, often in their own words, are adventures of the ocean explorers. Here are discoveries, including some of the latest, of the ocean scientists. Here are stories by eyewitnesses, among the first in all history, of what the depths and the bottom of the oceans are like. Those wonderful men in their new deep-diving machines are opening up earth's last, deep frontier—the seas that cover over seven tenths of the globe. "The sea," says Washington's Warren G. Magnuson, a United States Senator importantly concerned with oceanography, "contains complex forms of life yet unknown." In this book you will meet some of the more surprising of the ocean's known inhabitants. The seas, says Senator Magnuson, "have held in their dark depths multitudes of mysteries." You will learn how scientists and researchers and deep-divers have cleared up some of the mysteries. Yet many, many mysteries remain. You will read also of some of the ocean's riddles that still puzzle man.

MEN EXPLORE THE DEPTHS

JACQUES-YVES COUSTEAU, born in France in 1910, is the only man alive who does all three things: (1) prowls offshore depths of the sea as an aqualung diver; (2) designs and uses deep-diving submarines, the diving saucer and *Deepstar 4000;* and (3) designs undersea dwellings that men live in beneath the sea. In his Conshelf III (1965), men stayed and worked for three weeks 325 feet below the surface of the Mediterranean Sea. Cousteau, preeminent as an undersea explorer since with Emile Gagnan, in 1943, he had invented the aqualung, tells in the March, 1966, *Industrial Research* why men are today moving into the depths of the ocean:

The Oceans Always have raised formidable barriers to man's curiosity and understanding. Enormous distances and storms made early navigation uncertain and perilous. The sea was a hostile environment, where pressure, cold, and darkness discouraged or limited the diver. And even the fisherman, who draws his food from the deep, still is compelled to grope blindly—the only hunter who does not see or know his quarry. And even the oceanographer lowers his instruments more or less haphazardly, rather like an explorer setting out to discover a new continent with elaborate equipment and blindfolded eyes.

Seeing underwater—to understand and interpret what we are doing—is an obvious necessity. Only yesterday, it was an impossibility; today, it represents a conquest. Barely begun by aqualung divers, underwater vision has been furthered by the historic descent of the bathyscaphe *Trieste* to the very bottom of the Marianas Trench.

It now is technically possible for us to descend, to observe, and to take action at any level. I am not sure that we have realized this fact—I should say revolution—and it is clear that we are not prepared, psychologically, to take full advantage of it.

From the surface of the ocean to a depth of 40 meters (131 feet), there are 50 million cubic kilometers of "safe" water awaiting the aqualung diver. This is the sea's most living layer—where nearly all the plant life is produced by photosynthesis.

Life here obeys the alternation of day and night; it follows the rhythm of the seasons. At sunset, hosts of marine animals rise from depths as far down as 800 meters to come close to the surface and feed on microscopic algae or wage silent combat. At dawn, these intruders, fearing light for various reasons, disappear back into zones reached only by a dim glow.

Most of the time, seawater is clear. In the open sea, it is not unusual to find visibility of more than 60 meters. Here, sight is a vital and perhaps predominant sense. The diver, equipped with a face mask, can enjoy sight on equal terms with the fish. He feels reassured and at ease—often daring.

The crystal of the ocean waters turns milky in the spring, when the sea is in bloom. Along coasts battered by breakers and washed by tides, water often remains clear. But near harbors and estuaries, countless particles in suspension scatter the light, and at times divers cannot even see their own hands.

In these turbid waters filled with small grains of sand or alluvial material, many microorganisms die. Various species of algae and most corals cannot survive. But fish sometimes teem in these waters, either because of fear or hunger. Their eyes are of no use in such conditions, and other senses take over. The animals' lateral lines, for example, enable them to be aware of the slightest pressure wave and tell them what is going on in the fog.

In the "sunny layer," aqualung divers can stay down for an average of twenty minutes, and they enjoy considerable safety and freedom of movement. Diving to a depth of 40 meters is becoming so commonplace that it no longer is the privilege of professionals. Now it is a great deal easier to teach diving to a geologist than geology to a diver.

Milne-Edwards was the first scientist to dive with a helmet and make observations of interest to marine zoology. Later, Professor Pierre Drach pioneered scientific research with self-contained breathing apparatus. Under his leadership, divers from the research vessel *Calypso* methodically gathered harvests in the Red Sea in 1951.

In Germany, Hans Hass inspired university men to become divers. In the United States, Woods Hole Oceanographic Institution trained an underwater photography and exploration team. At Scripps Institution of Oceanography in California, young biologists dived to discover new species; geologists observed and filmed the phenomena known as "cascading," measured the sheer strength of sediments on the spot, and studied an active undersea canyon.

Underwater archaeology was born in the Mediterranean. Applied to hunt for offshore oil deposits, geological prospecting has made use of aqualung divers in the Persian Gulf, California, and the Gulf of Mexico. Diving rapidly has become an indispensable tool for scientific exploration, and its use now has been extended to polar expeditions.

Consider a comparison: On land, in our own element, the volume of space actually inhabited is a layer extending from a few feet underground to the tops of the highest trees. This adds up to about 4 million cubic kilometers—hardly more than a quarter of the sunny and crowded upper layer of the sea accessible to millions of divers.

THE TWILIGHT ZONE ONE STEP BEYOND

Below 40 meters, light seems to come from all directions—there no longer are shadows. When you look up toward the surface, you cannot make out the reassuring gleam of the sun. Aqualung divers begin to feel the first attacks of "rapture of the deep" —nitrogen narcosis—which threatens their safety by dulling the instinct for survival. Pressure, cold, and darkness underscore the hostility of the marine world to man.

At about 300 meters of depth, there is only a pale light left in the visible part of the spectrum. It is hardly sufficient to see the shape of objects a short distance away once your eyes have become accustomed to the darkness. Beyond, it is practically night.

The "twilight zone" of 80 million cubic kilometers includes all of those provinces of the sea known as the continental shelf. Often it infringes upon steep slopes beyond the drop-off line. This extremely rich zone still is not very well known, even though it remains the most widely exploited area for deep-sea fishing. This zone is believed to store at least as much mineral riches per square kilometer as the nearby dry land. The continental shelf represents about 8 percent of the surface of the sea—an area three times as large as the United States.

Self-contained diving apparatus has enabled us to venture into the twilight zone. Breathing air, Italian divers succeeded in reaching depths of 135 meters for a few seconds. With a mixture of helium and oxygen, Hannes Keller left his bell for less than a minute at 300 meters (1,000 feet) below the surface.

These forays are shaking old theories and generating great hopes. Nevertheless, a few seconds at such depth must be paid for with hours of decompression under medical supervision. Another approach had to be found to work longer and deeper with a higher degree of efficiency.

Gases breathed by a diver dissolve in his blood and tissues. If a diver returns to the surface without appropriate decompression stops, bubbles form in his blood vessels, block circulation, and cause accidents ranging from the "bends" to fatal embolism.

Safe decompression time depends on the nature of the respiratory gas mixture and the depth and duration of the dive. But, for a given gas mixture and a given depth, a diver's body becomes saturated in a few hours, and safe decompression time remains constant whether he ascends upon saturation or stays down for days or weeks. Such extremely long exposures to pressure are known as "saturation dives." Capt. George F. Bond, leader of the U.S. Navy's Sealab experiments, was first to emphasize the economic interest of saturation dives and to outline a project of "occupation" of the seabed by man.

The first saturation dive was made in September, 1962, by diver Robert Stenuit in a small submerged decompression chamber lowered from Edwin A. Link's vessel, *Sea Diver,* in the bay of Villefranche, France. Stenuit stayed one day at a depth of 60 meters. Unfortunately, the project was interrupted by bad weather, and the decompression procedure was hampered by an accident.

Due to inadequate diving equipment, Stenuit only could swim out of his chamber for very short excursions. But the new method nevertheless was demonstrated. Also demonstrated was the fact that weather conditions could endanger shelters hanging from a ship. Undersea stations of the future would have to settle on the bottom.

AT HOME IN THE SEA

Commandant Jean Alinat, my closest associate since 1957, already had been aware of that necessity when planning Conshelf, a step-by-step program that would make man "at home in the sea" anywhere on the continental shelf.

Conshelf I was the first manned undersea station. Built and operated by Office Français de Recherches Sous-marines, it was lowered for one week to a moderate depth of 10 meters off Marseille in that same vintage month of September, 1962. While living on the bottom in a heavily ballasted steel cylinder 6 meters long and 2.5 meters in diameter, Albert Falco and Claude Wesly averaged 4 hours a day each of hard work down to 25 meters of depth. After 7 days, they surfaced safely and suffered no ill effects whatsoever. Falco and Wesly were the first "oceanauts"—a new breed of men.

Since these historic breakthroughs, techniques of saturation diving have shown evidence of rapid progress. In the summer of 1963, in the Red Sea, Conshelf II permitted a team of five oceanauts to work at depths from 10 to 25 meters for a full month. At the same time, a second team of two oceanauts lived and worked 7 days at 25 to 55 meters, and the diving saucer, our small exploration submarine, was serviced and based in an undersea garage.

A daring attempt was made by Stenuit and Jon Lindbergh in June 1964 at the Bahamas in an inflatable structure 130 meters (432 feet) down. Again the experiment was interrupted after 48 hours, and decompression was extended to 92 hours following bends suffered by one of the divers. Soon thereafter, the U.S. Navy started the Sealab program. Sealab I took place near Bermuda—four men lived and worked for 11 days at a depth of 56 meters with complete success.

The latest achievements in the history of saturation dives were simultaneous: In Bond's Sealab II, three teams of ten "aquanauts" spent 15 days each off La Jolla, California, at a depth of 62 meters, with an average daily diving time of 50 minutes per capita. One of the aquanauts, who was also an astronaut, Scott Carpenter, stayed 30 days. Sealab II lasted altogether from August 28 to October 10, 1965.

At the same time, on the eve of September 21, our group landed a 140-ton spherical structure—Conshelf III—on the edge of Villefranche's undersea canyon at a depth of 100 meters. Conshelf III's six oceanauts worked 22 days substantially deeper—120 meters—daily averaging 2½ hours of extremely hard work per man. They successfully decompressed in 3½ days and have shown no aftereffects as of today.

Already it has become clear that any kind of extended hard work now can be undertaken anywhere in the world at least down to the very edge of the continental shelf. The consequences of this conquest for mankind should not be underestimated.

DIVING IN A SEA SHELL

Manned undersea stations have opened up the twilight zone to oceanauts. But, in order to remain safe, such operations are large, costly, and difficult to move from one work site to another. In that very layer between 40 and 300 meters, in many instances the explorer is better off when protected against pressure by a rigid shell. Spheres or cylinders hanging from a cable can hardly do the job; they belong to museums. Recently developed tools are the miniaturized free-moving exploration submarines.

The head of that family—the diving saucer—was developed in Marseille by Office Français de Recherches Sous-marines and put into service from the research ship *Calypso* in the Caribbean in 1959. Since then it has logged 430 scientific dives down to 300 meters (1,000 feet). Its smooth ellipsoidal shape earned it the name "diving saucer."

The saucer weighs 3½ tons, is easily stowed in the hold of a ship 40 meters long, and accommodates two persons—a pilot and an observer. It can remain submerged more than twelve hours, and it has enough electricity in its batteries to run five hours under normal conditions. Speed is modest (3 kilometers an hour), but adequate for exploration. The craft is propelled by hydrojets, and the unconventional shape of its hull was designed for extreme maneuverability. It is equipped with gyrocompass, sonar in three directions, radio telephone, tape recorder, still- and motion-picture cameras, and a "hydraulic hand" to take samples.

DROP-OFF LINE TOWARD THE OCEAN FLOOR

Practically speaking, the saucer is almost the equivalent in the twilight layer to an aqualung in the sunny layer. Thanks to its light weight, it probably was the first submarine to fly, and it has crossed the Atlantic four times by airplane. In the very near future, the twilight layer will be invaded by a number of vehicles of the diving saucer class.

When, aboard a diving saucer, you reach the edge of the continental shelf, you are struck by the abruptness with which the floor of the sea suddenly drops off. Under the bright gleam of searchlights, the bottom disappears in the blue. You have to reason with yourself to fight off a feeling of dizziness. Then you tilt your bow down, on occasions as much as 30 or 35 degrees, to follow the slope downward.

The slanting surface often is furrowed by undersea canyons, abrupt and extremely narrow, which sometimes exhibit steps carved into their walls like giant staircases. Over such landscapes, the best echo sounders in the world are unable to transcribe what you see through the portholes of a diving saucer.

Then, at 300 meters of depth, the diving saucer must stop and turn over the job of exploring the "medium depths" of the sea (from 300 to 600 meters) to vehicles with a stronger hull. Deeper craft belong to two categories—the bathyscaphes and the exploration submarines. I have had the experience of venturing a few times to this bosom of the sea, once as early as 1953.

The upper part of the medium depth is a slanting wall, sometimes broken into tormented shapes, sometimes covered by mud. The slope plunges sharply down toward flat and less interesting stretches of the seabed.

MOUNTAINS PIERCE MONOTONOUS PLAINS

Great ocean basins, occasionally pierced by isolated rocky peaks, volcanoes, or even mountain ranges, are mainly huge sedimentary plains. This zone, rather monotonous (in appearance only), is found at depths between 3,000 and 6,000 meters. It alone accounts for 67 percent of the total area of the seas and of the oceans. The boundaries of the medium-depth zone correspond clearly to physical and geological discontinuities; it excludes the continental shelf, the ravined sagging of the floor, the main thermoclines, and the great ocean trenches.

So far, the medium depths have been penetrated a few hundred times by the bathyscaphes *FNRS III, Trieste,* and *Archimède.* These machines are based upon the principle of the former Zeppelins: A heavy steel gondola is made buoyant by a large float filled with gasoline.

The bathyscaphes are elevators without cables. These large, delicate, poorly maneuverable devices are the glorious pioneers of deep-sea exploration. But their principle goes back to prewar days, their construction was considerably delayed, and, in fact, they were obsolete as soon as they were born.

Today, we should be able to get along without any float at all down to depths of 4,000 or even 6,000 meters. High-grade steel, light alloys, titanium, glass, or plastics, used separately or in combination, make it possible to conceive hulls that will withstand pressures of 5 to 600 atmospheres with an acceptable safety coefficient, and still be self-buoyant.

Such very strong and at the same time very light hulls are technically within reach because an acceptable value for safety coefficients becomes smaller as operational pressures rise higher. This is logical because *relative* changes in pressure due to a given accidental change in depth are smaller for a submarine designed to operate at 4,000 meters than one built for 400 meters.

For exploration submarines, as well as for aqualung divers, surface conditions might prove more critical than those encountered at great depths. Handling a sub to and from the water is a formidable challenge for the accompanying vessel. Light weight is essential to ease launching and retrieving. A small vessel also increases maneuverability for exploring complex topography.

Very recently, three small exploration submarines have become operational—the *Aluminaut,* the *Alvin,* and our *Deepstar 4000*. They just have started to roam in the heart of the sea.

Added up, bathyscaphes and deep-exploration subs have opened new vistas in our knowledge of the medium depths. The scientific balance sheet of these dives is firmly on the credit side. Two general conclusions have been brought out from numerous observations:

(1) In the open sea, the density of plankton does not decrease necessarily with an increase in depth (it is not at all rare to run through an extremely dense layer of plankton at 1,000 meters).

(2) The bottom of the sea, covered most of the time with thick layers of sediments, is the scene of intense underground life. There is hardly a square meter without holes —small, medium-sized or large—and these holes are dens whose inhabitants are still very much of a mystery to us.

THE ABYSS

The great ocean trenches (Marianas, Philippine, Tonga, and others) are deep narrow furrows, mainly located in the Pacific. Their realm, it can be said, begins at a depth of 6,000 meters, extends to more than 11,000 meters, and represents only 2 percent of the total area of the sea. But they are critical spots, where the earth's crust is very thin and generally the scene of intense seismic activity.

The proven existence of varied life under more than 1,000 atmospheres of pressure also is an exciting challenge to physiologists and biologists. The systematic study of these deep trenches is of such interest that it justifies the expense of building and operating "superbathyscaphes" such as *Archimède.*

A superbathyscaphe is a large vessel with enormous floats containing gasoline or another light substance and one or several steel spheres with enough room for several scientists and a substantial payload of scientific instruments. It has enough power for substantial range and adequate cruising speed. Since the *Tri-*

este has been downgraded from its historic "anti-Everest" conquest, there is an urgent need for superbathyscaphes other than the lone French *Archimède.*

All the recent achievements enumerated or described above may lead to outlining a new relationship between man and the sea. The surface (a mere interface) is the *last* place from which we should study the oceans. Vertical-takeoff and -landing seaplanes and helicopters, stable, manned sponbuoys anchored in key locations, and thousands of recording buoys, spread all over the oceans and interrogated by satellites, could provide us with many times more data than any number of oceanographic ships.

In addition to this formidable and permanent network, we would need a few large oceanographic submarines, some of them able to rest on the bottom and serve as mobile manned undersea stations, putting oceanauts into action when and where they are needed, and able to launch and retrieve—in greater depths—exploration submarines or even superbathyscaphes.

SECTION I

THE OCEANAUTS
Men Live Beneath the Sea

Within ten years as many as a thousand people will be working, and even living, for periods of days, or weeks, at underwater sites on the continental shelf.
—John H. Perry, Jr.—a builder of depth-exploring submarines—in the Palm Beach (Florida) Post-Times, *March 6, 1966.*

MAN'S FIRST MONTH ON THE OCEAN FLOOR

JACQUES-YVES COUSTEAU has placed three villages for men at increasingly greater depths on the seabed. The U.S. Navy has had two: Sealabs I and II. Both Cousteau and the Navy plan more and deeper living quarters for men beneath the sea. Here, from a National Geographic Society News Bulletin by Matt McDade, is the story of the very first—and successful—attempt by men, in 1963, to live for a month on the sea floor:

Five French Oceanauts have spent an entire month in an underwater village 36 feet down in the Red Sea without once resurfacing. Two other teammates lived and worked a week in a two-room capsule moored deeper, at 90 feet.

The men had underwater transportation—a two-man hydrojet diving saucer that was the world's first submarine to operate entirely from a base on the ocean floor. They even had guests—project supervisor Jacques-Yves Cousteau and his attractive blond wife Simone.

Cousteau says the venture "convinced our underwater team that industrial and scientific seabed stations will become a routine thing in our lifetime."

None of the oceanauts suffered injury or became ill, though the two men in the deep capsule lost their appetite. Wrote a member of the team before going back up to the utility ship *Rosaldo* and the research vessel *Calypso:* "We don't think of our return to the surface as a relief. To continue our experiment further beyond the limits planned would not be difficult."

Boredom was never a problem. Portholes offered TV-type entertainment such as this: "A thick school of sardinellas prances into view. We watch, spellbound, as they execute in unison a dance as precise as that of the Rockettes, then vanish as if the stage had fallen in."

The two Red Sea ventures (at 36 feet and 90 feet), were pilot projects in a long-range program to put divers on the continental shelf—the richest and most accessible part of the ocean—for extensive periods of work and research.

Manned undersea stations there will have many practical applications, especially for oceanographers, the oil industry, and the military. According to Captain Cousteau, military uses include antisubmarine warning installations, coastal defenses, and submerged bunkering stations for submarines.

The Cousteau undersea village was prefabricated and planted on a reef 25 miles northeast of Port Sudan in the Red Sea. This location was chosen because of the blistering heat, humidity, and remoteness from bases of supply. Expedition sponsors thought that if a base could be set up there, it could be done anywhere in the world.

Sinking and fixing the buoyant structures in place took weeks of aggravations, setbacks, and galling labor. Captain Cousteau said it was like "trying to tie down so many blimps in a gale."

When completed, the village consisted of four steel structures, several pens holding fish captured for study and for Prince Rainier's Monaco aquarium, and some antishark cages. With divers in aqualungs swimming about among fish to do their assigned jobs, the scene took on the air of a Jules Verne science-fiction tale come true.

The oceanauts lived in Starfish House, anchored seven feet above coral sand on stilts and so called because four oblong chambers radiated from a central room. Temperature was 80.6 degrees, humidity 85 percent.

In the central room were the living-dining area and the command center. Its operator had a three-camera closed television circuit, intercom, ultrasonic underwater wireless, and telephone.

Off the central room were two chambers used for sleeping. The third arm contained kitchen, laboratory, darkroom, and toilet. The fourth contained gear, showers, and the exit.

Nearby was an onion-shaped steel dome on stilts—the hangar for the diving saucer. It could pop up inside the dry dome for maintenance and battery recharges.

Part of the experiment required the oceanauts to spend several hours a day in open water outside their station. One chore was to set up color panels to test fishes' color perception. The capture of fish was easy with an ingenious new stiletto light—a narrow intense beam that has the power to mesmerize fish.

Men from the two-man capsule, called Deep Cabin and anchored lower on the reef, worked regularly at a depth of 165 feet.

"These manned stations exist only to permit men to work in the open water much longer and deeper than they can in surface-to-surface dives," Captain Cousteau explains in the April 1964 *National Geographic.* "Indeed, the shelf station does away with tedious and time-wasting decompression. If they live underwater, divers no longer need to decompress; they simply finish their work and return directly to the undersea billet. Only when they leave the undersea world altogether must they decompress."

Commenting on the purpose of the undersea program, Captain Cousteau writes: "There are many economic reasons for colonizing the continental shelf. The shoal waters of the world are rapidly acquiring offshore wells of oil, natural gas, and liquid sulphur. Troves of fine gem diamonds are being dredged from the South African continental shelf. Manganese nodules in almost pure state litter some ocean bottoms. Undersea fish farms, analogous to stock ranches on land, are now challenging man's imagination."

THE FIRST COLLEGE CAMPUS ON THE BOTTOM OF THE SEA

From All Florida *magazine, 1966:*

The Floor of the blue Atlantic just off Palm Beach has become a college campus.

At the edge of the Gulf Stream, where sea life swarms in abundance, students from Florida Atlantic University's ocean engineering department attend classes.

Their classroom is a great steel cylinder. It is called the Hydro-Lab, and from within the students study underwater activity.

Peering through portholes in the side of the lab—first of its kind in the free world—they make observations which will help them probe the mysteries of the sea.

Shortly there will even be an artificial reef near the Hydro-Lab, to attract sea life and marine growth.

The Hydro-Lab was constructed by Perry Submarine Builders, Inc., with funds made available to FAU by John H. Perry, Jr., the submarine firm's president.

She is submerged in 45 feet of water. Her top is 20 feet below the surface.

Below her is a 21-ton "anchor," an oblong metal box filled with steel and concrete. Two stainless-steel cables extend from the lab to the anchor.

On the lab's underside are two entry hatches—a small one for the students to enter with scuba-diving gear, a larger one to accommodate a Perry Cubmarine's conning tower.

With the Cubmarine's tower projecting inside the lab, occupants of the Cubmarine can make dry entry and exit.

The lab is supplied with compressed air from a surface mother ship, the *Sea Hunter,* a 60-foot motor vessel owned by Perry Submarine Builders, Inc.

Air within the lab is at a pressure equal to that of the surrounding water. Therefore, even with the hatches open, no water enters the lab. The action is the same as that with an inverted bottle or can. So long as the openings remain at the bottom, no water enters.

Capt. Charles R. Stephan, chairman of FAU's ocean engineering department—which also is the first such university department in the free world—directs the Hydro-Lab project.

As Captain Stephan points out, prospective students for the ocean engineering course might well do one thing:

Learn to swim.

"I LIVE IN A LITTLE HOUSE ON THE BOTTOM OF THE SEA"—*JON LINDBERGH*

DIVERS until recently were only able to work at the depths minutes before they had to be brought back up. Now, breathing new gas mixtures under pressure, divers can stay down indefinitely. In 1964, two Ocean Systems, Inc., divers, Robert Stenuit of Belgium, and Jon Lindbergh, son of Charles A. and Anne Morrow Lindbergh, dived, inside a steel cylinder or elevator, 432 feet near the Bahamas and remained on the bottom 48 hours. It was a breakthrough: man's longest deep dive. Here is Bob Stenuit's first-person description, from *The Deepest Days:*

JUNE 30, 1964: The sun, at the porthole over my bunk, wakes me up at seven o'clock. The weather is perfect, just enough breeze to make one realize [one] is in the tropics. On deck, Dan

Wilson is already working. He has discovered new helium leaks, and is trying to fother them (to stop the leaks), while Jon and I foresightedly stuff ourselves with bacon, eggs, and marmalade.

0900: The cylinder has just gone overboard. It floats alongside almost entirely submerged in a calm sea, as blue as the sky. Clayton puts the analyzer batteries, which must remain vertical, in their watertight case. My flippers, my mask, my cameras, have been ready in a corner since yesterday. It's getting closer. One can feel it from something floating in the air, from a certain expression on the faces of friends. Everybody is on deck, the observers, the sailors of *Nahant,* our National Geographic friends, looking through the viewfinder, and Jannis, who wants us at all costs to have a final cup of coffee with chocolate biscuits. The television screen shows us very distinctly the bottom where the ballast tray has settled. No tiger shark in sight, only two or three tiny fish, the same ones as yesterday. Our control gauge is positive—the tent has not lost a single gram of pressure overnight. It is ready to welcome us; everything looks fine down there.

Ed Link shakes hands. "There, Robert, everything is ready this time. Good luck to both of you." We have another round of handshaking. My last sight of the surface will be that of Marion Link, very moved, waving us a last good-bye. Then we stick our heads in the tepid water. Jon undogs hatch A, which spits a flood of bubbles and swings outward, wide open, and we climb one after the other into our elevator, which I lock tight behind me. We have just closed our door to the world.

1045: At the control panel, Dr. Dickson, who will supply air . . . slowly increases our internal pressure to 5½ atmospheres, 150 feet of seawater. We will hold to that pressure all the way down to the bottom. Helium already distorts our voices. Topside hopes to have less trouble understanding a Donald Duck with a proper American accent than a Popeye with a French accent, so Jon Lindbergh is in charge of telephonic communications.

1150: The depth gauge shows 60 feet. Through the porthole, I can see a diver working on our electric cable. I recognize Ed at his regulator. From the first sketch to the last check, he has insisted on supervising everything himself.

1215: The cylinder descends so slowly that only the creeping depth-indicator needle reveals it, just as the blinking signals show the floors in an elevator. . . . The cylinder slowly sinks, braked by its safety line from the surface, and guided by the braided 1½-inch line which angles gently to the SPID. [The SPID was the tent on the floor, in which Lindbergh and Stenuit would live—a *s*ubmersible *p*ortable *i*nflatable *d*welling.] When our hanging weight comes to rest on the sand, our elevator will regain positive buoyancy, and float gently like a balloon at the end of its string, six feet from the bottom.

1230: Three hundred feet. The water is still limpid, but it is getting darker, and the washday blue of the surface is tainted with gray. Joe McInnis calls us: "Stopping circulation for a few minutes to take samples." Even though the cylinder is 100 percent autonomous, the doctors insist on verifying our gas mixture regularly with their surface instruments, more accurate than our Beckmann.

"Oxygen one ninety; CO_2 four point five." Jon, when reporting to Jim "Topside" Dickson, articulates as if talking into the ear trumpet of a deaf old gunner. Since our interior pressure is still only 150 feet, he gets his message across. Topside confirms a little later: "Oxygen here one eighty-eight, CO_2 four point seven. All's well on top, the weather remains fine."

1234: "The SPID," Jon shouts victoriously into the mike. He saw it first. It seems to stand nicely on a grayish bottom, mottled with vague darker spots. It warms the heart, this view of a little house in a landscape more lunar than terrestrial.

1240: I call surface: "Hold it; we are descending plumb on the tent. If we continue, we will land smack on top of it. You'll have to slacken the nylon line to get us farther away from the tent."

And I watch the white rope unwind, slacken, and deposit its big, threaded biconical lead weight on the bottom, 20 feet from the tent. Our terminal is in place.

"Okay, resume lowering."

1258: Good, the needle is on 400. But . . . are we still going down?

1300: "On the bottom." A big smile lights up Jon's face as he reports. The depth gauge at the top of the cylinder reads 415 feet. If I add 11 feet, the height of the cylinder, and 6 feet for the chain of the hanging ballast, that puts us at a depth of 432 feet. I must mentally convert feet into meters to fully realize the depth in which I find myself: 130 meters! *Diable,* the captain of the *Nahant* [a surface ship backing up Lindbergh and Stenuit] has been generous.

1315: Through the long "umbilical cord" which connects us with *Sea Diver* [the surface ship Lindbergh and Stenuit dived from], the doctors send us helium to increase the internal pressure gradually to 14 atmospheres. Once in equal pressure, we will be able to open our double door. The gas we now breathe is a cocktail of 4 percent oxygen, about 5.5 percent residual nitrogen, and 90.5 percent helium, which positively prevents us from producing any intelligible sound. Filled with the absurdity of the situation when scribbling messages to Jon on the vinyl lining, I begin to regret we didn't learn deaf-and-dumb sign language.

1330: The needle of the interior pressure gauge has slowly caught up with that of the depth gauge. They could hardly go any farther. Our diving suits are flattened and wrinkled like old parchment. I blow them up, piece by piece, with a small tank of compressed air. Up there, I had taken the precaution to open my camera housings, my light-meter case, and the diving flashlights.

Now they are in equal pressure, and I may close them again to take them in the water. I am glad I did, since our three spare electric bulbs have just exploded with a boom like thunder, spraying us with ground glass. I had tested, in the chamber, three of the heavy-duty type, and they had held up perfectly, but I put them away so carefully in Miami that I was never able to find them afterward.

1345: Topside gives us the green light: "You may transfer to the tent whenever you wish." Jon secures the IN and OUT gas valves, and starts the CO_2 scrubber, which begins its familiar purr. I undog hatch B, pull it upward, and fasten it tightly. Dash-dot-dot-dot, dash-dash-dash, Jon signals, B.O.—that means "B open"; then hatch A, which finally opens on a brown bottom of coarse sand. And Jon signals on the sending key: dot-dash, dash-dash-dash, "A open." I slide into the water, from where I hear Jon's dash-dot-dot, dash-dash-dash, "Diver No. 1 out." The water feels cool, even at 72° F. Visibility is excellent, 150 feet maybe—I glance around, looking for the antipathetic fish which I have been told to expect. Nothing in sight. Three days ago, some sailors on the *Nahant* caught a 15-foot-long tiger shark on a butcher's hook baited with a 5-foot shark, and it took the ship's boom to hoist it aboard . . . fortunately, that monster did not seem to have a twin brother.

Our spotlights pierce the gray water with two emerald beams, and awaken on the sand glimmering splashes of sleeping color. Seen in profile, the tent is leaning like the tower of Pisa; it is tilted at 25 degrees on a bottom which slopes down as far as I can see, but it is perfectly habitable. It appears so tiny, my little black bubble in this immensity, that the old sailor's prayer comes to mind: "Oh Lord, thy sea is so big and my SPID is so small." It is hardly more than 20 feet away from the cylinder, so close that I decide not to use the rebreathers for our comings and goings. That is how I wanted it to be. Whatever happens, we will always get back to our elevator, even without flippers, mask, or light. A diver who has come from the surface or even from an undersea house settled at 85 feet and who suddenly finds himself in difficulty at 350 feet is not very likely to make it back. But here we have our return ticket in our pocket.

A deep breath, and let's go. Seen from below, the water surface inside the entry shaft of the SPID is a mirror of fluid silver. My head breaks through it as soon as I set foot on the ballast tray. Inside, the gas tastes like mountain-fresh air. I climb the ladder. Everything is in order. First operation: I must connect the Beckmann analyzer to its watertight batteries. Good, the little black needles come alive and slowly take the position I expected: oxygen, 4 percent, carbon dioxide, 0.25 percent. All is well. I sit down on the side of the well from which a Blue Grotto light is rising. At last, I am here. Ten months of working like a beaver, delays, dogged effort, but now I am here. How calm this other world! How silent! How peaceful . . .

Full of optimism, I have not put on my wet suit. The cold makes me shiver. Well, let's pull ourselves together, and act quickly.

1405: Fearing an inundation, we have taken a useless precaution by securing all our instruments, electrical connections, and internal gear in watertight containers, attached to the ballast tray. So much the better. But now we must get them unpacked and connected as soon as possible. I swim back to the cylinder to get dressed; in sliding into my isothermic suit, I feel as if I were going into a hot bath. We both return to the tent; I pass the first container to Jon. He removes our central power station connected to the generators by its cable. It is an octopus of big, black wires with waterproof plugs, carefully labeled. First he makes contact with the surface: dash-dot-dot, dash-dot-dot—"both divers in." On top, they congratulate us. Then he switches on the light. The light bulb glows. We look at each other, beaming. We won. It burns five seconds and goes out. We look at each other in consternation. Is the game up? Is it merely the bulb? If it's the current—that would be serious. To go on working, I light a diver's hand lamp. Immediately, a noise like a gunshot splits our eardrums. The "sealed beam" bulb of the lamp had just imploded, spraying the other half of SPID with thousands of sharp fragments. Fortunately, I brought along six cheap flashlights from some discount store which were not waterproof, thus not affected by the pressure. I plug in the radiator. Let's see: Nothing? No, no heat at all. Without light, without heating, without warm food, things don't look terribly good.

1410: Standing in the narrow access well, with water up to my waist, I wrestle with a 5-foot-long aluminum cylinder. It houses a big cartridge of granulated barium hydroxide and the turbo-ventilator which will continually drive the surrounding gas through the compact crystals so they will combine with the carbon dioxide produced by our respiration. At last, I have got hold of it. Its top is out of the water, the sill leaning on the last bar of the ladder. I open the vent and wait for a psst. Nothing happens. Catastrophe! Jon makes a long face. That can mean only one thing. Yes, indeed. I take off the cover: Everything is flooded. The motor and ventilator are useless. A thick white paste, bloated with craters, spills over the container. Our situation is not exactly brilliant—that apparatus is vital to us.

I glance at the Beckmann; the little needle already points to 12; 12 millimeters of mercury, that is 1.5 percent of CO_2. Our minutes here are numbered. Let's fetch the spare filter, quick. It is carefully tied up in a corner of the ballast tray. I cut ropes and more ropes of nylon, sisal, and cotton. This time the container is in ¼-inch sheet iron. It seems to weigh a ton, as I thrash around on the bottom trying to drag it behind me. "Containers made for human beings, not for a team of horses." That will be the first item on my list of necessary improvements. Jon hands me a line. He pulls, and I push, I grasp, I lift, I pivot, and I maneuver. I come back to the entrance well to breathe more and more often, more and more heavily. At last the monster is in place, but I am completely out of breath. Our disordered efforts have raised the level of carbon dioxide to 1.8 percent.

Now we discover that the cover has no pressure-equalizing valve. The surface crew has put on the wrong cover! I calculate rapidly: On every square centimer of this iron disk with a 10 cm radius, there are 14 kilos of external pressure and one kilo of internal pressure, so differential pressure is nearly four tons. . . . We won't try to pull it off. What we try to do is to cut or pry off the O-ring between the cylinder and its cover. No luck. I break a screwdriver and Jon snaps a scissors blade.

A glance at the Beckmann analyzer: 2.8 percent carbon dioxide. We begin panting now; we are breathing too fast. The symptomatic lead bar impinges on my forehead, and the pounding of my heart resounds through my whole body. I make a sign to Jon: "Let's get out of here," and we return to the cylinder—to the refuge, to the light, to the heat, to the pure air, to the antechamber of the world of men.

1430: I consider our condition: no scrubber, no light, no heat, possibly no electricity at all. The outlook is very, very bad. I write with a grease pencil on the cylinder wall: "In any case we will stay here 24 hours." From the upper level, Jon signals his agreement. A whole day at 432 feet in the cylinder—that would at least be a partial success.

In Morse code we report to topside. Link answers: "Wait one." I picture the powwow up there: Ed, Dan, Wardwell, Captain Wilson, all discussing. As Dan likes to say: "There are perhaps problems that have no solution, but personally I have never encountered any."

And then: "If we send you a line, can you attach it to the flooded container? We have a spare motor; we shall repair and send it down to you again."

Dash-dot (affirmative).

"Very well. We are sending you a line, along your safety line."

1500: I have received the line, and dragged the container up to the cylinder. I have attached it and sent it back up. Now the flooded apparatus is on the surface in the hands of the electricians.

1600: We wait and munch a few biscuits. Jim Dickson calls us: "According to my samples, you now have over 2.8 percent CO_2 in the tent. You can tolerate that fifteen minutes, no more if you move around." He is right; as soon as we reenter SPID, the carbon dioxide level will climb rapidly. At 4 or 5 percent we will have to get out fast, otherwise we shall be overcome by asphyxia, and down here, no rescue is possible. Those fifteen minutes will decide either the success or the semifailure of the entire operation.

1700: Still waiting. It is getting dark.

1825: Clang—the new air purifier which topside has just announced lands on top of the cylinder. I rig myself and leap into the water. *Brrr*—I shiver, and I swim for the new container up there and drag it toward the tent. The gas inside is heavy, and sticky in the mouth. With my heart pounding, I open the tap of the equalizing valve. Psst, the surrounding gas rushes into the container. The scrubber has arrived dry. Jon's face lights up with joy, but we have no time to celebrate. Six minutes have passed already. The little black needle has started to the left again far into the danger zone. We take off the cover, Jon pulls the heavy interior cylinder to him, I set it down in its cradle, I plug it in, the motor purrs, gas circulates, we have won! An outburst of joy answers from topside.

1930: We are installed under the tent. Wardwell has sent us spare electric bulbs in the scrubber container. Since they are smaller, they withstand the pressure. On tonight's menu: carrot juice and corned beef, canned water, fruit salad. The pressure has crushed and crumpled the tin cans, but their contents are intact.

2300: Dash-dot-dot, dash-dot-dot dash-dot-dot—BKI, "Beckmann readings unchanged." I have taken the first watch of our first night at 432 feet. I have wrapped up my head in towels and put on close-fitting woolens to fight the helium chill. I watch the instruments and the water level in the entry well. The radiator does not work, nor the air-conditioner, and Jon shivers on his cot in his three inadequate sweaters. Still, the thermometer registers 76° F. Through a porthole, I watch in amazement thousands of sardines dancing a gastronomic ballet with the shrimp in the beam of our projectors. Topside, the medical team takes turns at the control panel; through the eye of the closed-circuit TV aimed straight at my face, Big Brother is watching us. . . .

July 1, 0200: I lean over the well, and my heart suddenly rises. A huge . . . silhouette moves slowly against the ladder. Could it be the brother of the *Nahant* shark? Yes? No? No, I got a better look this time. It is only a peaceful grouper which nibbles on our garbage and on some spoiled ham which we have thrown in the water. It is as big as a boar; it must weigh 200 pounds.

0900: Breakfast. I have not slept well because I shivered too much, but as soon as we move around, the temperature becomes bearable.

1000: To work. I send the other container up to have a spare scrubber ready. We test our breathing apparatus: On a leash at the end of our 50 feet of hose, we take turns exploring around. When I put my mask close enough to the coarse sandy bottom, I can see it is teeming with life—sponges, worms, minute royal-blue fluorescent fish I would like to bring back to make into a ring or earrings. Is that why they are called jewel fish in Florida? Chunks of dead coral, scattered all about on the bottom, swarm like beehives with little flabby creatures. Sometimes, from the far end of a hole, a big round, yellow eye looks at you. The breathing apparatus works perfectly. The big grouper follows us everywhere. It sucks my feet when I descend the ladder, and it accepts all our caresses.

1330: Link on the intercom: "May I congratulate you for being the first men to have lived a whole day at 432 feet depth."

1530: I leap up to the cylinder to make our routine checks: Everything is in order and I inform topside—dash-dash-dash, dash-dot-dash. Jon joins me to try the breathing rig of the cylinder. We won't have another opportunity to use it.

1600: With parts and tools sent from the surface, Jon succeeded in repairing the air-conditioner. The electric radiator gives us more trouble. It sputters as soon as we connect it. It makes sparks and bites my fingers when I touch it. Perhaps, if I hadn't let it drop so awkwardly into the access well, when pulling it out of its container yesterday . . . ? Too bad. The air-conditioner gives us sufficient heat. After three hours in the water, it is a real pleasure to come back to a warm, cozy, and almost dry little haven.

2200: On the agenda: experiments in voice communication. Question: Below what percentage of helium in the windpipe can one make oneself understood at 400 feet? Lindbergh takes three deep gulps from a bottle filled with 25 percent helium and 75 percent air. His voice remains nasal and distorted, but I understand him clearly, and the surface does too. He takes the opportunity to dictate a telegram to each one of his children on the West Coast: "I live in a little house on the bottom of the ocean. It floats like your balloon at the end of a string. Through the window I see thousands of silverfish and a big grouper follows me on my walks like a poodle. A little while ago I gave him some ham. . . ." The wonderful story of Ondine, which has become reality. The radio up there will relay to four little children of the twentieth century a modern fairy tale, and, no doubt, they won't be astonished.

It's my turn. Now I take three deep breaths from a bottle of pure compressed air. The air is so dense that when I push the BYPASS button, I can see it flow from the regulator's mouthpiece like a thick fog. On the third gulp, the tent begins to swing back and forth, circles of light flare up and drift slowly before my eyes, and cumuli pile up under my skull. I feel my face twisting into ludicrous grimaces, I am drunk as a lord. I drop the mouthpiece: Now I know what narcosis is. It is the first time it has happened in my whole career as a diver.

2315: I am on watch. Every half hour I transmit to topside the figures I read on the dials on the analyzers: BKI, "Beckmann readings unchanged."

Why am I vaguely disappointed? I am here, at last, here where I had so much trouble arriving, where so many people had so much trouble keeping me alive, and it is not what I was hoping for. I expected the great adventure of my life. I expected the exaltation of effort and danger. Not at all. It happens exactly the way I predicted it would, swaggering a little bit, of course, to the reporters in London. It is routine, the humdrum life with its little works, the meals at a set time, the little problems which all have their little solution. But I should not regret it. After all, isn't that the real success of our operation—this normal development of a well-prepared program without really narrow escapes? A more thrilling, "heroic" adventure might not have had a tomorrow. What we are doing today, others, nonspecialists, will do just as calmly tomorrow. That is what matters, not the state of my soul. . . .

The second of the 1,000-watt spotlights of the cylinder, which burned night and day, goes out. Burned out, no doubt. Our interior light brightens immediately. Ten seconds later, the water in the access well is boiling. All the sardines which were whirling in the bright beam have now come around to the lesser light. They jump out of the water frantically and race on the surface and twist and turn like mad creatures. At once I see why: The water teems with tiny shrimp which turn round and round like mosquitoes, pursuing an invisible plankton, no doubt.

2335: A staggering blow shakes SPID. Jon wakes up, startled by the bang. What is happening? Another bang. We hold on to the cots. "The grouper." It is the giant grouper, charging the sardines in the well. With his enormous mouth wide open, he bores like a bulldozer, and gets entangled in the well, which is too narrow for his colossal body.

July 2, 0400: The grouper wakes us up ten times during the night. It is a real earthquake. Plankton, shrimp, sardines, groupers. The only ones lacking to complete the cycle are sharks. But if their size is related to that of the groupers around here, I prefer not to meet them at midnight. . . .

0900: At breakfast, Jon tries to tell me something. I look at him vacantly without understanding a single sound, while he repeats and articulates and repeats again. I can't get accustomed to these difficulties in communication. Finally, I hand him a scratch pad. He writes: "Weather on the surface excellent. Jim signaled dead calm. Sunrise on the surface 0510, first light here 0520."

0940: Getting dressed to spend our daily three or four hours in the water. To forestall a telephone breakdown, I have devised an emergency system—a plastic mustard dispenser ballasted with a lead pellet at the neck. I write a note on a sheet of paper and slip it inside, then I need only drop the dispenser in the water with its opening down. But one can't anticipate everything. I raise my eyes to follow the ascent of my small red-and-yellow plastic bottles, which bump along upward, sputtering their bubbles, only to see voracious packs of amberjacks rushing to pursue them. It is the first time I happen to look up. There is a whole carrousel of king mackerels and jacks far above the tent, and barracudas and other steel-gray fish which I can't name, all twisting and turning tirelessly. Are they attracted by the noise?

Topside calls: "Four dispensers with messages received."

"See, jacks don't really care for the taste of plastic."

Now, I take photographs of Jon; he breathes from the recirculating hookah, rearranging our gear ballast tray. It had to be done. We used the tray for a garbage can, and the sight of the debris-strewn bottom is no credit to the first colonists who came from above.

I used GE_1 and M_3 bulbs, the only ones small enough not to be crushed by the pressure. Immediately, the flashes attract around me half a dozen giant groupers. But where the deuce do they come from? It's a desert as far as I can see. No way to photograph them; they press against me in spite of the strong kicks I give them to get rid of them: They nudge the lens, bump into my legs, and fill up the whole field of my viewer with their bovine bodies, while their Ping-Pong paddles stir up opaque sandstorms in front of me.

Yesterday, while raising an arm too high, I tore my diving suit from shoulder to waist. Now deflated, it floats around me like a nightgown, weighed down by water, useless, and my teeth chatter helplessly. But I must continue, bones frozen or not. If they come out, my pictures will be the deepest pictures ever taken by a diver. After a roll of color film, I go and fetch my second Calypso-Phot, this one loaded with black and white, and begin to shoot again. But now, this is it; I can't go on, it's too cold, my fingers can no longer grip the flash bulbs. I dash toward the cylinder. I climb and turn on both radiators at once. Well, that doesn't help. To stop trembling like an epileptic and recover my energy, here as well as in caves, I know what I need: sugar. I return to the tent and greedily swallow six big spoonfuls of powdered sugar. My trembling hand spills more on the floor, but thirty seconds later, my composure returns and I stop shivering.

1330: We ate with big appetite: tomato juice, frankfurters, apple sauce, biscuits and Cheshire cheese, bananas and oranges. The thermometer registers 80° (27° Centigrade), and we relax—full, warm again, happy and content. Topside calls us—it's Ed with a ceremonious voice ". . . er, Robert and Jon . . . you . . . you have spent two days and two nights at 432 feet, and all our tests have succeeded. What we wanted to prove, is proved by now. Bravo! But now that the demonstration has been made, we'll gain nothing more by extending your stay. So pack up everything, and get ready to come up."

We stare at each other, nonplussed. The first night, when shivering with cold under our useless sweaters, we may have been willing to obey orders to come up without much discussion, but now that the air-conditioner works, and we are installed and organized, and have made friends and got into our daily routine, no need to consult each other: We would gladly spend the rest of the week here.

It is the voice of reason, however, and we have to obey. But while bolting the container tops in our little house, our hearts are filled with the kind of nostalgia which overcomes you when you close for the winter the shutters of a summer cottage.

Then comes the routine of the ascent, just as in the rehearsals: our comings and goings with the instruments, the elevator sealed, the order to topside—dot-dash-dot-dot, L for "lift"—the needle of the depth gauge coming back to familiar figures, the water luminous again, the glare of sunlight through the porthole, and the big white ship close by, the cylinder afloat, swiftly dancing on the surface and lying down under our backs to put us on deck, horizontally; and finally, the happy faces of the captain and all our friends who stick an eye to the porthole, their hands making a sunshade, to get a look at us in our box, and the smile of the cook when he promises a steak dinner to celebrate our return to civilization.

"Mating with Deck Decompression Chamber accomplished," the telephone tells us. "You may now switch."

It is 3:15 P.M. Jon opens hatch B, unlocks the DDC's door and crawls into it on his stomach. I follow him and straighten up, enjoying the simple and forgotten luxury of stretching my limbs.

At 3:50 P.M., Jim lowered the internal pressure from 432 to 399 feet. With one atmosphere of difference between the partial pressure of the helium dissolved in us and the pressure of the gas which our blood would encounter in our lungs, our desaturation had just begun.

My cameras and housings were open. For them, as for us, we had planned on a regular linear resurfacing at a rate of one foot per eleven minutes in line with Dr. Workman's successful dry exposure at 400 feet at the EDU (the Experimental Diving Unit).

But it would be longer, after all, Joe explained to us. "First, you were thirty-two feet deeper; second, you have worked harder and under much more strenuous conditions of comfort, and then, too, we did not have the means of controlling your percentages of inert gas on the bottom with as much precision as they did in the caissons of Washington. We are going to decompress you at one foot per twelve minutes, you will breathe oxygen on and off from fifty feet up, but just as an extra precaution, not to cut down your time."

I picked up a pencil: "Twelve minutes per foot, that amounts to 5 feet per hour. Five feet times 24 hours equals 120 feet per day. In other words, to resurface from 400 feet will take us 400 divided by 5, equals . . . er . . . equals 80 hours, or, let's see . . . 3 days and 8 hours."

Well, that is worth the trouble of sitting down.

Jim Dickson's voice in the intercom: "Robert, look starboard." Through the porthole of our decompression chamber, I saw our little rubber house slowly emerge from the blue water. The potbellied roof came first, sleek and shining, then the green and orange bottles glistening with color under the Bahama sun, and finally the access well, like a trouser leg, inflated by a muscular thigh.

At the exact moment when the base of the well emerged, the same sausage collapsed, lacking the counterpressure of the water; what the hoisting boom unloaded on the deck was just an empty sack, a dead and flabby skin.

I wrote in my notebook: "1630 o'clock, all's well that ends well, both divers recovered, all equipment on board, not a single bolt lost, complete success."

I took pictures also: Jon taking our first iced drinks out of the air lock; and then in the evening Jon attacking his steak, a plate on his knees; Jon shaving; and finally, Jon falling on his bunk to make up for a few forgotten hours of sleep. Then I climbed on the bunk above, and stayed such a long time that the next day our friend Wardwell suggested the name of the project be changed from Man in Sea to Man in Bed.

I learned that July 3 was a Friday. All cables and anchors recovered, *Nahant* left us after a polite exchange of foghorn blasts. She had assisted *Sea Diver* like a big, attentive brother—how could we have gotten along without her? I was glad to know that the crew would spend the Fourth of July with their families after all.

Tonight we listened to the tape recording of the dive. It was the same story but seen from the other side of the mirror, and once more I realized that experiments of this kind, just like cave diving, are much more frightening for those who wait and worry on the surface than for those who are down below active and happy.

At 4 A.M. on July 4, Jim woke us up. "You have arrived at two hundred feet. Please get up and try out your joints." Frequently, it is the joints where the first bubbles materialize, so we will watch ours closely. As perfectly ridiculous as the actors of the silent movies, we solemnly gesticulate, facing each other. Toes, ankles, knees and hips, fingers, wrists, elbows and shoulders: Everything works without creaking. Henceforth, every three hours we shall go through the same sophisticated mime's dialogue.

A very tired *Sea Diver* was heading back for Miami at low speed when we "reached 100 feet," then, on the fifth at about 2:30 in the afternoon, the skyscrapers of Miami Beach traced in the porthole their tourist-poster silhouette, and at 4:00 we were tied to our berth in the Miami River. Little details betrayed our ascent: a plastic bottle inflated; I could whistle again; our voices gradually resumed their human tone.

At 4:30, we strapped rubber masks on our faces to breathe pure oxygen. The amount of dissolved inert gases driven from the tissues and blood to the lungs, in which it diffuses and from which it is then eliminated, is proportional to the difference in partial pressure between the dissolved inert gas and the inert gas present in the lungs. If there is no inert gas at all in the lungs, the difference is maximum and the elimination quickest.

I felt a first slight pain at 33 feet, at about 5:00 P.M. It was internal, somewhere in the right knee and leg. I was expecting that. Bubbles always display a regrettable tendency to show up again in the same parts of the body where they have appeared before, following any dive too close to a first decompression accident. When the inside of my leg began to burn, I notified Jim Dickson, who brought me back to 50 feet, and the pain vanished. But now both of us had to resume the ascent at the rate of one foot per quarter hour only. We both were in the same boat, and poor Jon, free of any symptoms, now saw his purgatory prolonged for almost a whole day when he could probably have been through as planned, just as the first guinea pigs did at the Experimental Diving Unit.

Joe had himself locked in with us that evening; to tap my knees, look into my eyeballs, listen to our breathing, take our pulse and blood pressure. At this point I felt a strange tingling in the end of my fingers, which interested him a great deal, but which gradually faded away while we finished our last hours of desaturation on our cots.

At midnight, the caisson was ventilated with compressed air only. In the morning Jim announced: "There, see, your heads emerge." Indeed, we were only in five feet of imaginary water, and at eleven o'clock, the oxygen mask still glued to our face, we were "wading" in two feet of theoretical seawater.

[Lindbergh and Stenuit came out of the caisson. The longest deep dive men ever had made was ended.]

MEN AND A PORPOISE AT HOME ON SEA FLOOR

In 1965, three teams of ten men each lived, in turn, in Sealab II: a 57-foot-long chamber 205 feet beneath the Pacific. Sealab II was just off the La Jolla, California, beach of the Scripps Institution of Oceanography. The three teams stayed on the bottom of the sea for two weeks each. One man, M. Scott Carpenter, lived beneath those 205 feet of ocean for a month—the first man ever to do so. One member of the Sealab II team, a porpoise named Tuffy, trained by the Navy and by Dr. Sam H. Ridgway of Texas A. & M., carried lifelines to divers feigning "distress" in the dark waters. Thus Tuffy showed that the porpoise may become the ocean equivalent of the St. Bernard dogs in the Alps. Tuffy responded instantly and unerringly, *Naval Research Reviews* for November, 1965, reported, to acoustics (sound) signals from divers out of sight. "The animal," said *Naval Research Reviews,* "passed the tests with high marks and thus may have earned a place beside man in the exploration and exploitation of the undersea world." This may be a turning point for man: Hundreds of thousands of years ago, man domesticated —tamed—the dog and the horse. With their help, man became the ruler of the land. The porpoise, starting with Tuffy, may help man rule the depths. This is a Navy news release from Sealab II:

With Sealab II off La Jolla, California, October 12, 1965: Today, after 45 days on the ocean floor off La Jolla, California, Sealab II of the Navy's Man-in-the-Sea Program, is finished.

The Man-in-the-Sea Program began almost eight years ago with laboratory experiments. Since then, scientists and engineers have worked toward giving man the ability to explore and exploit the world's continental shelves with reasonable safety and freedom.

This goal is important for military purposes, but for civilian purposes as well. The continental shelves are rather shallow underwater extensions of the continents which, if combined, would equal an area as large as Africa. They hold great riches in terms of food, minerals, and ocean by-products.

The results of this experiment have been outstanding: Three teams of Navy and civilian divers have proved that men can do useful work while living in the hostile environment of the sea.

Three new concepts in diving and decompression techniques have been tested during Sealab II. They are: total gas saturation dives; deep excursion dives without decompression after saturation at living depth; and a single linear decompression after a prolonged stay under pressure.

Exploration of Scripps Canyon to a depth of 300 feet was carried out. The aquanauts have eaten fish, crabs, and even raw plankton to help prove man's ability to survive in the liquid space of the oceans.

Great strides have been made in the science of underwater living. Three teams of ten men each lived in a 57-by-12-foot undersea laboratory, spending almost 350 hours of actual work outside their home on the ocean bottom. They lived and worked under pressure for a total of three man-years.

There have also been engineering and physiological advances, bringing the diving art into a new dimension. It can now be said that the critical tools needed for man's conquest of the world's continental shelves are at last available and can be used with confidence.

On August 28, 1965, the first team of Sealab II entered the habitat. Comdr. Scott Carpenter, Wilbur Eaton, GMI; Cyril Tuckfield, EMC; Lt. Robert Sonnenburg, Billie Coffman,

TMI; J. D. Skidmore, PHC, and Fred Johler, ENCS, made up the Navy members of the team. Civilians were engineer Berry Cannon of the Navy Mine Defense Laboratory and Earl Murry and Tom Clark from the Scripps Institution of Oceanography.

The first team's main task was to get the habitat operating properly, establish an area of exploration, map the area they were located in, and to perform human factors and physiological experiments as well as marine biology studies. An underwater weather station was set up to measure current velocities, water temperatures, and other parameters at varying depths.

More tasks were scheduled for each team than they could possibly accomplish. This was to take care of any slack time which would result if an experiment were aborted. Aquanauts soon learned that it took a tremendous amount of work just to live at 205 feet.

In spite of a busy housekeeping schedule, checking equipment that was used for the first time in many cases, the first team on one day reached a total of 732 minutes in the water. All in all, they logged 6,067 minutes of time in the ocean and countless hours doing experiments inside the undersea habitat.

On Sunday, September 12, the first team (with the exception of Comdr. Carpenter) returned to the surface for 31 hours of decompression.

The second team was composed of Comdr. Carpenter, Robert Barth, QMC; Howard Buckner, SWC; Kenneth Conda, TMI; Glen Iley, HMC, who would serve as medical representative, and John Reaves, PHI, for the Navy. Civilian scientist-divers were George B. Dowling, research physicist, William Tolbert, Jr., oceanographer, and Wally Jenkins, equipment specialist, all from the Navy Mine Defense Laboratory, Panama City, Florida, and Arthur Flechsig, oceanographer from the Scripps Institution of Oceanography.

The second team was dubbed the Scientific Team by Sealab officials. This was due to the high number of physiological and marine biological studies that were carried on inside and outside of the habitat.

A major achievement of the second team was completion of excursion dives to a depth of 266 feet and the sheer brink of Scripps Canyon. Comdr. Carpenter and Wally Jenkins made the first dive, with the entire second team later completing the excursion.

The second team had great success with Tuffy the porpoise. The mammal proved to be an expert mailman and carried a line to a diver who called him as if the diver were lost. This demonstrated that the porpoise can be a valuable assistant to men working in an undersea environment. Tuffy finished with his chores, and accompanied his trainer, Wally Ross, to the Marine Sciences Division of the Navy Missile Center at Point Mugu, California.

The second team logged 5,850 minutes in the water, but a major portion of their time was scheduled inside the undersea habitat performing special physiological and marine biological experiments. They entered the personnel transfer capsule on Sunday morning, September 27, and underwent 35 hours of decompression.

The third team entered Sealab II in two shifts. Team leader Robert Sheats, Master Chief Torpedoman and Master Navy Diver, with Bill Meeka, BMI, and Navy Electronics Laboratory scientist-diver Bill Bunton entered Sealab on September 26. This was to enable the third team to become familiar with the routine and Chief Sheats with his leadership duties. The remaining seven men entered the habitat later. Navy members were Lt. Robert Sonnenburg, Medical Corps, Charles Coggeshall, GMC, John Lyons, EMI; Lavern Meisky, SFC, and Paul Wells, MNC. The civilians were scientist-divers Rick Grigg and John Morgan Wells, both of Scripps Institution of Oceanography.

Primary objective for the third team was to test new salvage procedures at a greater depth. They used a special foam to salvage an aircraft hulk and to raise barrels from the bottom. They used explosive tools in an important experiment designed to attach plates and lifting surfaces to a portion of a submarine hull. They also worked with specially designed tools, with torque-free characteristics, to test the tools' effectiveness. Two different kinds of sample mining, airlift and bottom coring, were also tested by the aquanauts.

The third team had two immediate problems, both of which were solved by aquanauts and topside personnel, working together. The first problem was headaches suffered by most of the third team, which coincided with the discovery of significant traces of carbon monoxide in the Sealab atmosphere. A chemical, Hopcalite, was added to the air-scrubbing system, and seemed to help. At least the headaches became fewer.

The second problem was one which all three teams faced. They had to send their air bottles topside for recharging with helium and oxygen, and this consumed valuable bottom time. A special high-pressure line was sent to Sealab II, and the third team was able to charge their own bottles inside the habitat.

Chief Bob Sheats and NEL diver-photographer Bill Bunton received permission from Captain George F. Bond, principal investigator, and Dr. John Craven of the Navy Special Projects Office, to make a 300-foot dive into Scripps Canyon. They completed the dive satisfactorily, and the remainder of Team Three also made dives to the 300-foot level. The last team also had the major job of preparing for ending the project. They prepared the habitat for raising from the ocean floor. This involved undoing many of the things the first team had done. All of the scientific gear had to be disassembled and returned to the surface, the Benthic communication laboratory had to be unhooked, and a general tidying up of the area made so that cables and wires would not foul during the raising operation. In all, the total ocean-bottom working time accomplished by Team Three was 8,678 minutes.

Members of the third team came to the surface in the personnel transfer capsule on Sunday morning, October 10. They underwent about 31 hours of decompression and emerged from the decompression chamber late Monday afternoon.

In addition to awarding all Sealab II aquanauts and project personnel the Navy Unit Commendation Ribbon, the Secretary of the Navy, Paul H. Nitze, sent the following message to Sealab II at the end of the experiment:

"Thanks to the teamwork and dedicated efforts of the scientific community, aquanauts and support personnel, Sealab II has accomplished its mission. You have proved that man can live and do useful work under the sea. Your accomplishments during the past 45 days have set one of the cornerstones for our future exploitation of the continental shelf. Admiral McDonald, Chief of Naval Operations, joins me in extending to all hands our sincere best wishes and the official congratulations of the Navy Department for a job well done."

NOW MEN CAN STAY IN THE OCEAN

Captain L. B. Melson in *Naval Research Reviews,* May, 1965, had concluded what Sealab II further underlined:

Thanks To The Wisdom, skills, and energy of the men who have pioneered in these efforts, the question of whether man can enter the hostile oceans and wrest from them their secrets has been answered in the affirmative. No longer must man venture hesitantly into the oceans like a toy encased in a protective coat dangling from the end of a string tethered precariously to a ship on the surface. His ability to live beneath the surface at depths greater than anyone envisioned a few short years ago has been proved. He now possesses the ability to live, work, eat, sleep, and participate within the oceanic environment—remaining not for minutes, but for days, weeks, or months if the need arises. With the facilities now available, man is no longer a spectator looking at the changing subterranean scenery through glass ports: He is a member of the aquatic fraternity.

SECTION II

THE OCEAN PROSPECTORS
Men Obtain Great Wealth from the Sea

"There are extensive mineral deposits that we know of in the deep ocean."

—Rear Admiral Odale D. (Muddy) Waters, Jr., Naval Oceanographic Program Director on the staff of the Chief of Naval Operations.

THE SEA'S BIGGEST GEOLOGICAL SPECIMEN

THE MINERAL wealth on the sea floor is enormous. Men are gradually learning about it. On one occasion a Scripps expedition hauled up a mass of evidence—the hugest rock we have retained from the deep sea. The following report is from *Deep Challenge* by Harris B. Stewart, Jr., chief oceanographer, U.S. Coast and Geodetic Survey, who was an eyewitness:

The Most Interesting accumulation of minerals on the sea floor, and probably the one that will eventually be most fully exploited, is the mineral lumps made up primarily of manganese, iron, nickel, cobalt, and copper, and called *manganese nodules.* These potatolike concretions of minerals were first dredged from the sea floor during the British Challenger Expedition in the last century. Since then has come the development of the deep-sea camera, and with this equipment we have found large areas of each of the three major arms of the global sea to be covered with these nodules. The largest one known to have been recovered weighed about 300 pounds and was brought up tangled in an undersea cable being retrieved for repairs. It was sketched and sampled, but unfortunately the men aboard were more interested in cables than in minerals, and the specimen was dropped back into the sea. The second-largest known specimen was brought up by the research vessel *Horizon* of the Scripps Institution of Oceanography during an expedition to the Gulf of Alaska in 1951. The method of recovery was sufficiently interesting that it might be worthwhile to quote from a description of the recovery of this amazing sea-floor specimen written at the time.

Yesterday, though, things began to pop. My watch again had the night station the night of the tenth and eleventh (September, 1951), and Al Smith and José secured after the deep cast was in, and Bill Riedel came on deck to help me with the core. It was to be core No. 10. We put the rig over in 2,750 fathoms of water—that is three miles straight down—and it would have taken 5,000 meters had the wire gone straight down, but even though there was a very mild swell and the wind was light, we had a goodly drift that managed to work up a 45% wire angle by the time 5,000 meters of wire were out, so we took her down some more to make up for the big wire angle. I wish someone would work out or discover what a wire suspended in water does as the ship drifts. It certainly doesn't stay at 45% all the way to the bottom. . . . We let out finally 6,300 meters or all but the last layer of turns on the winch drum. . . . We couldn't let out any more because "there ain't no more," so we started to haul it in and hoped we had a core. At 5,900 meters the winch ground to a groaning, complaining halt. Don Derringer was winchman—full beard and now waxing the much-fingered, almost microscopically small tips of his moustache—and I went up to the boat deck to check with him. He goosed up the power and the winch began to turn slowly, each roll to port putting enough strain on the thing to stop the winch. On the starboard roll a foot or so of cable would come up, and then the ensuing port roll would loosen enough so that the next roll back we could pull a bit more in. We had seen it do this before and knew it was the way a winch reacted when it was pulling a deep core out of the bottom, so our hopes rose. It would be a three-hour job at least—or should be if your wire has as many splices as this one has—to bring a core up from over three miles, so we settled down to some semiserious dipnetting and spearing. There were a few large sauries that broke water occasionally in short jumps as they streaked around under the light. I saw one flying fish and a few three-foot white-bellied devils just out of the range of good vision. Then the squids came up—probably after the sauries, and I missed eight of ten good ones with the spear.

It was then early in the morning. Derringer had given way to Fenton on the winch; pitch-black night had given way to the first faint subtle shadings of dawn, and my thoughts on fishing had given way to happy, if somewhat libidinous, thoughts of the girls back home, when I was startled by a splash followed by great dripping noises. I turned, and there, where the wire left the water and rose past the bucket to the sheave, a great gleaming black mass clung to the wire and was still dripping as it rose slowly upward, twisting lazily about the wire. I screamed at George to stop the winch and jumped into the bucket. What I had at first fleeting glimpse thought to be a turtle, I now saw was an immense rock that had somehow fouled in the $\frac{5}{32}$-inch wire we use for hydrographic wire and had been hauled all the way to the surface. The winch had stopped, and it seemed quiet without the usual straining whine that changes pitch with every roll, and I could hear the dripping as water still drained from "the thing." George shouted down "What the hell is it, Stew?" I was looking at it and still couldn't believe it. Three or four turns of hydrographic wire were wrapped around it, and I held my breath for fear it would come loose and drop back into the water. Who would believe me when I told them that "we brought up a big rock in the hydrographic wire, but it . . . ah . . . came off and fell back into the sea"? I knew at once that it was a real find and could now see that it was at least coated on top with MnO_2—

manganese dioxide—a typical incrustation often found on rocks dredged from the ocean floor. Mid-Pac Expedition had gotten some nice nodules from Sylvania, Hess, and Johnson Guyots, and they were ecstatic over specimens the size of your fist, and here before me dangling on a wire no bigger than a lead pencil was a piece almost three feet across. I shouted for Bill Riedel, and he came up into the bucket. We decided to have George raise it gently and we would pull it over and rest it on the edge of the bucket. Then the ship rolled, and I hung on to that thing for dear life. If it had gone to the bottom, I think I would still have been hanging on when it landed. Bob Haines brought the wire come-along, hooked it to the bucket rail, and took enough strain off the outboard part of the wire that we were able to unwrap the specimen, and Bill and I lowered it gently—even lovingly—to the floor of the bucket. It is without a doubt the finest geological specimen ever brought up from the ocean floor—certainly the biggest from that depth. It is the sort of specimen that should be placed on a pedestal in a museum somewhere with a brass plate identifying it, and a velvet guard rail on highly polished brass posts to keep people from touching it. We carried it into the lab, grinning like Cheshire cats. We knew it was a real trophy . . .

From dredge hauls and from bottom photographs, it is known that the average size of these manganese nodules is about that of the average potato, which they so closely resemble. Estimates of their concentration on the surface of the bottom are rough at best, but in an area of 16 million square miles in the eastern Pacific, the Institute of Marine Resources of the University of California has estimated that there are about 230 billion tons of these nodules. Manganese nodules are also found in the Atlantic, but they generally contain more iron and less manganese, nickel, cobalt, and copper than their Pacific counterparts. The Blake Plateau off the coast of the Carolinas and northern Florida has been found to be covered with abundant nodules ranging in depths of from 500 to 3,000 feet. These are considerably shallower than the great preponderance of the Pacific nodules, but they also assay out at lower values. Using 1961 prices, the value of the recoverable metals in manganese nodules ranges from $45 to $100 per ton of nodules.

Figures have been developed to determine the economics of getting manganese nodules up from the sea floor, and—at least on paper—the recovery appears to be feasible from both the engineering and the economic point of view.

BREAKTHROUGH UNDER THE OCEAN

THE MOST successful mining of the sea floor to date is for oil and gas just offshore. A higher living standard for Great Britain and Europe could come from natural gas just found beneath the North Sea. The discovery cost a great price: The rig (a barge on legs) that found the gas was later wrecked in a storm, with thirteen men killed and five injured. The reporting of the breakthrough is by Bryan Cooper, a journalist, and Dr. T. F. Gaskell, a British Petroleum oceanographer, in *North Sea Oil—The Great Gamble:*

The Morning of Friday, September 17, 1965, was bright and clear in the North Sea. The sun, rising through an early haze, warmed the men who had been working all night on the lonely drilling barge some forty-two miles out from Grimsby (England). They were glad of the break from the gales that had lashed at the slender tower of steel girders, and the fogs which had sometimes closed in without warning round the barge—fogs which had brought an even greater sense of isolation to this small, remote colony of oilmen.

But apart from the weather, it seemed just like any of the previous 104 days, during which time the men had been drilling deep into the seabed, searching for oil or gas. The barge, *Sea*

Gem, was being operated by the British Petroleum Company, one of sixty-six companies which, operating either singly or together in consortiums (a total of twenty-four groups in all), had paid for the right to search in the British sector of the North Sea and were risking well over £110 million in the project, without any assurance of success. And in the North Sea as a whole, these and other companies were spending over £250 million—the biggest industrial gamble ever undertaken in Europe.

The solitary barge stood sixty feet above the surface of the water, surrounded by the gray, somber 221,000 square miles of the North Sea, bounded on one side by the rugged cliffs of Scotland, tapering down to the flat coastline of the English eastern counties, and on the other side by Norway, Denmark, Germany, the lowlands of Holland, Belgium, and France. A dangerous, treacherous sea, often shrouded in fog and whipped by some of the fiercest gales in the world. Ever since man first fashioned boats and took to the water, the North Sea has seen many varieties of craft: high-prowed Viking galleys, Elizabethan men-o-war, schooners, steamships, diesel-powered liners. And now had come the strangest objects of all: man-made islands of steel, rectangular platforms perched high above the surface of the water on stiltlike legs.

Sea Gem was one such platform, a barge which had been specially converted for offshore drilling and towed out to the site from Middlesbrough docks at the end of May. The ten giant, self-elevating legs had been lowered to the seabed eighty feet below, and then the 5,600-ton platform had literally hoisted itself up on these legs and out of the water. Drilling started on June 5, and continued nonstop, twenty-four hours a day, as the drill bit deeper and deeper into the rocks beneath the seabed.

This was the fourth well to be "spudded in" in the British waters of the North Sea. Amoseas, for the American Caltex Group, had been first with the famous "Mr. Cap" drilling platform, which began drilling in December, 1964. "Mr. Cap" had then been subleased to the Shell/Esso Group, representing

British, American, and Dutch interests, who began their well at the beginning of April. Then Gulf Oil, another American company, had started drilling the third well on April 24, using a drilling vessel, *Glomar IV,* which had been brought across the Atlantic from Texas. All these were completed as dry holes, and although by September 17 a further four drilling platforms were at work in the vicinity—belonging to Gulf, Total, Continental, and Signal—these also showed no signs of success. The BP drilling crew on *Sea Gem* were becoming despondent. They knew that although several small oilfields had been found in England over the past twenty-five years, mostly in the Nottingham area, and one small gasfield at Eskdale, in Yorkshire, no really major discovery of oil or gas had ever been made in the British Isles, let alone the North Sea. The world average of finding oil- or gasfields is about one success in every ten exploration wells, and most of these fields are small. A discovery in the North Sea would have to be much larger to be worth commercial development, and the odds were something like fifty to one against.

Sea Gem's drill had reached a depth of some 8,500 feet, and although the rig was capable of drilling down to 12,000 feet if necessary, it was beginning to look as if this would be yet another dry hole. It was no more than was really expected—oilmen are trained to this kind of disappointment when drilling "wildcat" exploration holes. But although no one spoke of disappointment, it made itself apparent in the occasional petty grumbling and flashes of temper. To make matters worse, the rock they were drilling through at that time was extremely hard, and progress was slow and laborious. Only two feet an hour were being drilled, instead of the 100 feet an hour which had been possible earlier on. And because of the hardness of the rock, the drilling bit had to be changed every two hours. That meant that the whole 8,500 feet of pipe had to be brought up and unscrewed, section by section, until the bit could be changed, and then the whole length reassembled again—a back-breaking ten-hour job in the misery of the cold and rain of the North Sea. It was a misery these men felt even more keenly, for most of them had been brought over for this task from offshore wells in the hot climate of the Persian Gulf.

But at least the weather promised to be fine on this Friday morning. And the shift that had been laboring all night and was due to finish at 7 A.M. had an additional reason to be happy. They were due for five days' leave, being replaced by another shift which had just returned from leave. The drilling crew operated on a basis of three shifts, each working by rota ten days on and five days off. There were always two shifts on board. Each worked for five days and then five nights, twelve hours at a time, from seven to seven. In between, they rested and watched films and read in the crew lounge. Some of them had even run out hand-lines to catch fish, which seemed to thrive around the barge. Altogether, there were some forty men on board at any one time, and a shift would include a tool pusher in charge of the rig, a driller, several rigmen and roustabouts, an engineer, various maintenance men, and cooks and stewards. Sometimes, one of the two geologists allocated to the well would be present, as well as the drilling superintendent in overall charge.

The language they spoke was the language of oilmen throughout the world, from the swamps of Louisiana to the arid desert of the Middle East. The "kelly" is the hexagonal-shaped device which turns the drill pipe. It is kept in the "rat hole" when not in use. The "mouse hole" is where the next length of pipe to be used is kept. Being "on the brake" indicates that you are in charge. The "dog house" is the small office-shed on the derrick floor. "Hand over the dope" is a request for grease to lubricate the threads of the drill pipe.

The shift that had worked all night left happily on the helicopter for the half-hour journey to Cleethorpes—BP's operations base for the North Sea project—and then home for a well-earned rest. Home for most was either in the Midlands or in Scotland; over half the drilling crew lived in Fife. The new shift took over, and everything looked set for another routine day. Already, the men were talking about when they would be finishing this well and moving to the next.

But as the day wore on and the big diesel engines continued to roar and the ever-turning drill went slowly deeper, it began to appear that this might not be like all the other days. To begin with, the dials began to flicker on the electrical apparatus set up to detect the presence of any gas. This in itself was not very indicative—tiny pockets of gas could be present at any time and might have no significance at all. But then it was noticed that the drilling fluid returning from the bottom of the well—fluid constantly being pumped down the center of the pipe in order to cool the drilling bit and return back up the outside of the pipe with the rock chippings—was tending to froth and bubble. And what was causing these bubbles? Natural gas.

It was still much too early to get excited about this discovery. But the geologist on board made an extra careful examination of the rock chippings in his laboratory, specially built on the platform, and discussed the situation with the drilling superintendent. In their cautious report to the Cleethorpes base—sent in code by teleprinter—the words "natural gas" appeared for the first time.

Although they didn't know then, this was the beginning of a momentous discovery, the implications of which will take a long time to be accurately assessed, but which will have a far-reaching effect on Britain's economy. It is a discovery which will go down in the history books, and cause many of the textbooks on the geography of Britain to be rewritten.

By Sunday, September 19, it was obvious that this was more than a slight show of gas. The weather had changed; gales were now raging around the barge, and the wind and rain beat against the derrickmen as they worked high up on the 136-foot drilling rig. But the atmosphere among the men had changed. No one said very much, but there was an undercurrent of excitement. Maybe this would not be a dry hole after all.

The men in charge were faced with more than technical problems. Ever since drilling operations had started in the North Sea in 1964—and even before that, when the whole project was getting under way—the attention of the world's press had been focused on the area. Many conjectures had been made in numerous articles. Questions had been asked in Parliament. Every slightest happening was reported. And not only were the press and public closely following progress but other oil companies as well, for any geological information would be extremely valuable to others involved in the search. As one of the drillers had commented: "It's like working in a fish bowl, with everyone watching what you are doing." Security arrangements had to be tightened, and it was small wonder that careful consideration had to be given to any question of making a public announcement.

It was decided to stop drilling on the following day, September 20, and run a drill-stem test to make a preliminary assessment of the flow and pressure of gas. The results of this test were sent again by code on the teleprinter, to Cleethorpes, and from there to BP's headquarters for U.K. exploration at Eakring, in Nottinghamshire, and on to BP's head office in London. Here they were studied, and after much discussion it was decided to make an announcement to the press.

This historic announcement of the first discovery of natural gas in the North Sea was brief in the extreme:

"A test in BP's North Sea well now being drilled by the *Sea Gem* forty-two miles east of the Humber has produced gas, but not in sufficient volume to be commercially significant. The well is being drilled deeper in the hope that commercial production may yet be encountered."

No announcement could have been more guarded, but the reaction it sparked off from the press showed how intently the whole project was being followed. "BP Strikes Gas" . . . "North Sea Klondike" . . . ran the headlines the next day, and from that time on, North Sea gas was not just conjecture but a reality.

Interest grew as the oilmen drilled deeper. On October 1, BP made another announcement that gas had been found in a zone below the previous level. Further drilling and testing would be necessary to establish whether the find was commercial, but it was "encouraging." This time the headlines were even bigger, and BP's shares soared on the Stock Exchange.

The well was finally completed at a depth of 10,000 feet, and on Wednesday, December 9, further dramatic headlines appeared in the press when a fifty-foot flame was ignited at the top of the rig, signaling the start of tests to measure the quality and quantity of the find. Normally, several wells have to be drilled in a field before a company can be sure of a commercial strike. But by mid-December, BP was so confident of its discovery that the Minister of Power could announce in the House of Commons that BP's first well was yielding 10 million cubic feet of natural gas a day and was satisfied that sufficient quantitites could be produced to justify the building of a pipeline to bring supplies to land. The full extent of the discovery would not be known until further wells were drilled, but the field was expected to provide at least 50 million cubic feet a day, equivalent to 500,000 tons of coal a year, enough to supply all the needs of a city the size of Sheffield or Leeds. And not only was there sufficient quantity, but the quality of the gas was exceptionally good, almost pure methane, in fact.

And so ended much of the speculation which had been made ever since the first traces of gas were found. BP's *Sea Gem* had proved conclusively that substantial reserves of natural gas exist under the North Sea, a remarkable feat for the oil industry as a whole, since this was only the fourth well drilled. It gave new heart to the other exploration companies from America, Canada, Denmark, France, Germany, Holland, and Norway who were committed to exploration in the North Sea and who, since 1960, had been carrying out scientific surveys in the area, establishing shore bases and weather-forecasting stations, and all the other activities connected with this gigantic venture. By the time it was known that BP had been successful, a total of nine other wells had either been completed or were still drilling in the British sector of the North Sea, and since then the number has grown as more drilling platforms have been built.

It might have been felt at the time that BP was too cautious in its earlier statements about the gasfield, in view of its later proved success. But the cost of producing oil or gas from under the sea is extremely high, much higher than on land, in fact, and this caution is understandable when it is realized that BP is now having to spend an additional £20 million to construct offshore production facilities. The wells have to be "capped" by a complicated system of valves at the wellhead in order to control the flow, and pipelines laid along the seabed to transfer points on shore. Experts had estimated before the search began that for a gasfield in the North Sea to be economic, it would have to have at least three wells flowing at a minimum rate of 50 million cubic feet a day for twenty-five years. And, in the case of an oilfield, recoverable reserves would have to be about 175 million tons, that is three times the current annual consumption of oil in the United Kingdom.

Now, for the first time, Britain had found a cheap form of energy on its doorstep, and although supplies of North Sea gas were not expected to reach the consumer for a time, the price of gas would undoubtedly come down. The effects of the find will be far-reaching in many ways. It will hasten the further decline of the coal industry, lessen Britain's dependence on overseas sources of petroleum, which in itself could affect the nation's defense policy, particularly east of Suez, and lead virtually to a new industrial revolution.

SECTION III

THE OCEAN ADVENTURERS
Men Cruise at Great Depths

No other branch of human endeavor offers more adventure, intellectual or physical, than oceanography. The Age of the Abyss is upon us.
—C. P. Idyll in Abyss.

NEWLY INVENTED SHIPS TRAVEL FAR BELOW

THE WAY is open to the depths of the sea. For the first time in all history, men—many of them Americans—know how to build deep-diving ships to take them anywhere beneath the sea they want to go. Five hundred years ago, Portugal and Spain developed a new type of sailing ship, called a caravel, that was especially seaworthy and would take their sailors for the first time anywhere on the then-unknown open ocean they wanted to go. Among those who sailed in caravels was Christopher Columbus. The discoveries made by men with caravels opened up continents and outlined the geography of the whole world as we today know it. Ahead of men today, in their new deep-diving ships, are discoveries that will show us for the first time what the depths are like, and what they contain.

From a National Geographic News Bulletin by Edward Cornish, April 15, 1966:

Midget Submarines are starting to do a giant's job in the ocean.

The versatile metal minnows caught the public eye when a

hydrogen bomb was lost in the Mediterranean off Spain in early 1966. A sub only 22 feet long and known as *Alvin* located the bomb at 2,500 feet.

In the salvage operation, the sub was aided by the 50-foot *Aluminaut.* Though much larger than the *Alvin,* the *Aluminaut* is a midget, too, compared to the 300-foot-long World War II submarines. The bomb was actually lifted by an unmanned device, the Cable-Controlled Underwater Research Vehicle (CURV), directed from a surface ship.

CARGOES AWAIT SALVAGING

The United States Navy plans six 43-foot submarines for rescuing men who might be trapped in a disabled nuclear submarine.

Other midget submarines are expected to be useful in ship salvage. More valuable than all the gold that went down in ill-fated Spanish galleons are the cargoes of thousands of ships sunk off the Atlantic coast in two world wars. The tin in a single drowned cargo is reportedly worth $26 million.

Until now, recovery of cargoes from many deeply submerged ships has been considered impractical, but new techniques may make it economical. In one method, polyurethane foam is blown into a sunken ship. The light foam forces enough water from a ship to make it rise to the surface.

Small submarines such as the University of Pennsylvania Museum's two-man *Asherah* are hunting for ancient wrecks of interest to archeologists. The *Asherah* has explored wrecks in the eastern Mediterranean.

Oil companies plan to use midget subs increasingly in locating and developing offshore oil deposits. Oil is only one of many minerals lying within reach of the underwater craft. Diamonds, tin, and other materials are already being recovered from the sea floor.

COUSTEAU'S DIVING SAUCER

Today's midget subs owe much to Captain Jacques-Yves Cousteau's diving saucer, built by the French Undersea Research Center at Marseille with National Geographic aid. The jet-powered diving saucer, first tested in 1959, has made some 430 dives for scientific purposes. Only 6.5 feet in diameter, the saucer carries a pilot and observer.

Mass-produced underwater vehicles may someday be as common as automobiles, according to the American ocean expert Athelstan Spilhaus. He says advances in underwater breathing gases and apparatus eventually will make it possible for anyone to take to the sea.

"Underwater resorts will develop," says Dr. Spilhaus. "People will drive down under the sea, park their submobiles, check into submarines, and participate in one of the many recreations the resort will offer. . . . Submarine trains and guided tours will take people through the reefs and underwater world."

MEN REACH OVER SIX MILES DOWN

ON JANUARY 23, 1960, Jacques Piccard, a young Swiss, and U.S. Navy Lt. Don Walsh rode in the U.S. Navy Electronics Laboratory's bathyscaphe *Trieste* through over six miles of ocean to the bottom of the Challenger Deep in the Marianas Trench in the Pacific. Jacques Piccard in *Seven Miles Down* tells what the exact moment was like as, after sinking for four hours, they reached the deepest point any men in this world have ever seen with their own eyes:

The Bottom Appeared light and clear, a waste of snuff-colored ooze. We were landing on a nice, flat bottom of firm diatomaceous ooze. Indifferent to the nearly 200,000 tons of pressure clamped on her metal sphere, the *Trieste* balanced herself delicately on the few pounds of guide rope that lay on the bottom, making token claim, in the name of science and humanity, to the ultimate depths in all our oceans—the Challenger Deep.

The depth gauge read 6,300 fathoms—37,800 feet. The time—1306 hours.

The depth gauge was originally calibrated in Switzerland for pressures in fresh water, considering water a noncompressible fluid, as is usual in these cases. After the dive, the gauge was recalibrated by the Naval Weapons Plant in Washington, D.C. Then several oceanographers (especially Dr. John Knauss of Scripps Institution of Oceanography, and Dr. John Lyman of the National Science Foundation) applied corrections for salinity, compressibility, temperature, and gravity. Agreement was reached that the depth attained was 35,800 feet—or 5,966 fathoms. This computed depth agrees well with the deepest sonic soundings obtained by American, British, and Russian oceanographic ships, all of which had reported the round-trip sounding time in the Challenger Deep at almost precisely 14 seconds. The corrected figure confirmed that the *Trieste* had indeed attained the *deepest* hole in the trench.

And as we were settling this final fathom, I saw a wonderful thing. Lying on the bottom just beneath us was some type of flatfish, resembling a sole, about 1 foot long and 6 inches across. Even as I saw him, his two round eyes on top of his head spied us—a monster of steel—invading his silent realm. Eyes? Why should he have eyes? Merely to see phosphorescence? The floodlight that bathed him was the first real light ever to enter this hadal realm. Here, in an instant, was the answer that biologists had asked for decades. Could life exist in the greatest depths of the ocean? It could! And not only that; here, apparently, was a true, bony teleost fish, not a primitive ray or elasmobranch. Yes, a highly evolved vertebrate, in time's arrow very close to man himself.

Slowly, extremely slowly, this flatfish swam away. Moving along the bottom, partly in the ooze and partly in the water, he disappeared into his night. Slowly, too—perhaps everything is slow at the bottom of the sea—Walsh and I shook hands.

THE DEEPEST DIVE HAD A HAIRY MOMENT

From Time *magazine, February 15, 1960:*

Back From the deepest depths ever reached by man, Jacques Piccard and Lt. Don Walsh flew into Washington last week to receive decorations from President Eisenhower, and to tell how it felt as the bathyscaphe *Trieste* dropped seven miles down through the Pacific Ocean to the bottom of the Marianas Trench.

The *Trieste* passed through many thermal layers. When it came to the dense cold layers, it stopped. "We sat on them like going down steps," said Lieutenant Walsh. The crew had to release some of the buoyant gasoline in its upper hull before it resumed its dark, downward passage. Only contact with the surface was a telephone that transmitted their voices in sonar waves to a listening device on the mother ship. Part way down it conked out, and the *Trieste* men drifted on down, utterly isolated from outside contact. Probably the mother ship had drifted sideways and the sonar waves were not strong enough to penetrate at an angle. When the bathyscaphe reached bottom, contact was reestablished. From seven miles down, Walsh's voice reached the listeners, faint but clear.

At 30,000 feet a sharp crack rang through the ship, shaking it violently. The water pressure outside was 6,000 tons per square inch, and even a slight fracture in the hull would have meant certain death. It proved to be only an outer Plexiglas windowpane which had splintered under the pressure. The inner hull remained watertight. "A pretty hairy experience," admitted Walsh.

When the *Trieste* finally settled on the bottom, it raised clouds of fine white silt. Dr. Andreas B. Rechnitzer, the scientist in charge of the dive, identified the "dust" as diatomaceous ooze, the silica skeletons of small sea creatures, often used as scouring powder. In effect, the *Trieste* landed in a cloud of Bab-O.

Clearly visible when the dust settled was a white flatfish about one foot long. It seemed healthy and it had eyes, although the nearest trace of sunlight was more than seven miles overhead. Swimming six feet above the bottom were a shrimp and a jellyfish, neither of them bothered by the enormous pressure on their bodies. The very fact that these creatures were living and healthy proved that the water had oxygen in it. . . .

The *Trieste* stayed on the bottom for thirty minutes, but Piccard and Walsh could use its powerful lights for only short periods because the heat they generate made the water around them boil violently. In later dives *Trieste* will carry more instruments, take more pictures, and collect water and living creatures from the depths. Says Dr. Rechnitzer, "We'll go up and down like a Yo-Yo."

SECTION IV

THE OCEAN'S SURPRISES
Men Learn Some Amazing Things

The sea contains physical phenomena . . . not yet known.
—Warren G. Magnuson, U.S. Senator from Washington. Chairman, Commerce Committee, U.S. Senate.

WE FIND AN UNDERSEA GARDEN

By Don Seaver, Duke University Information Services, July 18, 1965:

180 FEET DOWN

Beaufort, North Carolina: Fifty miles off the North Carolina coast, a thousand-foot-wide garden of ocean life has been located by marine scientists here.

The garden teems with crabs, fish, vegetation, algae, and tropical coral.

Some 300 miles long, its structure poses a mystery to scientists who believe that the answer to the enigma may lie 15,000 years in the past, when the coast of North Carolina was vastly different.

Sports fishermen have known for years that the area produced a rich harvest. Now, researchers from the Duke University Marine Laboratory have turned up some answers as to why this is so while posing the riddle that may reach into ancient times.

The garden is a giant reef. It rises from the ocean floor at least 30 feet and extends to the north at least as far as Cape Hatteras. Southward, it runs to a point in the Atlantic roughly corresponding with the South Carolina border.

The reef has been tracked and charted with sonar soundings

from Duke's oceanographic research vessel, *Eastward,* a $1.2 million scientific ship that operates from the Marine Laboratory here.

The reef fades back into the ocean floor adjacent to the South Carolina border. But there is a possibility that this may only be a break and the rocky protuberance may continue southward, mingling with the waters of the Gulf Stream, according to Dr. Robert J. Menzies, director of Duke's cooperative program in oceanographic training and research.

Dr. Menzies, a marine biologist, is working closely with Dr. Orrin Pilkey, geologist from Duke, on the implications of this finding.

They believe that the reef, formed from skeletons of billions of generations of ocean life, may have been caused by an ancient shift in sea level.

Thousands of years ago, the Carolina coast may have extended an additional 50 miles into the Atlantic. But as the water rose, temperature changes killed off a myriad of tiny calcium-forming animals living in the shallow depths, and their skeletons formed the great reef.

This theory is backed up by the finding that the reef is composed primarily of calcareous (calcium-forming) algae of a kind that normally live in shallow waters.

Since the reef is for the most part under about 180 feet of water, there must have been a considerable change in water level.

Now, scientists hope to pinpoint the age of the reef and the time of the great shift in sea level by what is known as the Carbon-14 method.

They know that when the algae died the remains contained a certain proportion of C-14, an unstable radioactive isotope of carbon. The isotope gives off radiation constantly, and as it does, it disintegrates into another element.

Scientists also know the rate at which C-14 disintegrates.

Thus, by measuring the ratio of C-14 to a stable form of carbon, C-12, in the fossils at the bottom of the Atlantic, they can determine their age. They now believe that the reef is 10,000 to 20,000 years old.

"The reason the sea level was lower was because it was during the last Ice Age," Dr. Pilkey said. "Much of the water of the earth was tied up in glaciers."

In the past few months, the *Eastward* has cruised back and forth across the reef while sonar beams from a continuous depth recorder bounced off the ocean floor indicating the depth of the water. The depth figures were continuously and automatically recorded in graphic form aboard the vessel.

The graphs have enabled scientists to put together a profile of the ocean floor and the rocky outcropping rising out of the sand and silt.

The reef has been photographed continuously with a camera mechanism that shoots pictures six feet from the bottom.

This camera also has been used to take pictures of the Atlantic floor out to the end of the continental slope and beyond, in waters more than 20,000 feet deep.

"By the time you get out to 5,000 meters (17,000 feet) or 6,000 meters (20,400 feet), you often see nothing on the bottom but mud; no tracks, no trails, no indications of starfish or anything at all," Dr. Menzies said.

But the camera has picked up a wealth of life on the reef. This was living coral, usually found only in tropical waters.

"We see such an abundance of fish that you find some in almost every photograph," Dr. Menzies said.

AT SEA, JOHNS HOPKINS FINDS EARTH'S FOUR CORNERS

From The Johns Hopkins University Applied Physics Laboratory, Silver Spring, Maryland:

Man, by the use of orbiting satellites, which observe his earth from a distance, has learned more about the size and shape of his earth in the last three years than his laborious earthbound hypotheses have told him in nearly two hundred. . . .

The Navy entered this modern phase of geodesy because it had the tools in its navigational satellites and because a better map was needed of the seas upon which ships would travel. Precise data on the shape of the earth were necessary also to determine satellite orbits around it accurately. Accurate orbital information is essential to a ship's determining its exact position by means of satellite signals—the first continuous use of space technology in the fleet. . . .

Data . . . soon obtained from Sputnik told scientists that the bulge on the earth's equator was much larger than had been calculated. Then O'Keefe and Eckels, in 1959, determined that the earth has a slight pear shape, that is, the shape in the Northern Hemisphere is not like the shape in the Southern Hemisphere.

In 1961, Dr. Robert R. Newton of The Johns Hopkins University Applied Physics Laboratory, where the Navy's geodetic work is now centered, and Dr. Imre Iszak of the Smithsonian Astrophysical Observatory, found independently that the earth's equator is elliptical rather than round, and that the long and short axes differ by several hundred feet.

All of these facts have been published and are generally known today. In the last three years, new findings have appeared with much rapidity. . . .

Four major high and low areas have been found on the earth's surface. The four main high points or "corners" of the earth have been found situated in pyramid form with points near Ireland, off Peru, south of Africa, and across the equator near New Guinea. These highs are about 60 yards in altitude from the smooth geodetic mean surface and measure thousands of miles across.

Applied Physics Laboratory geodetic investigators say this means that the surface of the oceans is not level but varies by as much as 150 yards up and down. Charleston, South Carolina, they found, is 150 yards below Ireland, and the traveler would have to go "uphill" by that much to reach the Emerald Isle.

WE LOCATE A DROWNED ISLAND

MEN FIND a sunken island no one dreamed was there. They also find new evidence of terrific disturbances—turbidity currents—far beneath the surface of the sea. From the Columbia University News Office, January 13, 1960:

An Uncharted Submerged "island," which probably existed as a true island 8,000 to 10,000 years ago, has been discovered in the South Atlantic 550 miles west of the Cape of Good Hope, South Africa, by Columbia University scientists aboard the University's research vessel *Vema.*

The formation—termed a seamount by geologists—rises 15,980 feet from the ocean floor, higher than any peak in the United States, except Alaska. Its circular platform top is 210 feet below the surface of the ocean, with one isolated knob that rises to within 120 feet of the surface.

North America's highest peak is Mount McKinley, in Alaska, which rises 20,320 feet. The highest peak in the United States below Canada is Mount Whitney, 14,495 feet, in California. Pikes Peak, in Colorado, is 14,110 feet.

The cone shape of the newly found seamount "gives good assurance that it is an extinct volcanic cone," said Robert D. Gerard, of Columbia's Lamont Geological Observatory, who held the post of chief scientist aboard the *Vema* when the discovery was made.

The seamount is about 35 miles across at the base and about five miles across at the top. Coral completely covered the top, and kelp, a large, coarse brown seaweed, was growing from it.

Rounded cobbles of lime, about the size of large eggs and

baseballs, were dredged from the crest as well as coral and mollusk shells. A blanket of manganese-coated sand and gravel was spread around the foot of the seamount at 15,600 feet.

Dr. Maurice Ewing, director of the Lamont Geological Observatory, at Palisades, New York, said that "as is the case with most seamounts, this one is associated with a large anomaly in the earth's magnetic field, indicating that it is composed of highly magnetic volcanic rock."

"It lies about one hundred fifty miles west of a similar seamount," Dr. Ewing said, "suggesting that a new line of ancient volcanism has been found."

Columbia geologists said the seamount probably protruded well above the ocean surface during the last glacial period 8,000 to 10,000 years ago, even though the glaciation was largely in the Northern Hemisphere.

Since that period, the scientists explained, the melting of the ice changed the worldwide sea level, and the waters of the Atlantic rose about 180 to 240 feet, submerging the island.

A precision depth recorder, an instrument that maps elevations of the ocean floor by means of an electric stylus on photographic paper, recorded a sudden rise from the ocean bed as the ship reached the seamount. It leveled off when the *Vema* was over the top, and samples were dredged from the top and base of the seamount.

"We made no biological trawls because the rough coral would have ripped our nets to shreds," Gerard said. "However, the mollusk shells give a clear indication that there must be some animal life on the top of the cone."

The seamount, heretofore unknown to mariners, presumably could have proved a menace to navigation, Gerard said. A submarine with its sonar equipment turned off might possibly ram the formation before being aware of its existence.

The seamount was discovered on a fairly busy shipping lane between Recife, Brazil, and the Cape of Good Hope, near the tip of South Africa, both very active ports.

Less than 200 miles east of the seamount, the *Vema* found additional evidence to support the theory that great landslides occur periodically in the ocean, causing mud to race across the bottom at the speed of an express train.

Some scientists say such "turbidity currents" may reach eighty-five miles an hour and lay down 50,000 square miles of silt in a day.

The theory that mud races through seawater at such speeds has met with considerable resistance among scientists, but its supporters seem to be gaining ground. Two of its most prominent champions are Dr. Ewing and Dr. Bruce Heezen, research associate in geology at Columbia.

East of the seamount the *Vema* brought up cores with sand and shallow-water fossils from the sea bottom several miles deep and a few hundred miles off the mouth of the Orange River, which forms the boundary between South-West Africa and the Union of South Africa.

These cores, taken with metal tubes, bite forty feet or more into the ocean bed and bring up ocean sediment in layers, just as it was laid down by nature through the ages.

Dr. Heezen for several years has been collecting evidence to support the theory of periodic landslides beneath the sea. He divides them into two categories: one cut loose by an earthquake and the other by an unusually heavy flow of water from a river mouth. He said the rivers most likely to produce such phenomena are those with no visible deltas at their mouths.

Dr. Heezen and his colleagues have studied two of these in detail: the Magdalena, which flows from South America into the Caribbean, and the Congo, which empties into the Atlantic from West Africa.

Attempts were made to maintain a submarine cable along the African coast for more than fifty years, Dr. Heezen recalled, and at first it was laid seventy miles offshore. But, where it crossed the canyon off the mouth of the Congo River, it broke five times in seven years.

The floor of this canyon is more than 6,000 feet below the ocean surface, and retrieving and splicing the broken ends of the cable is a major operation. In 1893, the cable companies relaid the cable with a detour 125 miles off the mouth of the Congo, but this proved even worse, since the cable broke nine times in four years despite its great distance from the mouth of the river.

The cable company then relaid the cable close to the river, where repairs would be easier in shallow water, but in the next forty years repairs were necessary twenty-two more times. In 1937 the cable was abandoned.

Dr. Heezen believes turbidity currents provide the only explanation for this succession of breaks at distances up to 125 miles from shore. He has found that the breaks came at times when the river was in flood.

He believes that normally the river builds up submarine silt at its mouth, but when the water flow is heavy, the silt breaks loose and races down the canyon to spread out over the deepest ocean floor.

To explain the high speed of turbidity currents, Dr. Heezen cited two studies of avalanches in the Alps. In one, he said, a layer of snow slides down the slope, more or less intact, at speeds of less than twenty miles an hour. In the other, the snow mixes turbulently with the air and races down at speeds up to 190 miles an hour, often sweeping a considerable distance out over the valley. In turbidity currents, he said, the silt mixes with water and behaves in a similar manner.

WE MAP DOZENS OF UNKNOWN SEAMOUNTS

From the U.S. Coast and Geodetic Survey, December 27, 1966:

The Discovery of dozens of previously uncharted undersea mountains, mountain ridges, and sea basins in the North Pacific and Bering Sea was disclosed with the publication by the U.S. Department of Commerce of six new maps of the sea floor surrounding the Aleutian Islands.

Known as bathymetric maps, they cover about 400,000 square statute miles of seabed where thousands of earthquakes are spawned each year.

The maps, the culmination of almost a quarter century of painstaking work, are the most detailed of their kind ever made of this region. Produced by the Environmental Science Services Administration (ESSA), they were compiled using information gathered from more than 275 hydrographic surveys by vessels of ESSA's Coast and Geodetic Survey between 1943 and 1964. The two-year compilation was performed by Haven Nichols, of Hibbing, Minnesota, and Richard B. Perry, of Williamstown, Massachusetts, both of ESSA's Institute for Oceanography. Perry is a research oceanographer; Nichols, a research nautical cartographer, has recently retired.

The maps cover the seabed adjacent to the Aleutian Islands from Unimak Island on the east to submerged Stalemate Bank, 45 statute miles west of westernmost Attu Island. The area embraced by the maps extends from a few miles south of the Aleutian Trench to approximately 350 statute miles north, including the southern portion of the Bering Sea and all of the submerged mountain range known as Bowers Ridge, which extends northward into the Bering Sea.

The detailed portrayal of submarine topography of the island chain is expected to provide a much better understanding of the geologic forces which shape the ocean floor in this seismically-active area. For one thing, it will enable seismologists to determine changes in the sea floor resulting from major earthquakes. The maps are also expected to prove valuable to scientists in associated disciplines, such as physical and biological oceanography, geophysics, and commercial fisheries.

The authors named many topographic features on the ocean floor. Among the new undersea mountains, generally known as seamounts, was one which rises more than a mile above the seabed. This 6,510-foot seamount has been named after the late Rear Admiral K. T. Adams, a former assistant director of the Coast and Geodetic Survey.

A newly discovered submerged mountain ridge was named after the late Rear Admiral Jean A. Hawley, who was also an assistant director of the Coast and Geodetic Survey. This ridge, located about 45 miles south of Adak Island, rises 4,260 feet above the sea floor.

Many features, such as the immense Aleutian Trench, are shown in greater detail than on previously available maps. This trench, which parallels the arc about 75 miles to the south of the Aleutian Islands, has a maximum depth of over 25,000 feet.

The maps also pinpoint various other sea-bottom features, including the Murray Canyon, 12 miles wide and almost 3 miles deep, the Adak Canyon, 8 miles wide and more than 2 miles deep, and Bowers Ridge. This ridge of submerged mountains extends about 300 miles, rising from extremely flat areas more than 2 miles deep to 390 feet below sea level.

Positions of the soundings within sight of land were obtained by standard visual fixes, while positions of offshore soundings were located by the latest available electronic positioning devices. Depths were secured with echo sounders, which create a continuous profile of the ocean floor.

Among the ships which conducted the hydrographic surveys over a period of more than two decades were the U.S. Coast and Geodetic Survey's *Pioneer, Surveyor, Explorer,* and *Pathfinder.*

UNDERSEA SOUND HEARD ROUND THE WORLD

THERE ARE sound channels in the ocean. Like a cable on the bottom of the sea, they carry sound. They can let you listen to a noise made on the other side of the globe.

From the Columbia University News Office, July 5, 1960:

Underwater Sound Waves from depth charges fired by Columbia University's research vessel *Vema* have been picked up at a record distance of 12,000 miles—virtually halfway around the world.

The previous record was approximately 3,000 miles.

Scientists point out that the distance is almost as far as such sound waves can be received, because if they pass more than half the circumference of the globe, they naturally get nearer to the receiving station. The circumference of the earth at the equator is 24,902 miles, and through the poles is 24,860 miles.

The recording of the shots was reported by Columbia's Seismic and SOFAR station in Bermuda in a message to Dr. Maurice Ewing, director of Columbia's Lamont Geological Observatory, Palisades, New York, which operates the *Vema* and the Bermuda station.

The cablegram said the acoustic signals were received in Bermuda before arrival of a radiogram from the *Vema* announcing that three shots were fired by the vessel in a deep channel off the coast of Australia. Another message said the shots were recorded at five-minute intervals at 10:47 P.M., Greenwich mean time (5:47 P.M., Eastern Standard Time) March 21, 1960.

The acoustic waves from the shots, fired off southern Australia, reached the Bermuda station in approximately 144 minutes. They traveled through the water, following the sound-channel axis near the surface in the south and dropping to depths of around 4,200 feet near the equator. The sound followed a great circle path past the Cape of Good Hope. The sound waves could be picked up only in areas where there is a great circle path in deep water.

The highly sensitive instruments at the Bermuda station, one of which has been in service eleven years, are located in water around 4,200 feet deep. Scientists believe that an underwater atomic blast, if fired near the sound channel, could be picked up by SOFAR.

John I. Ewing, a member of the Lamont Observatory scientific staff and brother of the director, said recording of the shots was remarkable both because of the distance the sound waves traveled and the fact that there is no perfectly clear path in the water between the firing point off Australia and Bermuda.

"Sound waves traveling through the water between those two points have to feel their way around islands and through shallow areas," he said.

The *Vema* began its acoustic wave experiments shortly after it left the vicinity of Bermuda.

Small charges were fired at intervals en route to the Cape of Good Hope, South Africa, and as the ship got farther away from the Bermuda station, distance records were broken every day in the receipt of the waves in Bermuda.

Various sizes of shots were fired, and the largest—50 pounds—were fired off Australia.

Dr. Maurice Ewing discovered SOFAR during World War II.

While working with the Woods Hole Oceanographic Institution before the United States entered the war, he took countless seismic measurements up and down the eastern seaboard.

During an examination of seismographic records it occurred to him that aircraft or ships in distress at sea might signal their position by underwater sound by setting off small depth charges. The vibrations would carry through miles of water to listening posts, and the rest would be a simple matter of mathematics to figure the source of the underwater sound and the exact location of the craft in distress.

He wrote the Navy Department about the idea, but nothing happened until early in 1944, when Dr. Ewing told a young Navy lieutenant, Edgar L. Newhouse III, about it. Lieutenant Newhouse took the matter up with his superiors in Washington, D.C., and in April, 1944, tests were made.

Dr. Ewing was aboard a yawl anchored off Bermuda waiting for the Navy destroyer *Buckley*. An underwater detection device called a hydrophone ear was lowered 4,000 feet into the water from the yawl. The *Buckley* put out and at 100-mile intervals dropped 4-pound depth charges, set to explode at 4,000 feet.

With a loudspeaker and a recording machine at his side, Dr. Ewing waited for the acoustic waves from the *Buckley*'s depth charges, which were set off at 100 miles, 200 miles, and finally at 1,200 miles away. A few days later in Washington, Dr. Ewing played back the recording to Navy officials, and they heard the explosions. The Navy quickly found a name for Dr. Ewing's discovery—Sound Fixing and Ranging—abbreviated it to SOFAR, and authorized Dr. Ewing to perfect it, with Lieutenant Newhouse as project officer. Late in 1945 Dr. Ewing finished his work. Sound had been transmitted underwater from Dakar, French West Africa, to Bermuda, a distance of 3,000 miles, in 62 minutes.

In 1955, Dr. Ewing was awarded the Navy's highest civilian honor—the Distinguished Public Service Award—for SOFAR, called by many the most important discovery in communications since radar.

AT LAST WE KNOW WHERE BERMUDA IS

THE ECHO I and Echo II satellites are big, 100-feet-in-diameter, balloonlike objects. They have orbited the earth so many times that they have become probably the two man-made objects seen by the most people in all history. They also located exactly the Bermuda Islands. This would have helped skippers of the sailing-ship age who kept missing Bermuda because of inexact charts, but who often found nearby rocks and shoals very easily. The results from the Echo satellites showed, according to a front-page headline in the *Bermuda Mid-Ocean News,* that "Bermuda Is Not Where You Think It Is!" From that newspaper, September 19, 1964:

Through the Use of the artificial earth satellites Echo I and II, science has finally determined the precise location of the Bermuda Islands in the Atlantic Ocean, 449 years after they were first visited by a Spanish voyager.

This was disclosed today by the Coast and Geodetic Survey, U.S. Department of Commerce, after three months of intensive and painstaking work.

Rear Admiral H. Arnold Karo, Director of the Commerce Department agency, said the study revealed that the Bermuda Islands lie 220 feet farther north and 105 feet farther west of the last determined location. This, incidentally, brings the islands closer to New York, which is approximately 750 miles northwest of the islands, and to Cape Hatteras, North Carolina, the closest point on the North American continent, 650 miles distant.

Using the satellites as space targets against star backgrounds and employing the most scientifically advanced cameras, geodesists of the Coast and Geodetic Survey were able to determine the location of the islands with an accuracy previously unknown.

Heading the study, in which thirty persons participated, were Lt. Comdr. Eugene Taylor, Chief of Satellite Triangulation Observations, and Dr. Hellmut Schmid, Scientific Adviser to the Director.

IN 1937

The location of the popular resort islands has been in question since the earliest geodetic surveys, performed by the British Admiralty before the turn of this century, determined their position by astronomic observations. In 1937, the islands were resurveyed by the British Admiralty, starting from a new astronomic position, and this resulted in a new location for the islands.

During the last war, the Naval Oceanographic Office and the Coast and Geodetic Survey surveyed the islands again with a higher degree of accuracy, in order to establish military and naval bases. Astronomic observations at two stations were used to reposition the islands. These two astronomic positions were not compatible, so the final position of the islands was arbitrarily taken as the average of the two conflicting astronomic positions.

1943 DATUM

This constituted the so-called Bermuda 1943 Datum, the mathematical base which enabled surveyors to determine its position in the Atlantic in relationship to positions on the North American continent. This location remained fixed for fourteen years, when it was supplanted by the so-called Bermuda 1957 Datum.

The latter was the outgrowth of submarine gravity and astronomic surveys conducted by the Naval Oceanographic Office, and it resulted once again in a new position for the islands, 100 feet south and 525 feet west of the 1943 position.

But the islands did not remain fixed in this position very long. In August, 1959, the Air Force provided a two-dimensional connection between Bermuda and the North American continent through the simultaneous observance of high-altitude flares in Massachusetts, Virginia, and Bermuda. This moved the position of the islands 220 feet to the north and 60 feet to the west.

FINALLY ANCHORED

The Coast and Geodetic Survey has finally anchored the islands once and for all with a three-dimensional satellite triangulation connection between Bermuda and points in Maryland and Florida. The position of the islands was moved another 220 feet to the north and 105 feet to the west.

In determining the precise location of the Bermuda Islands,

the Coast and Geodetic Survey made use of a new system of measurements known as satellite triangulation, or satellite geodesy.

REFLECTION

This system involves the use of passive satellites, such as the Echo, which reflect the sunlight.

In practice, satellite triangulation is the photographing of an identified satellite simultaneously from three or more points on the earth's surface.

This system of measurement will help determine with more accuracy than in the past the distances over water—as between continents and islands.

WE MAP HATTERAS SUBMARINE CANYON

By Don Seaver, Duke University Information Services, May 10, 1965:

DOWN TO ABYSSAL PLAIN:

Beaufort, North Carolina: Some 26.5 miles due east of Cape Hatteras and 80 fathoms deep in the Atlantic is the beginning of the continental slope and the Hatteras Submarine Canyon.

The canyon is 500 feet deep and a mile and a half wide here. The deep gash in the ocean's bottom runs southeasterly and may continue for several hundred miles.

For more than twenty-five years, it has been a subject of much speculation—suspected but not proved.

But a group of Duke University scientists has been shadowing the chasm with sonar soundings—a cone of electrical impulses that ranges from 550 to 6,900 feet in width.

As the cone probes the ocean bottom and graphically records its configuration aboard Duke's new oceanographic reasearch vessel, *Eastward,* the picture of the long-sought canyon is slowly unfolding.

In the next nine miles of ocean water it broadens to a width of three miles. And Duke scientists believe it will get much deeper as it continues down the continental slope, into the continental rise, and, finally, to the Hatteras Abyssal Plain.

Charting the Hatteras Canyon is only one of several research projects already under way.

Duke scientists are seeking basic knowledge about the ocean's wonders, and this knowledge may have important implications for commercial and sport fishing off the Carolina coast.

"The basic knowledge collected will be made available to any agency, to everyone," said Dr. Robert J. Menzies, director of the cooperative oceanographic program at the Duke Marine Laboratory.

"Much of this basic information will have application to commercial problems."

For instance:

They hope to compile precise and accurate chartings of the meandering of the Gulf Stream.

According to Dr. Menzies, who is a Duke marine biologist, this current of warm water, which flows along the coast and is a rich repository of marine life, varies in its location.

Dr. Menzies believes that the fluctuations are seasonal.

The *Eastward* is equipped to constantly monitor and record water temperatures. With this equipment, Dr. Menzies hopes to determine just when the Gulf Stream will be located where.

In the past . . . months, he has found that it begins about 20 miles off Cape Hatteras. It begins suddenly, with an abrupt increase of some five degrees in water temperature, he said.

Duke researchers and others also are interested in a peculiar phenomenon of the deep which confounded sailors for a number of years and led to the appearance on many marine charts of dangerous shoals that did not exist.

In scientific terminology this curiosity is known as the deep scattering layer.

According to John G. Newton, assistant director of the cooperative oceanographic program, it is composed of a dense layer of marine microorganisms. These organisms stay deep in the ocean during the day and at night rise to the surface to feed.

Consequently, many fish rise with them to feed on the organisms.

On sonar readings, the deep scattering layer shows up as a solid dark mass. At dusk in World War II, when the organisms were nearing the surface, many Navy sonar operators read them as the ocean bottom and rapidly receding water depth.

"Many shoals still shown on Pacific charts made during World War II are not really shoals but simply where sonar picked up the deep scattering layer," Newton said. "This caused many ships to suddenly stop and back up."

Newton said that researchers hope to determine just what the organisms are, what fish feed on them, and exactly what the fish feed on.

Currently, Dr. Menzies' chief research interest remains the Hatteras Submarine Canyon.

Scientists once thought such canyons might have been caused by river outflows during periods when the sea level receded, such as the Ice Ages. But this theory collapsed when midocean canyons were discovered.

"It is the general belief now that this canyon was cut by submarine erosion caused by turbidity currents," Dr. Menzies said.

Turbidity currents are strong currents with a high degree of sand or sediment suspended in the water. The current and suspension grind away at the ocean floor.

Dr. Menzies explained that canyons act as traps for organic material floating in the water, and that currents in the canyons wash the organic material down into the oceans' deepest waters.

"Theoretically, this could either furnish food for deep-sea life, or it could be a mechanism for preservation of ocean fauna," he said, "by burying life on the bottom and preserving it as fossils."

"An enormous amount of organic material is being carried to the bottom of the sea where ordinarily there is none. I want to find out if it is feeding life there or burying it," Dr. Menzies said.

With additional equipment soon to be installed on the *Eastward,* he will be able to take large core sections of bottom samples. This equipment will enable him to take cores up to 60 feet in length at one scoop.

And it may cause the Atlantic to surrender some more of its secrets.

SECTION V

THE OCEAN'S FALSE BOTTOM
Just What Is the Deep Scattering Layer?

The recent discovery that a living cloud of some unknown creatures is spread over much of the ocean at a depth of several hundred fathoms below the surface is the most exciting thing that has been learned about the ocean for many years.
—Rachel L. Carson in The Sea Around Us.

DIVE EIGHTY-FOUR: INTO THE "SEA SNOW"

THE U.S. Navy Electronics Laboratory bathyscaphe *Trieste* made a series of numbered scientific dives off the Southern California coast to study at first hand the biology, geology, underwater sound characteristics, and physics of deep waters. Dive 84, the subject of this article, was made by Lt. Don Walsh, USN (who along with Jacques Piccard in 1960 piloted the *Trieste* to a world-record depth in the Pacific) and Dr. Eugene LaFond in order to observe the deep scattering layer, bottom currents, and sea floor. By Eugene LaFond in *Sea Frontiers,* May, 1962:

Since Her Record-breaking descent 35,800 feet into the Challenger Deep of the Marianas Trench, the *Trieste* has undergone extensive alterations, including structural improvements and the addition of new sensing and recording equipment. On the twenty-fifth of October, 1961, Dive 84 was directed to a depth of 3,870 feet in the San Diego Trough. This is a flat-bottomed trench extending in a north-south direction and connecting with the Catalina Basin over a deep sill of 3,000 feet about a hundred miles to the northwest, while to the south it is open to greater depths.

The bathyscaphe was towed by a fleet tug from the Navy Electronics Laboratory (NEL) dock to the diving site fifteen miles away. A bright sun, a calm sea surface with swells of only a foot or two, and a wind velocity of less than five knots made the day ideal for diving. At this site, the echo sounder of the fleet tug was turned on before the dive to verify the distance to the sea floor and to measure the depth of maximum scattering in the scattering layer, that peculiar sound-reflecting layer of concentrated zooplankton which, at mid-depths, causes an echo from the sounder and appears on the instrument chart as a "false bottom." The sounder showed that the layer began at 840 feet and faded out at about 1,080 feet.

THE DESCENT TO THE BOTTOM

The dive was characterized by a rapid vertical descent. The ocean became darker as the descent progressed, and at 480 feet the battery-operated floodlights were turned on. These were directed downward past the gondola viewing port to illuminate the particles in the water and brightly etch all organisms and inorganic material against a black background.

It was at this depth that the water first seemed placid, still, and clear. The larger biological organisms coming into view—arrow worms, copepods, siphonophores, medusae, comb jellies, and others—seemed fixed in space. There appeared to be no relative movement among them, and they looked as though they were frozen in clear ice.

Previous experience diving with scuba gear to depths of 100 feet has shown that the upper water is always in turbulent and surging motion because of the surface waves. Underwater television, employed at a 60-foot depth from the NEL Oceanographic Research Tower, has also recorded surges due to the surface waves, in which particles of water move in vertical circles or ellipses. But at the 480-foot depth, the water seen through the

Trieste's window was calm and clear. Upon close scrutiny, tiny copepods were observed moving with erratic jumps, and although small fish too were actually swimming very slowly, life in the cubic yard of water under floodlight still appeared suspended in space. After this pause, the bathyscaphe proceeded slowly downward.

The clarity of the ocean at these depths was much greater than in the shallow waters near the San Diego shoreline, where abundant phytoplankton hampers visibility. No plants were present to obscure visibility of the many other organisms, including shrimp, isopods, euphausids, and small fishes.

The most unusual feature observed during Dive 84 was the presence of white particles called "sea snow." This phenomenon consists of organic wastes that resemble very fragile flakes of white ashes. The sea snow seemed as thin as wet tissue paper, and it is questionable whether it could be collected in a conventional plankton net. The water motion at shallower depths would ordinarily disintegrate such material. These flakes vary in shape and size up to 2½ centimeters across. It is doubtful that the nature of sea snow in its environment could be detected by means other than close visual observation from a submersible.

FIREWORKS

When the lights were extinguished, the variety of bioluminescent forms was startling in front of the *Trieste*. Strings and circles of individual lights, bright single bursts, and blazelike flares gleamed in a color spectacle of blue-green, yellow, and orange. These appeared to be concentrated in front of the bathyscaphe gondola which, in descending, was ahead of the main chamber. The explanation seems to be that the pressure wave ahead of the descending bathyscaphe has a triggering influence on the organisms which causes them to bioluminesce.

Although the species of organisms changed with depth, the most conspicuous change was in their abundance. For example, the deep scattering layer was marked by an increase in the population of creatures whose size was between 1 millimeter and 15 centimeters across. The number in the layer per 6-inch cube was estimated as ten. The lowest count at any level in the water column was one. Most surprising was the continued abundance and variety of living things from surface to bottom, with life in all stages of growth and decay.

At a depth of 3,600 feet, organic life of all kinds seemed to increase in numbers, and a greater mass of organic matter was especially obvious through the last 360 feet. Near the bottom, however, the water became crystal clear, although not entirely free of suspended particles.

The descent to the bottom was slowed by dropping ballast. The gondola, or steel sphere for the crew, was placed gently on the sea floor, but a cloud of mud billowed up alarmingly in front of the port. This sudden, upward motion of dense, muddy water outside the window gave the impression that the bathyscaphe gondola was sinking completely under the bottom mud, and produced what must be described ruefully as a sinking feeling within the author! The television camera at the stern, however, revealed the clarity of the water there and the distance of the camera from the bottom.

ON THE BOTTOM

As the gondola settled into the bottom, the brown and gray mud curled up around it in clean layers to a height of about 5 inches, almost like toothpaste squeezed from a tube. The subsurface mud was gray, but the undisturbed surface was covered with a fine, brown material which contrasted sharply in color. The sea floor was unusually flat, with small worm-tube projections protruding above it a centimeter or two. Other mounds measured 2 or 3 centimeters in diameter. The remains of old borings were also apparent on the flat floor, which was devoid of prominent ripples. A patch of the small iron pellets that the *Trieste* discharges to control descent lay . . . in front of the gondola window.

After ten minutes on the bottom, the water around the *Trieste* cleared, and the base of the inclinometer grid suspended in front of the port was determined to be 6 inches from the sea floor. A large, black sablefish (*Anoplopoma fimbria*), about thirty inches long, moved close to the window, then veered off, but remained within the light beam fringe for the two hours the bathyscaphe was on the bottom.

Besides the solitary sablefish, the most conspicuous organisms at the bottom were the white brittle stars (ophiuroids), about 5 to 6 inches across to the tips of their expanded rays. A smaller variety was also present, and these did considerable moving. About a hundred brittle stars were visible in the floodlights, averaging nearly two per square foot. Television showed them to be equally numerous under the stern of the vessel.

Three sea cucumbers (*Elasipoda holothurbidea*) were observed. These creatures were blue-gray and nearly transparent, with tentacles in pairs about 3 centimeters out from the 12- to 13-centimeter-long body. One cucumber moved close to the gondola and affixed itself on the freshly upturned mud, possibly looking for exposed food. Two others were also noted in the television field under the stern, and the speed at which these specimens ambled across the sea floor was determined by periodic photographs. One moved at varying rates up to 5 centimeters per minute, possibly stimulated by the presence of the freshly turned mud.

The principal purpose of Dive 84 was to determine currents near the sea floor. Although an observation of bottom-current speed of half a knot had been reported, much slower movements had been anticipated before the dive. To measure these currents, a grid tied with nylon-yarn streamers had been suspended between the forward ballast tub and the gondola in full view of the port. These nylon streamers, when soaked, are just slightly heavier than water and hang downward from their point of attachment to the grid. The streamers then follow the water movement in any direction.

The nylon-yarn streamer technique is used successfully from

the NEL Oceanographic Research Tower to study motions caused by surface and internal waves. Investigations conducted from the tower require only a 2-dimensional grid because local surface and internal waves move in a known direction. However, an observation from the *Trieste,* without advance knowledge of its orientation on the sea floor, coupled with lack of information on deep-water currents, required a 3-dimensional view, which was obtained with a mirror arrangement at the sides of the grid. One advantage of such a current indicator is that almost nothing can go wrong with it. This has not been a feature of other current meters. A second advantage is its quick response and ability to measure weak currents. No other known meter can record, accurately and reliably, speeds with an accuracy of 0.01 knot.

The *Trieste,* which settled about 2 feet into the mud, with a heading of 175 degrees, and remained still, formed a good reference for motion studies. The motion of the streamers was photographed with a 16-mm movie camera. Although the period of observation was short, the results were reliable and would be difficult to obtain by use of other oceanographic facilities.

These results showed that the current on the sea floor was exceedingly slow, averaging 0.04 knot to the north-northeast, which is in a direction opposite to the usual surface currents. The maximum speed was only 0.06 knot. An unexpected factor was a pulsing in the current with changing speeds and directions. The cause of this variation is unknown. (The sea lacks constancy to such a degree that its one constant is variability.) Visible particles moving across the grid were also timed during the 2-hour observational period on the sea bottom.

ASCENT TO THE SURFACE

The speed of the bathyscaphe ascent was not favorable to detailed oceanographic studies. Occasional clouds of mud washed upward from the gondola hull and obscured visibility. The circulation in front of the port, now being in the wake of the large flotation tank above, was upward, and the streamers hung in that direction because of an eddy in the wake. This turbulence effectually precluded further data collection. The *Trieste* surfaced after 3 hours and 23 minutes.

WHAT WAS LEARNED

On Dive 84, certain measurements and observations were made that could not be accomplished by other means. The nature of biological sound scatterers in the water column, and especially the deep scattering layer, were observed firsthand. Many such organisms cannot be caught in a net, and others disintegrate on contact with a net. Dive 84 demonstrated that a wide variety of organisms exist through the entire water column from surface to sea floor. There were about ten times as many organisms in the deep scattering layer as at some other levels.

Panoramic features of the benthos [the sea floor], its geology, and the biology of benthonic forms, were studied more effectively at firsthand from the *Trieste* than by sampling. The sea floor in the area explored by the bathyscaphe was nearly flat, and microtopographic features such as worm tubes and animal borings were evident. There are obvious advantages to direct visual observation of the habits and movements of organisms living on the bottom, such as the brittle stars and sea cucumbers viewed on this dive. Repeated photographs were made for further detailed examination. Such observations are only possible from a manned submersible.

Dive 84 showed that weak bottom currents and their variations can also be studied easily at the bottom. The operation of a current meter to measure similar currents would be impractical if suspended to the sea floor by a long cable. The sensitive nylon-streamer inclinometer showed a north-northeast-directed current that averaged 0.04 knot, and in addition, oscillations in the current up to 0.06 knot.

Dive 84 demonstrated the new opportunities opening in oceanography through the development and operation of the bathyscaphe.

SECTION VI

THE DIVERS' ASSISTANT
The Porpoise Helps Men in the Sea

Friendly and intelligent, porpoises are being trained to carry messages to and from divers, locate sunken objects, and aid in scientific research underwater.
—Popular Science Monthly, *June, 1966.*

THE PORPOISE—MAN'S BEST FRIEND?

AFTER man thousands of years ago tamed the horse and dog, he went on to gain dominance over dry land. Now man is taming the porpoise—and may obtain from the porpoise help he needs in the sea. From United Press International in *The Houston Post* in April, 1967:

Point Mugu, California: It may turn out that man's best friend is actually the porpoise.

By population and/or nuclear explosion mankind could some day run out of standing room on the land and have to start living in the sea. In that case the porpoise, a mammal with 60 million years' experience, could provide the know-how to enable man to make the switch.

In fact, the porpoise (or dolphin), along with the seal and the sea lion, is already providing some of that know-how at the U.S. Naval Missile Center at Point Mugu, California.

Dr. Sam H. Ridgway, 30, research veterinarian at Point Mugu's marine bio-science facility, feels that much has been accomplished since the Navy became interested in porpoises in 1959, but that much more remains to be discovered.

"I am interested in the physiology of the marine mammals,"

Ridgway says. "How can they go so deep in the ocean? How can they come up so fast? How can they stay underwater so long? How do they maintain their water balance? What is their water economy? How does their sonar work?"

The marine bio-science facility was established at Point Mugu in 1962 and now has twenty or more marine mammals undergoing tests and training.

The most famous of these is Tuffy, the Atlantic bottlenose porpoise that took messages, tools, and lifelines to the divers of Sealab II during their 45-day experiment of living 205 feet below the surface of the ocean off the coast of southern California.

Ridgway, a cigar-smoking graduate of Texas A. & M., is intensely interested in the water economy of the porpoise.

"They need fresh water just as much as we do," he says. "Yet being in the ocean is just like being in the middle of a desert as far as fresh water is concerned.

"We believe they get most of their fresh water from the fish and squid they eat, but exactly how do they do it and maintain a salt concentration no greater than ours?

"The animal's physiology is not a great deal different from ours; he has made some vital adaptations because these animals have been living in the sea for some 60 million years. We want to find out what these adaptations are—they might provide clues that will help man as he goes farther and deeper into the sea."

The porpoise is also far ahead of man hydrodynamically. Some scientists believe it shoots through the water at high speeds without producing turbulence, or drag. If this is true, the Navy would like to know how it is accomplished. It could lead to a breakthrough in ship design.

Its sonar is especially highly developed, too. Tests at Point Mugu and elsewhere have shown that porpoises can distinguish size, shape, and even materials by means of this sonar. They can tell the difference between a copper disc and an aluminum one, for instance.

And they communicate. Some scientists believe that porpoises may even possess a true language capability. Bill Powell of the Naval Ordnance Test Station at China Lake, California, doing research at Point Mugu, said:

"We are trying to determine the level of porpoise communication. We would like to find out if porpoises can do any better than such animals as the dog or the chimpanzee."

WHAT I'VE LEARNED ABOUT PORPOISES

CAPTAIN WILLIAM B. GRAY, director of collections and exhibits at the Miami (Florida) Seaquarium, is in his seventies, and has been fishing—much of the time for live, unharmed specimens—for over fifty years. At the Seaquarium, tens of thousands of people have seen performances by porpoises he has netted. Some of the Seaquarium's porpoise performers have been Carolina Snowball, the only white porpoise ever seen anywhere; Clown, who counts to three (she puts three oranges in a tub); and Sparkle, who tosses a basketball and sings duets. This is Captain Gray telling about porpoises:

Porpoise Means "pig fish," a stupid name for fleet, smart, beautiful animals that are neither piggish nor fishes. Also called dolphins, they are entirely unrelated to the fish of the same name.

There are about fifty kinds of porpoises found in all the waters of the world. The most common porpoise of the Atlantic Coast south of Cape Cod are the bottlenose dolphins, which weigh about 600 pounds when mature and grow to be about 8 feet in length. They have been trained at the Miami Seaquarium to jump out of the water more than 20 feet in the air and grab a cigarette from a man's mouth. (That's higher than the world's pole vault record of 17 feet 6¼ inches, set in 1966 by John Pennel.)

The porpoise has a built-in grin, breathes air through a hole in the top of his head, and has a lot of love in his heart.

At birth a baby is about 3 feet long, weighs about 25 pounds, and is born tail first. The mother's labor is prolonged. The moment the newborn baby floats free in the water, the mother noses it to the surface for its first breath of fresh air. Other porpoises huddle close around as though to protect the baby.

For the first thirteen months of its life, the baby swims very close to its mother. During all that time the infant lives entirely on its mother's milk, nursing on a demand feeding schedule every few minutes. We can get them to eat no fish or anything else until they are about eighteen months old.

The adolescent porpoise matures at about four or five years. [Porpoises] can outthink and outrace all their enemies except the killer whale, the orca, which hunts in packs and kills them wantonly. Sharks are no problem to them, for they are far faster and more maneuverable, and have brains.

The porpoise naps dangling in the water, with its blowhole out in the air, for a few seconds at a time. At the Seaquarium, where they have no enemies, they relax and take longer naps. Though porpoises can stay under water for about five minutes without breathing, they usually come up for a gulp of air once a minute.

Some fishermen libel them by claiming they eat their weight in game fish every day. We stuff them with all the fish they will consume five times a day at the Seaquarium, and the average porpoise will eat no more than 25 pounds of fish a day.

Mullet up to one foot long are the natural staple of their diet in this area, though they also like catfish, sardines, and thread herrings. In captivity they must be taught to eat dead fish and only eat them live in nature. At the Seaquarium they soon recognize their feeders as individuals, and are reluctant to take fish from a stranger.

Though the porpoise is a cetacean, and related to whales, many attempts to capture them for their hide and oil have failed commercially. The flesh has no market value. So, at present, the porpoise family is one of the few sea mammals not headed toward extinction, though they were mercilessly slaughtered by fishermen in the early days of trawling on the Grand Banks, and used to bait codfish trawls.

Headed south in Biscayne Bay one day, we saw a porpoise continually pushing a dead baby porpoise to the surface. We watched a long time, proceeded on our trip, and came back the same way two hours later. With the mother instinct, she was still pushing that dead baby to the surface, vainly hoping it would breathe and live.

NAVYMAN'S BEST FRIEND: THE PORPOISE—OR IS IT A DOLPHIN?

By Jim Teague in All Hands, *The Bureau of Naval Personnel Career Publication, February, 1968:*

You Are Lying in the rack listening to the dull groan of the engines as you head toward the Mediterranean at 20 knots. Not much to do. You're bored. Then the 1MC blares out a welcome message: "Porpoise off the starboard bow."

You grab your camera and join the general rush topside. You can be sure of one thing: You're in for an entertaining performance. When you reach the bow, you can see the show has already begun. There below is a school of gamboling porpoises easily keeping up with the ship.

They play follow-the-leader. One jumps high out of the water, then several others shoot up together like hedgehogs from a destroyer. Some skate on their tail flukes, raising high out of the water and grinning up at you as if to say, "Ain't I the greatest?"

How can you disagree?

The show-off with the natural grin has been delighting Navy and civilian audiences for many years. At outdoor aquariums in California and Florida, porpoises perform all sorts of tricks to entertain tourists. With very little training, they have learned to play water polo, basketball, and even to bowl.

There's really no need to describe a porpoise, especially if you have a TV set. If so, you've probably seen one starring on his nationwide show at least once.

For the uninitiated, a porpoise looks much like any other fish, although he's really not a fish at all. He's a mammal, classified in the same zoological order as the toothed whale—Cetacea.

Thousands of years ago, his ancestors lived on land, but he's been on sea duty so long that he now looks like a fish to most people, even though he can't breathe under water and has to come up for air every few minutes.

In popular usage the name "porpoise" has come to include not only porpoises, but also bottle-nosed dolphins and assorted other mammals which belong to the cetacean family. Since that usage helps keep the mammal known as the dolphin from being confused with the gamefish of the same name, it's the one this article will use.

Seafaring men have long considered the porpoise a friend. As an example, some years ago there was one known as Pelorus Jack who was well known among the sailors who visited New Zealand because of his habit of escorting ships as they steamed through Pelorus Sound.

There is abundant lore concerning porpoises, some of it provable, some not. One of their accomplishments that has been observed is their ability to act as seagoing cowboys, skillfully herding schools of fish in whatever direction they wish. Often, they will herd a school to shallow water, where, acting like a well-coordinated fishing team, they will dart in one at a time to take a fish, then return to the circle while another streaks in to get a strike.

Over the years, many people have related stories about porpoises having saved them from various dangers such as shark attack and drowning. Scientists know that porpoises are, indeed, the natural enemies of sharks.

When a school of porpoises decides to attack a shark, they again use the herding technique, and will cut out a lone shark from the school and surround it. Then they drive in and butt the shark with their hard noses, again and again. This finally ruptures the shark's internal organs, and kills him.

One of the more recent incidents in which humans were saved from an attack by sharks was told by a Florida couple who, along with their dog, were adrift in a small disabled boat for five days.

On the second day adrift, a school of sharks surrounded the boat. The dog began barking, and shortly thereafter a large school of porpoises arrived on the scene and drove away the menacing sharks. From then on, the porpoises stood guard over the boat, driving away the sharks each time they came back for another try.

Many people have told of being in trouble swimming, and of having a friendly porpoise push them toward shore, apparently saving them from drowning.

Some scientists believe such stories should be taken with a grain of salt. They point out that porpoises simply like to push things around, and they would just as soon push a mattress around as push a human toward shore. It stands to reason, they say, that if a man were pushed toward shore, he'd have a good story to tell. If he were pushed the other way, he could not tell his tale.

It has been well documented, however, that porpoises do seem to like their human cousins. People who have experimented with porpoises report that these creatures, for some reason, will let human beings do things to them for which they would kill a fish or any other animal. Porpoises will keep right on smiling while blindfolds are put into place, harnesses are strapped on, and a swimmer grabs a dorsal fin for a free ride. This friendliness is one of the reasons the porpoise is such a good subject for Navy-backed experiments.

The Office of Naval Research has been sponsoring research involving porpoises since the early 1950's. Navy scientists have been, and continue to be, interested in three principal areas of research—hydrodynamics, sonar, and communications.

One of the most-studied aspects of porpoise capability is their swimming ability. As many sailors know, a porpoise can keep up with a ship which is making 30 knots or more, apparently with little effort. Yet, analytically speaking, a porpoise can swim only about 11 knots. The final answer has not been found yet, but several experiments have thrown some light on the subject.

One theory which has often been advanced maintains that a porpoise's speed is achieved by using a boundary-layer control to reduce drag. A porpoise's skin is nearly bloodless at its forward end, where a smooth water flow exists. Toward the tail, where turbulence and drag normally build up, there are progressively increasing numbers of vessels supplying blood to the skin area. It is possible that this greater vascular circulation aft could produce a smoother flow by decreasing water turbulence through heat transfer.

Another theory concerns the action of the porpoise's body in moving its tail flukes up and down like a skin diver's flippers. Scientists know what happens when a rigid body is moved up and down in such a way, but they are not sure what happens when a mobile body, such as a porpoise's, is moved likewise in the water.

Recent tests in Hawaii by two noted scientists in the cetacean research field, Dr. Thomas G. Lang and Dr. Kenneth S. Norris, of the Naval Ordnance Test Station in Pasadena, California, have proved pretty conclusively that porpoises aren't as speedy as we think they are.

Star of the tests was a three-year-old Pacific bottle-nosed porpoise named Keiki.

Keiki was first trained to race in a 10-foot deep lagoon about

30 feet wide and 200 feet long, enclosed by a chain-link fence. An entrance cut out of one end and an exit on the other marked the start and finish lines. Keiki learned to sit with his trainer's hand on his back at the rear of the pen. When the hand was lifted, Keiki sped to the entrance of the course. As his nose passed through the entrance, or starting line, an underwater signal was given which told him to "turn it on." He then raced the length of the course. If he made a good, fast run, three fish were given as a reward. If his time was outstanding, he got six fish.

Seafaring men's observations notwithstanding, Keiki's best speed was 16.1 knots. And that was in the smooth water of the lagoon. Other tests were conducted off Oahu, where Keiki had to chase a homing signal transmitted from a moving speedboat. Keiki's best speed in the rough water was 14.5 knots. During the tests, accurate speed-measuring devices included motion-picture cameras, stopwatches, and a speedboat with a highly accurate speedometer.

What's the explanation? Are sailors seeing things when they watch porpoises swim with their fast destroyers and cruisers? The scientists do have a couple of answers. For one thing, the observers riding in the speedboat all guessed Keiki's speed to be more than 20 knots. The sea was rough, and the boat crashing from crest to crest greatly added to the illusion of speed.

But more important is the discovery that porpoises are adroit surfers, and know a lot about riding bow waves and making use of various hydrodynamically favorable pressure fields which can give them a free ride.

The porpoise you see keeping up with your fast destroyer is probably riding the favorable pressure field caused by your ship's bow. This pressure field, scientists have discovered, extends a short distance out in front of the ship, which explains why many porpoises seem to be easily winning the race with your 36-knot destroyer. They are simply hitchhiking.

The use of favorable pressure fields created by moving bodies is old hat to porpoises. They often get free rides from each other, too. A small porpoise will position himself behind and slightly to the side of a larger animal, and thus will be dragged along by the big fellow's energy. This is, presumably, the same kind of phenomenon which racing drivers know as "drafting," that is, positioning one's car in the pressure field right behind a speeding competitor.

Navy scientists—and those sponsored by the Navy—are also intensively studying the porpoise's amazing sonar capabilities. Some of the early research sponsored by the Navy in this field was undertaken by Dr. W. N. Kellogg, then professor of experimental psychology at Florida State University.

He studied the echo-ranging ability of two porpoises named Albert and Betty in a large pool on the Florida coast beside the Gulf of Mexico.

The pool was usually so muddy that the average visibility in it was only about 20 inches. Yet, by bouncing sound pulses—"clicks"—off objects, they could identify and locate the objects through their echoes. The porpoises performed all sorts of feats to show off their sonar.

In one series of tests the 55-by-70-foot pool was studded with metal poles which, if touched or struck lightly, gave off a bell-like ring. During their first 20-minute session of swimming through the maze, the two porpoises together brushed the poles a total of only four times.

In the second session with this obstacle course, the porpoises made even fewer contacts with the poles, and after that they negotiated the course in test after test without touching the poles at all. Even in the dark, the porpoises swam all over the pool without touching the obstacles.

How does a porpoise's sonar work? As we might expect, much like the sonar used on our submarines. Sending out clicks while he swims, a porpoise scans by moving his head from side to side. When he gets an echo, he sends out more clicks, and at a faster rate. Like our subs, he knows how far he is from his object by measuring the time interval between the clicks and the echoes.

From the early experiments by Dr. Kellogg, researchers went on to find out just how good the porpoise's sonar is. Can he, for example, discriminate between subtle differences in the size of two objects? Dr. Kellogg had already found out that the animal's sonar was capable of picking out a 6-inch spot fish (which he likes better) over a 12-inch mullet, but that's quite a considerable difference in size.

Dr. Kenneth S. Norris decided to find out how small a disparity between sizes the porpoise could detect. He suspended two nickel-steel ball bearings beneath the water, with a lever in front of each. If the porpoise picked out the right (smaller) ball, she got a fish. The animal was blindfolded, of course.

When one ball was 2⅛" and the other 2½" or larger, the porpoise's sonar enabled her to pick out the right ball every time. When the difference between the two balls was brought gradually down to one quarter of an inch, the porpoise's performance fell to 77 percent correct.

During the animal's attempt to discriminate between the two ball sizes, she was sending out clicks at rates ranging from 20 clicks per second up to 230 per second. The harder the choice, the more clicks she sent out.

The number of clicks rose sharply in one phase of testing, Dr. Norris reported. Two balls of the same size were lowered into the tank. The porpoise sent out many more clicks than usual, but she would not try to choose between them. Somehow, she knew it was impossible. She turned away as if to say, "Don't be ridiculous."

Other scientists have found that a blindfolded porpoise, asked to distinguish between two disks, one aluminum, the other copper, can pick out the copper one every time.

Probably the most well-known among porpoise researchers is Dr. John C. Lilly, a research neurologist and head of Communications Research Insitute, in Miami, Florida. He has been studying the porpoise's intelligence and his language for many years.

From what he has learned about these animals through the

years, Dr. Lilly is convinced porpoises are the most intelligent beasts on earth. He ranks them far above the chimpanzee, which is generally considered the brightest land animal, and way ahead of such sentimental favorites in the animal IQ derby as dogs, cats, and horses.

A porpoise's brain is larger than that of a human being, and his cerebral cortex, or gray matter (the seat of consciousness, where the higher mental functions take place), is apparently just as complicated, if not more so.

The porpoise can learn some things just as quickly as a human does, and much faster than any other animal can.

In one experiment porpoises learned in a single demonstration to operate a device it takes a chimp dozens of tries to master. The device consisted of an electrical apparatus which gave the animal a pleasant tingle whenever he worked a switch correctly. The gadget gave the porpoises such a charge that their eyes would light up and the muscles around their blowholes would break into a sort of a smile whenever they got their electrical treat. When this was used as a reward, the porpoises would do their darndest to earn it.

Dr. Lilly's experiments of late have been aimed at communications between man and dolphin. He has had some success teaching porpoises to say English words and phrases, but so far the porpoises have only managed parrot speech, or mimicry. His research is continuing.

Even if we can't teach porpoises to talk to us in our language, it may someday be possible to talk to them in theirs. One Navy-sponsored project is to develop an electronic device which turns words into whistled tones, like those emitted from porpoises. A device has been manufactured, but this research is still in its infant stages.

While research into man-porpoise communication is still in progress, other Navy experiments have proved that the animals do talk to each other.

Dr. Jarvis Bastian recently conducted tests at the Marine Biology Facility, Naval Missile Center, Point Mugu, California, in which two porpoises first had to learn a pattern of instructions.

The animals, Buzz, a male, and Doris, a female, were first trained to press one of two paddles, depending on what kind of light signal they received from an automobile headlight. A continuous light meant to push the right paddle; a flashing light indicated the left one. If they got it correct, they received a fish for their efforts. The two porpoises quickly mastered it.

The next step was to train Buzz and Doris to work together in coordination. Doris was taught she was to wait until Buzz had pressed his paddle before she pressed hers. Again they learned fast. There was, after all, a fish involved.

Next, a partition was lowered into the tank to separate the two porpoises. They could no longer see each other, and Buzz could no longer see the headlight. The partition was not sealed tightly, however, so the two could still hear one another. Then the light was turned on. While Doris waited for Buzz to push his paddle, she gave off a combination of whistles and pulse trains—and Buzz pushed the correct paddle. They got it right every time.

Finally, several layers of acoustic paneling were placed between Buzz and Doris. Now they could neither see nor hear one another. Still they tried, but Buzz's performance dropped to the level of chance. Obviously, he was no longer getting the message.

Why does the Navy provide funds so that scientists like Dr. Bastian can play complicated games with porpoises? There are many reasons. By studying porpoises, scientists hope to acquire knowledge which human beings can use in all sorts of ways. For instance, if we could find techniques for understanding porpoise talk, we might be able to use these same methods to learn to say "Take us to your leader" in the languages of other planets. Chances are whomever or whatever we meet on other planets won't be much more unusual than the porpoise.

Porpoises are known to be capable of descending to 1000-foot depths and of absorbing enough oxygen to remain there for a long (as far as we're concerned) period of time. Why can they withstand these deep ocean pressures which are beyond the physiological limits of other mammals? Scientists say an explanation of this may lead to the development of techniques enabling divers to work deeper and men to escape submarines without long periods of decompression.

Does the porpoise know a lot more about hydrodynamics than we do? If we can find some of his secrets, we could perhaps reduce the drag of underwater missiles and torpedoes, and thus use smaller power plants to propel them.

Can we improve our sonar so that it approaches the capabilities of porpoise sonar? Our antisubmarine warfare experts would like to know. They would also like to be able to communicate with porpoises. It is, after all, only a little bit fantastic to imagine a school of porpoises assigned to an ASW task force. An imagined communication might read: "Hunter-killer leader to Albert, Buzz, Betty, Doris, and Tuffy. Any contacts?'"

Tuffy, by the way, has already proved himself to be quite a helpful animal. During the Sealab II Man-in-the-Sea experiments, Tuffy became a familiar sight to the inhabitants of the Navy's underwater house.

Instead of carrying a warming flask of brandy to aquanauts lost in the Pacific, Tuffy was trained to carry a lifeline to undersea travelers who lost their way in the murky depths.

Each of the aquanauts had an acoustic signaling device strapped to his wrist which, when turned on, would contact Tuffy and send him rocketing with his lifeline toward the "lost" diver. Tuffy also acted as the Sealab messenger, carrying bags of mail and tools in a special harness from the surface base to the aquanauts below.

Tuffy is scheduled to provide similar, more advanced services during the coming Sealab III experiments.

Which all brings us back to the basic question: Are porpoises really very smart? One aspect of their behavior provides us with a helpful clue.

Porpoises will eat only live fish when they are roaming the

open ocean, and have to be trained to acquire a taste for dead ones. After a while in captivity, however, they learn to enjoy their handouts, and will swim patiently all day in a pool full of fish until they are fed from a pail of dead fish. They're at least smart enough to let their keepers do the fishing.

SECTION VII

THE OCEAN'S MYSTERIES
In the Seas Are Many Riddles

The sea is a mysterious wilderness, full of secrets.
—Lionel A. Walford, Living Resources of the Sea.

WAS THERE AN EARTH-SHAKING ENCOUNTER?

EVIDENCE from the bottom of the sea suggests that a huge body from outer space once met up with the earth. From the News Office, Columbia University, April 20, 1967:

Columbia University scientists have lifted from the bottom of the Indian and Pacific oceans hundreds of curious glassy objects which point to the possibility of "an encounter" of a large cosmic body with the earth some 700,000 years ago.

The encounter, the scientists calculate, spread 300 million tons of extraterrestrial material over 10 percent of the earth's surface and may have triggered the latest reversal of the earth's magnetic field.

The scientists are Bruce C. Heezen and Bill Glass of Columbia's Lamont Geological Observatory in Palisades, New York. Their findings were reported at the annual meeting of the American Geophysical Union in Washington, D.C.

The geologists believe the glassy objects are tektites, which are widely regarded as being of cosmic origin. Called microtektites, they are less than four hundredths of an inch in diameter and all were discovered in deep-sea sediment cores extracted from the ocean floor. Most of the objects are spherical, but others have been found in disk, teardrop, pear, dumbbell, and cylindrical shapes.

The microtektites were found in each of nine deep-sea cores in a thin layer just above the point at which magnetized material in the core reverses its magnetic direction. It is widely believed that the magnetic poles of the earth have flipped positions every half to one million years in the late geological history of the earth. That would mean that prior to the last known reversal of the earth's magnetic field 700,000 years ago, compasses would have pointed to the South Pole rather than the North.

This magnetic history of the earth can be measured in the vertical sediment cores. As free-floating magnetic materials pile up on the ocean bottom, they align themselves in the direction of the magnetic field of the earth at that time. The direction of those alignments can be measured magnetically in the core materials, and the ages at which the direction reverses can be pinpointed.

"The cause of the reversals is not known," the Columbia scientists say, but the discovery that the deposit of microtektites "coincided with the latest reversal of the earth's magnetic field suggest that a common cause was responsible for both phenomena. An encounter of a cosmic body with the earth 700,000 years ago may have produced the tektites and triggered the last reversal of the earth's magnetic field."

The geologists note that their "examination of over fifty cores reveals that the glassy objects were deposited in the oceans adjacent to the Australasian tektite-strewn field which extends from Thailand to Tasmania."

The estimated total weight of all the microtektites believed to have fallen over this area is 300 million tons, the scientists state.

"An encounter of a cosmic body with the earth which left 300 million tons of identifiable debris spread over nearly 10 percent of the earth's surface might have had mechanical or electromagnetic consequences on the magnetohydrodynamic motions of the earth's core," the Columbia geologists write. "One might thus speculate that cosmic encounters caused at least some of the geomagnetic reversals which have occurred each half to one million years throughout the late geological history of the earth."

DO TINY ANIMALS DIE WHEN EARTH'S POLARITY CHANGES?

From the National Science Foundation, May 27, 1967:

Confirmation of Evidence indicating that some changes in the polarity of the earth's magnetic field occurred almost simultaneously with the extinction of certain microscopic animals in the sea has been obtained by two Florida State University geologists.

Their report raises again the question of whether increased cosmic-ray penetration of the earth's atmosphere, occurring when the magnetic field is weak or absent during a change in polarity, may increase genetic mutation rates. Such increased mutation could lead to rapid elimination of some species and changes in others. The possibility was suggested by the scientist R. J. Uffen in 1963.

The new study, by Drs. Norman D. Watkins and H. Grant Goodell, is reported in the latest issue (May 26, 1967) of *Science* magazine. Their evidence was obtained through studies of deep-sea sediment cores taken from the Pacific-Antarctic Basin. Dr. J. D. Hays, Lamont Geological Observatory of Columbia University, earlier detected boundaries showing the extinction of certain microscopic animals in the same cores.

Geophysicists have recently established that the earth's magnetic field has two stable states: It can point toward the North Pole, as it does today, or toward the South Pole, and it alternates between the two orientations. While the mechanism of reversal is not fully understood, scientists, through the study of earth cores and volcanic rock, have drawn up a time scale that shows at least nine reversals of the earth's field in the past 3.6 million years.

The research by Drs. Watkins and Goodell is based on the fact that fine-grained magnetic particles become effectively oriented in the direction of the earth's magnetic field as they settle through the water. Core samples of sediment may, therefore, record a series of magnetic changes. They found that such changes did occur almost synchronously with the disappearance of certain fossil microorganisms in the cores, as detected by Dr. Hays.

The scientists said that although the two phenomena occurred at almost the same time, the direct cause of the faunal disappearance is not yet known. The disappearance could have resulted from mutations due to cosmic-ray damage or could have resulted from some other cause occurring coincidentally with a magnetic-polarity change.

The Pacific-Antarctic Basin cores used in the Watkins-Goodell study were obtained from the USNS *Eltanin,* the only vessel devoted exclusively to Antarctic research. This ice-strengthened vessel is operated by the Military Sea Transportation Service for the National Science Foundation, which funds and manages the United States Antarctic Research Program.

Florida State University is the home of the Antarctic Geological Facility which preserves and classifies the ocean-bottom cores collected by scientists aboard the *Eltanin.* The facility, which supplies the cores for the research, is also funded by the National Science Foundation.

Drs. Watkins and Goodell hold a grant from the Foundation for a study of the magnetic properties of submarine sediments and volcanic rocks from the Antarctic seas. Their *Science* article reports preliminary findings.

HOW DOES THE SEA CHANGE ITS LEVEL?

IF YOU are puzzled as to when—and how—the sea has lowered its level to expose coastlines, or has raised its level to drown coastlines, don't be surprised. Scientists are puzzled too. We don't know much about it. The Scripps Institution of Oceanography is working on it. The following was sent to me from Scripps by Mrs. Diana Midlam (February 6, 1967):

What Are the evidences of sea-level fluctuations in the central and eastern Caroline Islands and the Marshall Islands, in the southwest Pacific?

There are two schools of thought on this subject, and scientists from the University of California, San Diego's Scripps Institution of Oceanography, and other organizations hope to reach some conclusive answers.

Dr. Joseph R. Curray, Scripps associate research geologist, says there are diametrically opposed thoughts on some aspects of the subject of sea-level fluctuations, and the South Pacific area was chosen for study in an attempt to resolve the controversy. The two schools of thought are represented among the participating scientists, who are examining field evidence from the islands and bring samples back to the states for further intensive study.

"We have evidence of sea-level fluctuations during the last one million years from various other parts of the world. Sea level has been hundreds of feet below its present level during at least four or five glacial epochs in this period of time.

"For example, we know that sea level 18,000 years ago was some 400 feet lower than it is today.

"The sea probably approached its present level 5,000 to 6,000 years ago, but whether it was really a few feet below or above its present position we don't know and will try to find out," he said. "In most areas, we cannot determine whether the land has been going down or the sea has been going up.

"There is controversial evidence of a postglacial high stand of sea level which some scientists believe has caused 6-foot-high terraces, or benches, on some of the islands, during the past 5,000 years. In some areas we know that this terrace was formed more than 100,000 years ago, but in other areas the evidence appears to be very convincing that this sea-level high stand was only 2,000 to 3,000 years ago.

"On the other hand, this evidence conflicts with many studies made by investigators on both sides of the Atlantic and from western North America in which carbon-14 dates appear to indicate a rapid postglacial rise of sea level, probably with some fluctuations, followed by a gradual rise to the present level."

(Radiocarbon dating, a dating method first conceived by Nobel laureate Willard Frank Libby, has produced important new data about worldwide climate changes, recent geologic events, and man's prehistoric development. This dating method has enabled scientists to determine the absolute ages of such organic materials as wood, charcoal, parchment, shells, and skeletal remains formed within the past 50,000 years. It is a laboratory technique whereby the amount of radioactive carbon in a substance is measured and compared to the amount presumed to have originally been present in the substance. This is in a sense like measuring the spring tension in a watch and determining how long it has been running on the assumption that it was wound tightly to begin with.)

Dr. Curray said the area to be studied was chosen because of reports of uniformly submerged 60-foot terraces on the islands. These suggest a certain stability during the period of time under consideration; that is, the late Quaternary period, or about the last 100,000 years of the Cenozoic era, which dates back some 60 to 70 million years.

He indicated, for example, that borings in the Eniwetok Island area reveal recent coral growth above the submerged 60-foot platforms, probably extending slightly above the present sea level. The reefs also provide excellent material by both carbon-14 and ionium-uranium dating methods, and there have been many reports of the raised 6-foot terraces on islands in both the Carolines and the Marshalls.

The investigators sample terraces and sea shells to determine whether the sea level was formed in the past few thousand years, or whether they are as much as 125,000 years old.

Scientists from Scripps, Cornell University, the American Museum of Natural History, the U.S. Geological Survey, and Yale University are studying the sea-level fluctuations. The National Science Foundation provided a grant to fund the study. Senior scientist is Dr. Francis P. Shepard, active professor emeritus of submarine geology at Scripps. Dr. William A. Newman, assistant professor of biology, is chief biologist for Scripps. The scientists use the Scripps research vessel *Horizon,* Capt. Noel P. Ferris, Master.

WHAT HAPPENS TO THE SEA AROUND ISLANDS?

From the Scripps Institution of Oceanography, March 2, 1967:

A Long-Range Study of surface water movement around islands has begun by scientists at the University of California, San Diego's Scripps Institution of Oceanography.

"Irregular circulation systems have been observed in ocean water surrounding islands, and we hope this research will help explain the factors responsible for these variations," said Dr. William G. Van Dorn, Research Oceanographer at Scripps Institution, who will serve as the project's principal investigator. The research is being funded by the National Science Foundation.

"In the past, little oceanographic attention has been paid to the circulation of water around ocean islands," commented Dr. Van Dorn, "since oceanographic research vessels are not ordinarily equipped with the instrumentation necessary to observe and record the large number of factors contributing to this phenomenon.

"Our investigations will include a three-week preliminary field study of the circulation system around several islands of the Tokelau group near Samoa to determine the scope and distribution of ocean variables to use as a guide in establishing instrumentation requirements and techniques for a more detailed survey," Dr. Van Dorn said.

"In addition, we will carry out small-scale model studies in Scripps' Hydraulic Facility, using wave-tank models to simulate ocean island conditions."

Dr. Van Dorn said that results of the investigations are expected to have practical as well as scientific implications of interest and importance to commercial fisheries, maritime navigation, and general oceanography.

"Normally, the sea consists of relatively dense and nearly motionless subsurface water covered by a warm mixed layer that moves slowly due to wind action; there is little intermingling. Our studies of the sea around islands, however, have indicated two factors that suggest that an unusual vertical circulation of ocean water is taking place," Dr. Van Dorn explained.

One is the fact that marine life is often abundant in a region that is otherwise nutritionally poor and where marine life does not ordinarily flourish. The other is that strong, intermittent, nontidal currents have been reported in these island areas, indicating that there are internal disturbances taking place. Both factors can be attributed to a unique vertical exchange of water, Dr. Van Dorn said.

He said research will center around three theories considered as possible causes of the irregular ocean circulation associated with island areas:

(1) Internal waves (waves created below the surface of the ocean), more easily formed and often larger than surface waves, may combine with the piling up of surface water on the upstream side of an island, causing a break in the thermocline (boundary zone between mixed warm water and the deeper cold water). This break could produce mixing of deep and surface waters and therefore replenish nutrients in the surface layer in sufficient quantity to support marine life.

On the lee, or sheltered, side of the island, the reverse would occur. Nutrient exchange could result from an upwelling, or the replacing of surface water which has been carried away from the island, by cold water beneath the thermocline.

(2) Mixing of bottom water with the upper water may also be attributed to a variation in evaporation and rainfall in an island area. In areas of little precipitation, evaporation taking place within a semi-enclosed atoll can increase the salt content of the surface water, making it denser than usual. The water then transported out of the lagoon would be denser than that in the outside surface layer and would sink to a level of equal density (downwelling). The downward movement is capable of breaking the thermocline and mixing the water.

(3) The strong variable currents reported by divers in the vicinity of islands may well be associated with the whirlpool formation in the wake behind the island. The island acts as an obstacle in the normal current pattern and the wake which forms behind it is generally characterized by strong, alternating whirlpools which eventually dissolve downstream.

CAN WE FIND TWO MISSING "MICROCONTINENTS"?

A SUPERCONTINENT may have broken up and drifted apart 150 million years ago. We will be sure if we can find, at the bottom of the sea, the missing pieces of the biggest jigsaw puzzle on earth. From the Department of Commerce, Environmental Science Services Administration, October 3, 1965:

An American Scientist has proposed that a search be made in the Atlantic and Indian Oceans for submerged "microcontinents," the missing fragments of a supercontinent which broke apart some 150 million years ago to form all of the Southern Hemisphere continents plus India.

Dr. Robert S. Dietz, a geological oceanographer of the Environmental Science Services Administration, U.S. Department of Commerce, said "a major effort would be required to discover and survey such microcontinents, but it would lead to the conclusive solution of one of the earth's major mysteries."

For years, scientists have debated the theory that the earth's continents are fragments of two former supercontinents, Laurasia and Gondwanaland, which broke apart and formed the modern continents which then drifted to their present positions.

Another version held by some advocates of continental drift is that of a single supercontinent or Pangaea (universal continent), which combined all the world's continents, but Dietz discounted this. "It seems more likely," he stated, "that there was never any Africa-North America juxtaposition, which is critical to the Pangaea concept. Speaking in jigsaw-puzzle terms, these two pieces show semblance of a fit by their shape, but this is a false clue, as the 'picture' provided by the pattern of the surface rocks simply doesn't match." Instead, Dietz suggested there was a Northern Hemisphere continent (Laurasia) combining North America, Europe, and Asia, and a Southern Hemisphere continent (Gondwana) combining South America, Africa, Madagascar, Antarctica, Australia, and India.

Dietz said that "any reconstruction of the Gondwana supercontinent results in several Texas-sized missing pieces to this jigsaw puzzle. A large submerged microcontinental block, capped by the Seychelles Islands in the Indian Ocean, is one of these, but there must be others as well. Their discovery is crucial to the drift theory. These missing pieces constitute the 'lost Atlantis' of the continental drift theory.

"Once these pieces are found and the true edges (the continental slopes) of the Southern Hemisphere continents are precisely surveyed, the Gondwana jigsaw puzzle will fall nicely into place."

Dietz noted that proponents of continental drift have found inspiration in the fact that the opposing outlines of Africa and South America across the South Atlantic appear to dovetail. He added that one prominent British scientist dismissed this keystone of drift theory on the grounds that "there is actually a misfit between Africa and South America of 15 degrees."

But Dietz countered that this misfit arises only when comparing shorelines, which are not the true edges of continents. "It is not correct to fit the shorelines, nor even the edges of the continental shelves," he added. "Instead, the proper fit must be made along the mile-deep contour on the continental escarpment."

Dietz said that properly controlled and independent matching by scientists in both Australia and England has produced a remarkable result. The continental edges fit with a precision far beyond the expectation of even the most ardent advocates of continental drift. "Not only is there a general fit of the bulge and stem of South America into the great recess and stem of Africa," he stated, "but the various bumps generally fit, and so do the bumps on the bumps!"

He asserted that the earth's continents "are literally light, tabular bodies of rock buoyantly resting in the earth's dense mantle, the part of the earth's interior which rests above the molten central core. If the mantle is a quasi-liquid, which sometimes undergoes solid flow and convective overturn, then the continents would be drifted passively by the movement of the mantle in a way similar to icebergs which are drifted by the ocean's currents."

Dietz, who specializes in marine geology, pointed to Arabia as providing an especially convincing case for drift. "This block of subcontinental size, formerly a part of Africa, rather recently has split away and drifted 125 miles to the northeast while rotating eight degrees, opening up the Red Sea and the Gulf of Aden," he declared. "Eventually, Arabia and Africa may be separated by an ocean."

Dietz described the movement of a sizable portion of California along the famous San Andreas Fault as "a prima-facie example of drift on the small or subcontinental scale."

"Along this fault," asserted the scientist, "southwestern California is slowly moving en bloc northward at about two inches per year, relative to the remainder of North America. Accordingly, Los Angeles is slowly coming ever closer to San Francisco. If such movement can occur, it would seem that there can be no mechanical objection to continental drift. Continents drift like icebergs, and giant icebergs move every bit as well as small ones."

Dietz cited continental drift as "an example of an outrageous hypothesis which may well be true." He added, "It was also outrageous in the seventeenth century to believe that the earth spins in space supported by nothing at all."

Dietz said the "clinching proof" of continental drift may come from the other planets, rather than the earth. "We know," he stated, "that the earth's core is liquid, and continental drift requires that the earth's mantle be quasi-liquid. On the other hand, the moon with 1 percent of the earth's mass has a rigid crust like a rock in space. And we have just learned by the Mariner IV photos that Mars, with 10 percent of the earth's mass, is quite like the moon. It would seem that our earth may be just big enough to have developed a sluggishly mobile mantle. She acts almost like a rigid body, but not quite. Her crust has moved about, resulting in our drifting continents."

DID THE CONTINENTS DRIFT APART?

From a National Geographic News Bulletin by Edward Cornish, May 21, 1965:

North America may move a few inches away from Europe each year as powerful currents in the earth's plastic interior slowly push the continents apart.

The theory that the continents are in motion has not won universal agreement among scientists, but it seems more widely accepted today than at any time since the idea was expounded by German meteorologist Alfred Wegener in 1912.

Wegener suggested that all the continents were once joined in a single supercontinent he called Pangaea. Wegener died a laughingstock in 1930 while searching in Greenland for evidence to bolster his ideas.

Minute movement of the continents is only one line of argument for the drift theory. In 1620, Sir Francis Bacon noticed that the eastern coastline of South America fitted neatly into the western coastline of Africa. Later, geologists found that the rock structures in South America resembled those in Africa. Using a computer, British scientists recently found that the two continents could be juxtaposed with errors of less than one degree.

If the conformity is not due to union in the past, a geologist once said, "surely it is a device of Satan for our frustration."

Continental drift might explain the similarity of animal and plant life on widely separated continents. Similar species of freshwater fishes are found in Africa and South America, even though oceans are a greater barrier to them than to land animals. Continental drift might also account for the tropical fossils and coal deposits found in Antarctic and Arctic regions.

Since many rocks become magnetized when first formed and then indefinitely retain polarization, geophysicists have obtained "fixes" on the North and South Poles relative to rocks formed in different geological periods. The older the rocks, the farther the mean magnetization departs from the present north. One way to reconcile the differences would be to assume that the Atlantic was half its present width a hundred million years ago.

EARTH'S PLASTIC INTERIOR

Geophysicists report that the earth's mantle is plastic; it flows very slowly, like extremely sluggish molasses. In Scandinavia and Canada the land has risen and fallen in response to the load of ice on it. If land can move upward, perhaps it can move to the side as well, the scientists theorize.

Some scientists believe that huge convection currents may rise slowly from the interior of the earth. When a current hits the brittle crust, it spreads sideways, dragging the crust with it. Where the current rises, the crust thins and cracks, producing a zone of earthquakes and volcanoes. Where the current descends, it tends to drag the floor down, producing the deep ocean troughs.

Undersea areas suspected of being on top of convection currents reportedly have a heat flow much higher than normal, whereas the heat flow is exceptionally low near the ocean trenches.

All the evidence isn't in yet, but onetime laughingstock Alfred Wegener is now taken very seriously.

OR HAVE THE CONTINENTS STAYED IN THEIR PLACES?

From The Lamont Geological Observatory, Palisades, New York, October 8, 1965:

New Evidence that appears to confirm the geographical permanence of the continents could help to upset the widely held theory that the continents drifted apart and settled into their present locations as geologically late as 300 million years ago.

Jerome B. Carr, a geophysicist at the Sperry Rand Research Center, has matched recently discovered geological data with a strangely symmetrical, worldwide pattern of land and ocean-bottom features. This pattern was theorized eighteen years ago by the Dutch geophysicist F. A. Vening Meinesz. The European scientist said then that proof of the existence of his "shear pattern," which he based on the natural physical laws of rotating bodies, would indicate the geographical permanence of the continents.

Mr. Carr sees the match as evidence that both the continents and the oceans are very old, having been formed in their present locations at least 2,800,000,000 years ago. The Sperry Rand scientist says that the earth's crust is a single continuous shell, and that there is little possibility that individual continents could have drifted thousands of miles from their original positions.

Opposing this view are the geophysicists who see the continents as islands literally drifting on a viscous mantle. The fifty-year-old continental drift theory is based largely on the apparent similarity of certain continental coastlines, especially the east coast of South America and the west coast of Africa. This theory states that the oceans are still young and quite unstable, and that the continents split apart and settled in their present locations less than 300 million years ago.

Mr. Carr presented his statistical analysis to the annual meeting of the Eastern Section, Seismological Society of America, at the Lamont Geological Observatory. He supported the continental-permanency theory based on his geographical matching of cool subcrust regions of the earth to Vening Meinesz' shear pattern. To this he added a correlation of the age of rock samples taken from the earth along the lines of the shear pattern, plus new data on ocean-bottom topography that also matches the shear pattern.

The study is an offshoot of Mr. Carr's oceanographic work at

Sperry Rand. The shear pattern can predict major undersea features yet undiscovered, he said, and could be applied to the improvement of bottom-mapping techniques.

SHEAR-PATTERN BASIS FOR PERMANENCY THEORY

Vening Meinesz' shear pattern is based on observations that major features of the earth, including continental shorelines and undersea ridges, generally follow a series of intersecting northeast-southwest and northwest-southeast lines, rounding off toward the poles.

The theory explains that this pattern results from the earth's effort to maintain its rotational balance during the buildup of continents billions of years ago. In order to maintain its balance as the land masses heaved up, the entire crust of the earth was forced to shift as a unit, causing the symmetrical pattern of crustal shear, or breaking.

The pattern shows two areas of the world with unusually intense shear—one centered off the west coast of Africa and the other north of the Fiji Islands in the western Pacific. Both are some 2,000 miles in diameter, and lie precisely across the equator on almost exactly opposite sides of the world.

These two areas overlie almost perfectly two areas of low heat flow from the earth's mantle through the crust, Mr. Carr said. Geophysicists had begun to make heat-flow measurements about five years ago, but had not related any pattern to the worldwide shear pattern. The low heat flow indicates that a large quantity of the heat from the earth's mantle was bled out a billion and more years ago through the crustal shears of continents and oceans that already existed.

The natural laws of physics applied to unbalanced rotating spheres show that these two regions were indeed the areas under greatest stress from the rotation of the earth during continent buildup, the scientist said.

These new findings—together with matching to the shear pattern of well-dated features of the earth, plus new knowledge of ages-old ocean-bottom features that conform to the shear pattern —point to solid confirmation of the theory that the continents emerged and grew to present maturity in much the same locations as they are today, Mr. Carr said.

MARINE GEOLOGY: WHAT WILL IT SHOW US?

THE BOTTOM of the sea may tell us the history of the earth. This, by Maurice Ewing, is from *Ocean Sciences,* edited by E. John Long, and published in 1964 by the U.S. Naval Institute, Annapolis, Maryland. One of the world's foremost authorities on marine geology, Dr. Maurice Ewing, *Ocean Sciences* says, has been a pioneer in detecting and analyzing underwater sound, in exploring the ocean floor, and in developing underwater photography and sonic devices. Dr. Ewing is director of the Lamont Geological Observatory of Columbia University.

Geology Has Been defined as the science of the earth's history and structure. It might be expected that the principal branch of that subject would be marine geology—the geology of 70 percent of the earth. The fact that geologists until recently have been concerned almost exclusively with the continents has been mostly a matter of accessibility and of motivation. In marine geology it was usually harder to get data, and the economic and military needs for the data were not considered pressing. Financial support was consequently infinitesimal and intermittent, and very few qualified scientists worked in this field.

This situation has changed greatly in the last few years. Improved and newly invented instruments and methods facilitate data collection greatly; and awareness of the scientific, economic, and military importance has increased the available support and attracted many new workers to the field. The study of marine geology is, in fact, enjoying a boom.

A major difference between land geology and marine geology is the difference in the extent to which erosion has been effective in removing large masses of material. On the continents, the effect of erosion has been so great that we often find roots of mountain systems as the only remaining evidence that mighty ranges of mountains once existed. Only recently was it realized that there were any erosional effects at all taking place in the ocean basins.

Even so, erosion in the oceans has negligible effect in comparison with the enormous changes made by erosion on the continents. In other words, the oceanic crust has been far more stable —freer from major tectonic disturbance and possibly also from volcanism—than the continental crust. Were this not the case, we would expect to find in the oceans not only the same proportion of great mountain ranges which are found on land today, but also the counterparts of the much greater number of land mountain systems that have been removed by erosion throughout the past.

The foregoing argument does not allow for a new and very interesting speculation, which is identified mainly with R. S. Dietz. He proposes that a combination of continental drift and mantle convection could cause new crust to emerge from the earth's mantle, overriding some crustal areas while giving fresh exposure to others. If such activity is indeed the rule, then we will have to revise our interpretations of the processes which cause the topography to be as we find it on the ocean bottom.

The aim of geophysics is to know the history of the earth and solar system and to understand the physical processes taking place within them. In this context, it is the mission of marine geology to (1) discover by geophysical means the shape and composition of the basement and crustal rocks of the ocean basins; and (2) to learn the thickness, composition, age, and method of deposition of the sediments contained in them.

The lowest part of the earth, in the deep ocean trenches, is about 10,000 meters below sea level. Mount Everest, the highest part, is about 8,850 meters above sea level. The earth's topographic range from lowest to highest is thus nearly 20,000 meters. But it is a startling fact that most of the earth's surface is at one of two levels—either within a few hundred meters of sea level, or 5,000 meters below sea level. Other heights or depths are rare.

As Alfred Wegener said in 1924, "In the whole world of geophysics there is scarcely another law of such clearness and certainty as this one, which states that there are two favored levels on the earth, which occur alternately side by side and which are represented by the continents and the floors of the oceans." Despite the fact that most of the existing geophysical data from the oceans was gathered since Wegener's time, his statement is as strikingly true today as it was in 1924.

From geophysical evidence (principally seismological) it is known with virtual certainty that the continents consist of a crustal layer of granite and basalt about 30 to 60 kilometers thick, separated from the underlying mantle by the Mohorovicic discontinuity and overlain by a veneer of sediments usually less than 2 kilometers in thickness. The ocean basins are typified by a much thinner crustal layer (about 5 kilometers), with the Mohorovicic discontinuity (the division between crust and mantle) rising to within about ten kilometers of sea level. This discontinuity and that which appears to divide the crust into volcanic and basaltic parts are known only from seismic measurements.

The continents and oceans are in isostatic equilibrium with each other. This is known from measurements of the force of gravity, i.e., the continental crust stands higher than the oceanic crust because it is thicker and lower in density. It is as though the continents were large tabular icebergs of thick granitic crust "floating" in and rising above a "sea" of denser basaltic and mantle material. The prevailing level of the continents is about 100 to 700 meters above sea level, and that of the ocean basins is about 5,000 meters below sea level.

These two "favored levels" imply a permanence for the continents and ocean basins which is not violated by the observation that a large fraction of every continent is covered by marine deposits. Many of the rocks of our highest mountains are made from sediments deposited in shallow seas and folded into mountain chains by enormous forces. On the other hand, there are almost certainly no deposits from great ocean depths in the continents.

Our knowledge of the structure in each of the two types of crust is based upon concordant results from gravity measurements, seismic refraction, and reflection measurements, and observations of the dispersion of earthquake surface waves. All data support the conclusion that, with very minor exceptions, the crustal structure of the entire earth can be represented by one or the other of these two widely contrasting types of structure—a continental crust about 35 kilometers in thickness, rising from 100 to 700 meters above sea level; and an oceanic crust about 5 kilometers thick, lying 5,000 meters below sea level. There are variations from typical structure within the oceans and the continents, but the variations are small in area compared to the extent of these two structural types.

How did all of the low-density crustal material get to be collected in plates about thirty-five kilometers thick, covering only one third of the earth's surface? Why is it that the crustal material is not spread out uniformly? Furthermore, why have these plates collected almost entirely in one hemisphere? These are among the great riddles of geology, and no one knows the answers yet.

There are two interesting regularities in the pattern of distribution of continents. The first is that already mentioned—concentration in one hemisphere. The second is that they can all be fitted together neatly, as can the parts of a jigsaw puzzle, into a single mass. This reconstruction is associated with the names of A. Snider, F. B. Taylor, Alfred Wegener, and A. L. Du Toit, and was based on the observation that the pieces not only fit together, but that by fitting them so, continuity between similar geologic forms was established. For example, Du Toit has emphasized the continuity of the "Samfrau" geosyncline across South America, Africa, Antarctica, and Australia.

The oceans which now separate these continents supposedly were created when the continents moved to their present positions. Those oceans—the North and the South Atlantic and the Indian—all have as a characteristic feature a median ridge, the continuity of which is still being investigated by soundings in remote parts of the oceans. The extent of the ridge and rift system as we now believe it to be has been inferred by using the narrow, midoceanic seismic belt to guide us through unsurveyed areas. This seismic belt coincides with the ridge wherever it has been accurately mapped by surveys.

There are many difficulties with the view of motion of the continents to the extent implied by this theory of continental drift, but the sharpness and continuity of the earthquake epicenter belt along the ridge strongly suggest the median ridge as the line along which the separation (if it occurred) took place, and also give a suggestion of a possible mechanism.

It has recently been suggested that convection currents in the earth's mantle shift the continents about, with an outpouring of new crust occurring under the midocean ridges. Such a theory has been offered by the Dutch geophysicist F. A. Vening Meinesz. He has assumed that in a primordial earth of uniform composition, prior to the formation of a core, thermal instability from radioactive heating produced convection in a single cell. This convection caused a slaglike layer of low-density material to form over the region of the sinking convection currents. This mass of slaglike material he considers to constitute the single continental mass—the "Ur continent."

During the period of quiescence following this first cycle of convection, i.e., at the time when the instability had been corrected and temperatures equalized, the core material collected together by gravitational differentiation. Thus, when temperature differences had again built up to the point where convection would recommence, the convection pattern was constrained by the core to form a number of cells. . . . According to Vening Meinesz' theory, the forces exerted by the drag of these convection currents broke up the continent into pieces, and moved each piece to a region of sinking currents. The rising currents coincide with the ridge system.

While the mechanism by which continents and ocean basins came into their present forms is not yet understood, the general shape of the earth beneath the ocean water is known with certainty.

A typical configuration for the edge of a continent shows a broad coastal plain of small elevation and gentle relief, which continues under the sea as the continental shelf. The shelf sometimes extends as far as several hundred miles before it is terminated by the continental slope, a relatively steep drop to oceanic depths. The widest continental shelf borders Siberia in the Arctic Ocean. As other types of continental margins, for instance, where very young mountains border the coast, neither the coastal plain nor the continental shelf is well developed, and depths far greater than two hundred meters may be found within a few miles from shore.

During the last million years, there have been big changes in the sea level, due to the withdrawal of water from the oceans to form the great continental ice sheets of the glacial ages. When such a quantity of water is withdrawn or returned, it causes a worldwide shift in a sea level known as a eustatic change. During the stages of maximum glaciation, the coastline shifted out near the edge of the continental shelf, while at some intervening times it was farther inshore than its present position. This record can be read clearly, particularly the most recent part of it, when we can separate eustatic changes from changes caused by warping of the coast.

For example, on the Argentine continental shelf (one of the broadest and apparently the most stable in the world), we have taken more than one hundred sediment cores, mostly spaced along several traverses perpendicular to the coast. These cores reveal a consistent pattern: a layer of sand a few meters deep, covering a thick layer of heavy shells. These shells are from forms which live only in very shallow water. As the water became too deep for their survival, they died out. Gradually their shells were buried by sand. Thus the thick layer of shells provides a clear record of a continuous movement of the coastline from the continental slope to its present position.

Preliminary radiocarbon dating shows that this rise has occurred within the last twenty thousand years. Additional studies will probably permit us to put dates on the successive positions of the coastline.

Evidence from cores taken on voyages of Columbia University's R.V. *Vema* shows us that, during the Pleistocene glaciation, the American shore of the North and South Atlantic was along the contour where we now have water about 150 to 200 meters deep. Similar results have been reported by other research groups.

Cores of more typical sections of a continental shelf, which have not been shorelines for any extended periods of time, show layer upon layer of sediment washed from the continents—sands pounded by waves from the rocks and stones on beaches, and mud and silt washed out by streams. Seismic profiler records indicate that the shelf sediments are multilayered, one atop the other, as in a huge river delta. The "layered effect" seems to be characteristic of the sediments bordering continents.

The outer edge of the continental shelf slopes off rapidly, down to the general level of ocean basins. Lying in thick piles on the edge of such slopes, the sediments are in a position from which they can easily be dislodged. They are indeed dislodged sometimes, both by earthquakes and by much less violent forces. In simple "slumping," the sediments just tumble off the edge of the slope. In the case of major disturbances, many tons of sediment race hundreds of miles across the ocean floor at speeds of up to sixty miles per hour. These are called turbidity currents—currents of sediment-laden, heavy seawater.

Major rivers and recurrent turbidity currents have scoured out undersea canyons on as big a scale as the Grand Canyon of the Colorado River. Many such canyons and their tributaries cut the face of the steep continental slopes.

There are many patterns of transition from continent to ocean basin, but the great majority of them may be put into three classes. In the first pattern, the sequence of form is shelf, slope, rise, and basin (east from New Jersey). The second pattern is represented by the sequence shelf, slope, trench, ridge, and basin (westward from Peru). The third pattern differs in having a marginal sea and island arc between slope and trench (north of Venezuela).

Seismic refraction measurements have shown that in some instances the three patterns are structurally similar, apparent differences having arisen from filling in by younger sediments. For instance, a trench filled with sedimentary rocks has been found to border the continental slope off New England. It is possible that trenches once marked the boundaries between all continents and oceans.

The island arcs around the Pacific Ocean are bordered by deep trenches. These trenches, the deepest parts of the oceans, are in some way connected with the earth's mountain-building process. The processes by which long, narrow, deep trenches are found filled with sediments, metamorphosed, and elevated to form new mountain chains are by no means clear; but it is certain that the deep circum-Pacific trenches are centers of tectonic activity (earthquakes and volcanoes) and that they are associated with young, active mountain belts.

The deepest such trenches are the Mindanao Trench, off the Philippine Islands and the Marianas Trench near Guam. The sediment from continents bordered by trenches instead of shelves pours into the deep-bordering trench instead of either spreading out on the shelf or slumping off into the basin.

The deep basins lying at a depth of about 4,000 to 5,000 meters constitute the truly oceanic level of the earth. These basins make up about one half of the whole earth's surface. How it came about that there are these two prevailing levels, continents five hundred meters high and oceans five thousand meters deep, remains a mystery and a challenge to geophysicists.

The mid-oceanic ridge province goes through the ocean basins as a broad, rough rise. The crust under the ridge differs in composition and thickness from that under the basins. The configuration at the border between these two provinces is not known with certainty, but is inferred to be transitional. In all cases the rough rock surface of the ridge appears to be merely a continuation of the rock below the sediments in the basin.

The ridge in the Atlantic is a median ridge, remaining approximately equidistant from the bordering continents. On a typical transatlantic profile between New England and the Spanish Sahara, the Mid-Atlantic Ridge appears as an elevation about one thousand miles wide, reaching about two miles above the basin floor. It occupies approximately one third of the whole Atlantic Ocean area, continues through the Indian Ocean, and, with alteration of some features, through the southwestern Pacific.

There is a narrow, continuous belt of epicenters of shallow-focus earthquakes, which coincides with the crest of the ridge (wherever this is known) along a world-circling belt through the Arctic, Indian, and Pacific oceans. This epicenter belt marks the locus of the principal present tectonic activity in the ocean basins.

There are a number of ridges tributary to the mid-oceanic

ridge system which do not exhibit seismicity. Their relation to the active belt is not yet clearly established.

Sediment profiles and ocean-bottom photographs from traverses of the ridge show that in some places (for example, in the South Atlantic) the ridge is draped with a uniform cover of sediment from 100 to 200 meters thick. More frequently we have found that the sediments on the ridge are extremely sparse, and what little there are have been collected in pockets between the peaks. We are only beginning to accumulate information about sediment distribution on the ridge. Much more data must be examined before we can deduce by what physical mechanism such oddly dissimilar patterns of sediment distribution can be accounted for. At this stage our best guess is that sediments are uniformly thick where the local slopes of the ridge are too gentle to initiate the turbidity-current action which would slide them downslope into pockets.

Although the mid-ocean ridge system is the largest by far of the topographic features variegating the ocean basins, there are other geologic forms, both conspicuous and important structurally.

Smooth abyssal plains occupy large parts of the ocean basins in the Atlantic, the Indian, and the northeast Pacific. It had been long known that there were flattish regions in the ocean basins, but just how incredibly flat could not be realized until accurate depth measurements in deep water were available. The flat regions were discovered during a seismic reflection survey from *Atlantis* in 1947. That survey found abyssal plains extending for hundreds of kilometers, with the depth varying no more than a few meters. This observation stimulated the production of echo sounders of high precision, with which the widespread occurrence of abyssal plains was soon demonstrated.

The solid crust of the earth beneath the sediments of the abyssal basins and plains appears to be very rough. The rough rock surface of the mid-ocean ridge seems to be a continuation of that beneath the basins. In some places, the basin sediments do not continue all the way to the mid-ocean-ridge province. Rather, between the basin and the ridge there is a region where the rough basement is not covered by much sediment. These are the abyssal hills, a region of nearly bare, rough, rocky hills. On the landward side of the abyssal hills, the rock basement is covered by sediment; and, consequently, the ocean floor lies higher in the basin than in the hills. On the seaward side of the abyssal hills, the mid-ocean ridge rises. On the ridge, too, there are sediments. Thus, there is between the abyssal basin and the flanks of the mid-ocean ridge a region which lies lower than both bordering provinces, and yet has not been heavily covered by sediments.

Because of the abyssal hills' lower position, one would expect that the sediment would gradually move from both sides, covering the abyssal hills to the level of the basins. Yet on all traverses we have found them devoid of more than a very thin sediment cover.

One possible explanation is that the basic source of ocean-basin sediments is the continents, and that the abyssal hills are too far from land to receive continental sediment and so deep that the sediments which originate in the sea itself, as the remains of plankton, are dissolved by the corrosive deep water before they reach the level of the abyssal hills. Another explanation is the erosional action of deep currents, which keeps the hills swept bare of sediment.

Seamounts are the conical peaks which have been found in all regions of the oceans. They are volcanoes, either active or extinct; and like their counterparts on land, they occur sometimes as isolated peaks, but more often as groups of peaks. There are thought to be at least 10,000 such seamounts which rise 900 meters or more above the ocean floor. The Hawaiian Islands are great dome volcanoes, as are many other Pacific mountains, both emerged and submerged. In the Atlantic there is a seamount group extending 640 kilometers south of the Azores. The

Kelvin Seamount group is still longer, stretching 1,300 kilometers from the Gulf of Maine toward the Mid-Atlantic Ridge.

Some seamounts are truncated, having flat tops. The most reasonable explanation seems to be that these were once emerged peaks which were worn flat by erosion. A difficulty with this view is that these truncated seamounts, called guyots, have been found as deep as 1 ½ miles below the surface of the water. A good deal of subsidence and emergence through geologic time has been the rule in all parts of the earth, and perhaps even these extreme cases of deep guyots may be accounted for in that way. Most of the known guyots are in the Pacific, although there are several in the major Atlantic seamount groups.

Coral reefs are an important feature of the topography of the Pacific and Indian oceans. Tens of thousands of people live on islands built on such reef formations.

Coral is found in waters in cold climates and at great depths, but significant reefs have been built up only in shallow, warm water because the particular coral organisms which build reeflike masses are dependent on a type of algae (zooxanthellae) which is restricted to shallow, warm water.

The coral organism is a small polyp similar to a hydra, which lives in a stony cup secreted by its epidermis. The aggregate mass of these cups, which are basically calcium carbonate, makes the rocklike substance coral.

Charles Darwin's writings about coral reefs, in 1837, were the first to attract wide scientific interest. Darwin divided reefs into three principal types: the fringing reef, the barrier reef, and the atoll; and considered that subsidence accounted for the change from one type to the next. With the addition of a fourth type—coral-based islands, called table reefs—modern reef theory has remained essentially unchanged since Darwin's time.

Drilling on Eniwetok Atoll, in 1952, showed that the idea of subsidence as the dominating mechanism was correct. There the 1,342-meter-thick deposits of foraminifera, corals, algae, and mollusks were found to be underlain by basalt, the top of an extinct volcano. Geologists on Eniwetok found evidence that the basaltic mound projected far above sea level at the time the volcano became inactive. Yet the first sedimentary layer deposited on the basalt contains much coral (of Eocene age), indicating that by that time the high volcanic peak had subsided and was covered by shallow water.

The reason why either a rise in the general sea level, or subsidence of the preexisting land is indicated by all reefs except fringing reefs is that the typical coral-reef ecological associates do not grow well below a depth of five meters, and largely die out below one hundred meters.

Marine sediments may be classified as terrigenous (from the land), or pelagic (from the sea). These broad classifications may be further subdivided according to the material of which the sediment is composed.

Pelagic sediments are those which have been long held in seawater, widely distributed by its motion, and very slowly deposited. The most common constituents of the pelagic sediments are the calcareous and siliceous remains of planktonic organisms, and the red clay, which is colloidal lutite particles (extremely fine clay particles in suspension). Minor constituents of the pelagic sediment are volcanic ash or pumice, meteoritic dust, and such chemically precipitated incrustations as manganese nodules.

Calcareous sediments consist largely of the remains of organisms which concentrate calcium carbonate. It is principally globigerina ooze, and is generally deposited in regions far from land. Calcareous sediments dominate in the deep oceans in water depths of less than 4,500 meters (two and one half miles). At depths greater than that, seawater is more corrosive and dissolves the carbonates. Great expanses of the oceans lie at depths of less than 4,500 meters. These include the broad mid-ocean ridges of the Atlantic and Indian Oceans, which form between one third and one half of the area in these oceans. The accepted rate of accumulation of the carbonates is greater than that for any other major type of ocean sediments, 1 to 4 cm. per 1,000 years.

Siliceous ooze predominates on the bottoms of the cold Antarctic and Arctic Oceans. These silica-rich remains of radiolarians and diatoms (minute, single-celled animals and plants, respectively) are found in cold waters where deep water is upwelling, bringing the abundant nutrients on which the plants thrive. A belt surrounding the Antarctic continent is the major region of the oceans where deep water is upwelling. Another belt is in the high northern latitude in the extreme North Pacific. There is also a carpet of siliceous sediment, principally radiolarians, along an equatorial strip across most of the eastern Pacific. Here, too, there is upwelling of cold, rich bottom water.

Lutite (e.g., red clay) is the other important deep-water sediment type, covering about one third of the ocean bottom. It is deposited in water depths greater than about 4,500 meters, i.e., in the basins between mid-ocean ridges and continents. Since red clay is the small residue remaining after the corrosive deep waters have dissolved the carbonates, the rate of accumulation is exceedingly low, about 1 mm. per 1,000 years (the thickness of a dime in 1,000 years). There are still difficulties in the radiochemical and faunal dating of red-clay deposits, for the fossils that would be useful for dating here have been removed by corrosion.

Also, there are differences of opinion about whether some of these lutite particles can be identified as coming from specific continental sources, despite the fact that they have been carried so very far from land. It is thus a possibility that a high proportion of the red-clay deposits, now considered pelagic, may come to be considered terrigenous. There may well be some process, unrecognized as yet, which is able to take the fine, clay-sized particles of continental debris out many hundreds of miles to sea and deposit them in such a way that they fill the depressions to form and maintain a smooth, almost level surface at all stages of accumulation, even on a rough rock floor. The greatest deposits in area and thickness, which we find on expeditions of R.V. *Vema,* appear to have originated in this way.

Terrigenous sediments are those which have come rather directly from the continents by slumping down the steep continental slopes; by the turbidity-current process which has sorted out sands and silts and spread them over the modern abyssal plains; or by the as yet poorly understood mechanism mentioned in connection with red clay, which carries fine particles great distances from the continents.

There are, of course, many areas which are receiving a mixture of two types of sediments. In general there are not sharp boundaries, but transitions, where the composition changes gradually from clearly one type to clearly another type. Hence, the boundaries drawn on maps of sediment distribution should really be considered as broad zones of transition.

Just as there are regional transitions in the sediments on the surface of the bottom, there are also transitions from one type of sediment to another as we penetrate to greater depths in individual cores of sediment. These changes in sediment type represent changes in the regime of the ocean, and by studying them we are able to decipher the climatic changes of the past for each region investigated.

For many years now geologists have fully realized that the sediments, if properly known and understood, ought to yield the history of the earth. In 1899 the British scientist W. J. Sollas tried to estimate the duration of geologic time. He added together the greatest thickness of the strata representing each period of geologic time and divided this total by the present rate of sedimentation.

It was an ingenious idea; but, of course, it is not possible to fix an "average" rate of sedimentation. Even the present "rate of sedimentation" can be little more than a guess. The results of such guesses have been interesting, but necessarily meaningless as long as our real knowledge of the sedimentary processes and rates is so fragmentary.

Until now our knowledge of the sediments has come mainly from several techniques: dredging, which skimmed to only a few centimeters within the sediment; coring, which penetrates up to ten or twenty meters; rock dredging, in which we try to break off rocks exposed on steep cliffs; echo sounders, which in some areas show stratification in the sediments to depths as great as forty meters below the sea floor; and extensive use of ocean-bottom photography, in which we confirm the existence of large areas of bare rock.

Finally, there are the seismic-refraction methods, which give us some information about the degree of consolidation of the sediments and the rocks on which they rest, as well as the layer thickness. Refraction measurements, until now, have been our principal source of knowledge about the total volume of deep-sea sediments. Though far better than none, they are a poor source because from them we can obtain not the thickness at a chosen point, but only the average thickness over a line twenty to fifty miles in length.

Before the refraction measurements were introduced about twenty-five years ago, we had only estimates or guesses of the amount of deep-sea sediment, and the range of estimates was wide. Very low values were given by those who viewed the continents as the source of sediments, tried to calculate the maximum loss which the continents could have sustained, and imagined this material spread over the much larger area of the ocean floors. On the other hand, impossibly large estimates were obtained by those who measured or estimated a rate of deposition and (assuming that the present conditions are representative of the past) multiplied that rate by the billions of years during which the earth has existed.

The age of the earth, the nature of its original crust, the total thickness of sediments and their distribution, continental drift, convection currents—all of these exciting questions will not for much longer be "academic questions." Within the last two years, enormous strides have been made both in our ability to sample the entire column of sediment and our ability to map the worldwide sediment distribution and to pinpoint the places where it will be most important to drill deep columns of sediment.

In January, 1961, a method for measuring the total thickness of the sediment layers on the floor of the deep sea and observing its stratification was developed under the direction of John Ewing. All of my subsequent studies of this subject have been made in collaboration with him.

Recognizing the importance of this measurement, we have added it to the list of our standard underway measurements, which include water temperature and depth, and gravitational and magnetic field strength. We have also chosen the tracks of Columbia University research expeditions to favor the study of sediment distributions.

The measurements of sediment thickness are made by means of sound waves. A cap or small bomb, weighing from one half to two pounds and usually exploded just beneath the sea's surface, produces the sound. Part of the sound is reflected back from the sea floor and part of it penetrates into the bottom and is then reflected back from stratifications in the sediment and from the rock floor on which the sediment rests.

The separation of the echoes indicates the thickness of the layers. The measurement is repeated at intervals of two or three minutes along the entire track, while the ship is underway, at speeds up to ten knots. This ability to work while the ship is moving at its normal speed is of great importance, for it makes it possible to obtain continuous, worldwide lines of data without delaying the other important programs of the ship. In general, there is no doubt about the continuity of reflecting horizons mapped over distances of hundreds of miles.

Sediment thickness has now been measured along about 150,000 miles of track—mostly in the Atlantic. The thickness ranges from nothing up to a few kilometers (except along some continental margins, where it is greater).

The pattern of sediment thickness has provided many surprises, and promises many more. The greatest surprise has been the thinness of the sedimentary layer. Had sediments been deposited at a steady rate (even as slowly as 2 cm. per 1,000 years) over geologic time, they would be piled many, many times thicker than we find them. Either the time of accumulation is far shorter than the age of the oceans, or the mean rate is far less than the present one.

Despite the difficulty of estimating ocean-wide average values for rates of sedimentation (either in the present epoch or in earlier times), it is certain that the mean thickness of sediment measured by seismic surveys is small. It is remarkably small if it represents the accumulation through the several billion years during which we believe that the oceans have existed.

This dearth of sediment, plus the fact that no fossils older than about 100 million years have been found in ocean basins, has led to speculation that the ocean floor is somehow undergoing continuous rejuvenation. One suggestion is that convection cells within the mantle extend outward to the sea floor, so that the sea floor—sediments and all—is carried to the earth's interior.

Continental drift, and particularly the stage of the earth's development at which one believes it took place, would have an important bearing on the age of the present ocean bottom and, consequently, on the amount of sediment accumulated on it.

There are not yet enough observations of regional variations in sediment thickness to shed much light on any of the speculations about the relative ages and means of formation of the continents and oceans.

It is the solution of such fundamental problems that marine geologists seek. To find these solutions, we need first of all the facts about the oceans. From the facts we can build up our theories about what happened, and test these theories by further specific experiments.

Data are being accumulated rapidly, thanks to the increased interest and support of both governments and universities. Friendly relations among workers in oceanography have long prevailed. This cordiality, combined with the establishment of world data centers, facilitates the free flow of data. Thus, we may confidently look forward to a time when there are no longer vast areas on our charts of the oceans where the topographic and crustal data are based on only a few observations.

SECTION VIII

THE OCEAN MONSTERS
We Study Biggest Animals in the Sea

Since it is clear that sharks do not drift at random in the sea, we are concerned to learn . . . how . . . they navigate.
—Office of Naval Research.

WE FIND OUT HOW THE SHARKS FIND US

A Fish can *feel* sounds, the *National Geographic* says; sensitive nerve endings along the length of the fish's body can detect vibrations such as a fisherman's footfalls on the bank. A common fish of the mid-ocean depths, the brotulid, has along its side a row of sense organs (called a lateral line) so sensitive that it can detect currents produced by nearby creatures as they swim, feed, or even as they breathe.

The biggest of all fishes, the sharks, it has just been discovered, similarly appear able to detect movement or sound in the water. From the National Science Foundation and the University of Miami, September 16, 1964:

Tracking His Quarry by airplane, a University of Miami scientist has found evidence indicating that sharks can use underwater sound waves to home in on a suspected food source—possibly including human beings—with remarkable speed and accuracy.

This follows an earlier discovery that a struggling fish or a threshing swimmer generates a "dinner-bell" sound wave himself—announcing his presence and location to the cruising shark.

The findings resulted from a continuing study of hearing and related senses in fishes being conducted by Dr. Warren J. Wisby of the University of Miami's Institute of Marine Science. Dr. Wisby reported his current findings in a paper presented at the 94th Annual Meeting of the American Fisheries Society, Atlantic City, New Jersey, September 14, 1964. His investigations, supported by the National Science Foundation and the Office of Naval Research, could serve as a basis for understanding the amazing ability of fish to orient themselves in an environment that, to most humans, seems without landmarks.

Dr. Wisby's work has shown that sharks, and perhaps other predators such as barracuda, have the ability to pinpoint the source of particular kinds of sounds and to recognize them as coming from possible food sources. Sharks tested by Dr. Wisby could detect and locate the source of low-frequency sound waves when cruising over 200 yards from the sound source—far beyond visual range and with no blood in the water for sharks to smell.

Though the shark feeds mainly on shrimp, squid, lobsters, crabs, and fish, Dr. Wisby explained, "like any predatory animal, he preys most upon victims he finds easiest to catch. The easiest of these, other than a dead animal, is a cripple struggling or dying in the water. In this connection our early experiments showed that (1) struggling fish create underwater sound waves of low frequency, and these waves are transmitted in bursts as the fish struggles, (2) the frequency of these sound waves is easily within the hearing range of sharks, and (3) sharks rapidly appear near the source of such pulsed low-frequency sound waves but do not appear when a low-frequency continuous wave or a high-frequency pulsed wave is transmitted."

Dr. Wisby and associates at the Institute of Marine Science have repeatedly attracted sharks up to 14 feet long, of all the commonly known kinds, by broadcasting underwater taped signals of pulsed low-frequency sounds. Predators such as barracuda, jacks, and groupers also appeared regularly. As a result of his experiments he believes sharks use the lower part of their hearing range, from about 7½ to 100 cycles per second (cps), for hunting food. It was sound of this frequency range that was broadcast to sharks in his experiment this summer. Sharks can hear, he said, up to about 400 cps. The range of human hearing is between about 40 cps. and 20,000 cps.

"At the outset we were not sure, however, whether sharks could swim directly to the source of the sound or whether they conducted some sort of random or organized hunting pattern that eventually brought them to the right place. The speed with which they appeared seemed to rule out both methods. But they were still possibilities.

"Also, sound transmitted underwater produces near the source an area of sound turbulence often called the 'near-field effect.' Physicists have generally believed that fish could only localize a sound if they were swimming inside the turbulent sound area."

Using a light plane to find and track sharks, and a surface vessel with equipment that transmits underwater the dinner-call sound wave, Dr. Wisby found the sharks most efficient at locating the source of the sound, even when beyond the near-field effect.

"They hear the sound and then swim rapidly and directly toward it, usually staying fairly deep," he said. "They stop suddenly one or two boatlengths away and then swim off." Dr. Wisby and his associates flew about twenty shark-tracking missions in conducting their research this summer.

How the sharks can pinpoint the location of a sound source is still not certain. In humans, part of the ability to locate particular sounds is due to the fact that the ears are set far apart and are outside the skull. One ear hears a sound slightly before the other one, the mind performs a subsconscious problem in triangulation, other information is considered, and the answer is presented.

Dr. Wisby believe this process may not be true in the case of sharks. The ears of a shark are set inside its cranium and are very close together. This fact, coupled with the high speed of sound waves traveling through water (1 mile per second, or five times faster than sound in air), suggests that sharks receive all sounds in their ears almost simultaneously. A location solution through triangulation is unlikely.

It seems more probable, says Dr. Wisby that sharks are locating the source of a sound through a group of sensitive cells along their sides. This group of cells, called the lateral line, has been a controversial subject among fish experts for a number of years. It is possible that their function, never certain, is connected with sound reception and orientation.

Laboratory experiments testing this theory will be a next step in his research, the University of Miami scientist said.

THE WHALE THAT TALKED

KILLER whales, which are related to porpoises, are believed to hunt in packs for food (seals, porpoises, larger whales) and, while doing so, to communicate with each other. A wounded whale may communicate; whales—air-breathing mammals—have been seen holding up a dead whale on the surface. Men not long ago had their first chance to hear whale conversations in detail. By Ray Thomas in *Boeing Magazine,* February, 1966:

The Name of the male killer whale, Namu, briefly became a household word in many parts of the world. This 24-foot, 10,000-pound teen-ager blundered into fishing nets near Namu, British Columbia, in June of 1965. Namu was transported inside a floating pen to a Seattle aquarium. Other killer whales—still free—surrounded the pen. Namu talked to them. Scientists listened to the conversation.

"We had a unique situation," said T. E. Heindsmann, an ocean scientist. "There had never before been an opportunity to make continuous acoustical measurements of a mature, unharmed killer whale which was still in communication with others of its species."

During the five days the scientists operated, twenty-three reels of tape were obtained, each reel some fifteen hundred feet in length. After editing, these tapes will yield about nine hours of meaningful data, which is being correlated with underwater movies and ocean measurements which were made at the same time. There is enough information to permit statistical analysis; before Namu there were only isolated samples.

The men had not been very long on station before it was apparent that Namu possessed and used a complex pattern of communications skills. There were squeals and chirps in numerous variety, some clearly audible though emitted far underwater. In addition, there were inaudible signals used. In Heindsmann's words from a report to the Office of Naval Research, "Namu emitted several types of sonarlike impulses and we were able to observe the returning echoes and reverberations, something never done before with killer whales."

These whales have signals as individual as the voices of human beings, making it possible to tell which whale is talking. During the study, free killer whales swam outside the pen and held what sounded like an excited conversation with captive Namu.

The expedition produced a carefully documented study of a species about which little was known. This adds to a body of oceanographic knowledge which has an almost desperate need for more and new data.

"We know more about the moon than we know about our own ocean," says Heindsmann, who works for the Boeing Company, a builder of jet passenger planes, Saturn IB and IC boosters (for the Apollo, the moon-trip spacecraft), and hydrofoil submarine chasers for the Navy. Harley Bowdish was skipper of the *Maribo II,* that carried the scientists. Boeing's Mario Peila and Earl Pace helped. So did John Donaldson. "The oceans," Heindsmann continues, "cover more than two thirds of the earth. We hear a lot about growing populations and increased demands for food and minerals that possibly, at some future time, only the ocean can supply. But we know relatively little about the place where this is all supposed to happen."

One question unanswered is how a whale—an air-breathing mammal—can dive and return from astonishing depths in minutes. Fish hooked on the bottom and rapidly pulled to the surface from deep water are incapacitated by decompression, just as a man would be.

The possibility that man might learn to communicate with whales by sounds is not too farfetched. Dogs are trained to herd sheep; could whales or dolphins be trained to herd fish?

The communications aspect has another angle which interests naval planners. A person sitting in an office hears typewriters, telephone bells, people talking, doors opening and closing. The listener selects whatever he wishes to hear from this welter of sound, automatically identifying each element.

The sea is an equally noisy place—so much so that a sonar operator's toughest job is not to hear something over his headphones, but to know what it is that he is hearing. Can man learn to listen to underwater sounds as discriminatingly as a whale?

"Identifying the sonic patterns emitted by whales and understanding how these are used can help in the design of sensitive and discriminatory equipment for underwater listening," said Heindsmann. "This is one of the most immediately useful aspects of our Namu measurements. All of this will not come about tomorrow or next week, but our data adds to our knowledge, and it is from this that technical advancements are made."

"Namu" means whirlwind and is from the language of the Bellabella Indians who live in the rugged coastal region of Canada where the killer whale was captured. The killer is not a true whale but a member of the dolphin family. To confuse things more, the British call porpoises (another sea mammal) dolphins, which is not correct either.

Perhaps some of Namu's chuckles are caused by humans who say one thing which is interpreted to mean something else by other humans. This problem doesn't occur in whale talk.

Namu was taken—inside the floating net—into the harbor at Seattle. Fenced in, he became one of the city's most popular tourist attractions. His owner, Ted Griffin, learned to ride around on Namu's back. A song was written about Namu; children's shirts and toys had his name on them. There was even a Namu dance. In July, 1966, Namu tried to escape. He attempted to break out of his pen, and became entangled, beneath the surface of the water, in some of the shrouding that surrounded him. There—because he could not get up to obtain air to breathe—Namu drowned.

HOW TO (TRY TO) CATCH A SEA MONSTER

WILLARD BASCOM is president of Ocean Science and Engineering, Inc., Washington, D.C. The company, among many other things, helps mine diamonds in the ocean off South Africa. Here Mr. Bascom writes, in the March, 1967, *Geo Marine Technology,* of how he failed to catch a monster:

There Are Ways to catch monsters and ways not to catch them. The *Oceaneer* expedition to the deep terrace off Baja California in early October, 1966, successfully tested some of the latter ways. On our next expedition, we will try the positive approach, but in the meantime, our strategy is to let public interest build up. It's not wise to be successful on the first try—that makes the game look too easy.

First, you establish that monsters exist. That is easy, not only because tales of sea monsters go back two thousand years—documented by Homer himself and confirmed by generations of able seamen—but because recently they have been photographed by a Ulysses-like character with flowing white beard named John Isaacs. For years, fisherman-engineer-oceanographer Isaacs considered ways of building a baited camera that would attract bottom fish to a camera instead of scaring them away from it. As the great camera took shape, it became known somewhat whimsically as the monster camera. What do you photograph with a monster camera? But of course!

The first lowerings of the camera to the sea floor were made about 80 miles southwest of Ensenada, Mexico, where the depth is about 6,000 feet. The downward-looking camera, suspended 12 feet above the sea floor, photographed a can of bait and its surroundings every 15 minutes for several days. The area of sea floor visible in the photos is about ten feet on a side. The early photos on the roll show a herd of sablefish and grenadiers clustered around the bait—and in this clear, deep water, where picture quality is excellent, details are unmistakable. But then, a bit further along, a brute shape appears in the pictures—obviously part of a huge animal which extends outside the ten-foot span of the camera's field. Clearly it is a great fish—perhaps only one-third visible. It is old, barnacled, and scarred, and probably wise to have survived so long.

Probably it has never seen the blue haze of surface water and the underside of the waves; in turn, probably no man has ever seen such a creature on the surface in these latitudes. Dr. Carl Hubbs, the encyclopedia of ichthyology, tentatively identified it from the photos as a variety of Greenland shark—like those occasionally caught on the surface near Thule. Perhaps, he thinks, such animals are widely distributed around the world, but live unknown in very deep, cold waters and come to the surface only in the Arctic.

On a subsequent camera lowering some 50 miles away, another such beast was photographed. Again the head extended beyond one side of the picture and the tail beyond the other, but the scarred flank was clearly visible. This time the pattern of scars was different. This was a different animal. Two monsters such a distance apart means there must be more, and, of course, that is an irresistible attraction to a fisherman. A chance to catch the biggest fish in the world! So, we rigged to go fishing. John Isaacs, of the Scripps Institution of Oceanography, was the expedition leader, Dick Rosenblatt went as chief ichthyologist, Don Wilkie represented the Scripps Museum, Ed Horton was engineer, Alec Winton was captain, and Dan Brown went along to do the work.

I got to go in return for contributing the *Oceaneer* and acting as photographer. Oh, yes, we took four wives along, too. However, on the second day the sea roughed up a bit and they all got seasick. We dropped 'em in Ensenada and went back fishing. Monster hunting is a man's game, anyhow. Isaacs and Brown had a plan and some gear ready. The ship would return to the spot where the photos had been taken and fish there with a buoyed-off line. This fishing line would be ½-inch nylon, anchored by a section of steel wire to a small Danforth, so as not to drag along the bottom. Then the ship would move off a dozen miles and fish with the ⅜-inch wire on *Oceaneer*'s winch, presumably dragging the bait slowly along the bottom. Remember, the water is over a mile deep.

The hooks were made specially by a somewhat dazed-looking blacksmith who ties trout flies for a hobby. They were about a foot long, with a 6-inch throat and secured to the main line by ¼-inch leaders about 30 feet long.

Bait was a bit of a problem. Rumor has it that Greenland sharks have been caught with nearly whole reindeer in their stomachs (all except head and antlers). Reindeer being in short supply in San Diego, Isaacs decided he would fool the monsters with horsemeat. Horsemeat is tougher than it sounds—to find. But by swearing it would not be fed to human friends, he got several hundred pounds from the San Diego Zoo in 30-pound chunks. I thought it looked pretty good, but the girls were horrified and guessed (rightly) that monsters wouldn't like it. Then, reasoning that monsters may prefer seafood, other hooks (there were eight on each line) were baited variously with mackerel, bonita, and bags of anchovies. In case monsters were cannibalistic, we bought an 8-foot hammerhead shark from a Mexican fisherman for $5. We tried the hammerhead for lunch; it was acceptable, but not delectable.

The *Oceaneer* winchline was on bottom about ten hours on the first try. Nothing. So we went back to the buoy that marked the nylon line, found it, brought the end aboard, and wound it in. The bonita was gone and the horsemeat frayed by the nibbling of small fish, but no monsters. We tried again and again for a total of five lowerings. Our techniques of handling line, baiting, and station-keeping steadily improved, but the results were the same. However, one double-hook pennant, baited with a sea bass and a large flying fish, came up snarled and rammed tight, as one might expect if a great shark had rolled with it.

After the first cast we wound wire, hooks and all, on the main winch drum; in doing so, on one occasion a large hook caught in the winch frame and was partly straightened out. When we returned to San Diego and the curious came aboard to ask if we'd caught any monsters, Isaacs would suggestively massage this unbent hook, shake his head, and murmur darkly, "Not quite." The lubbers would depart, much impressed with the strength of sea monsters. Why didn't we catch a monster? Perhaps they didn't like any of our bait; maybe they feed only on living fish and in the photos they had been attracted by the fish that were feeding on the bait. Or perhaps they mouthed the bait, felt the hook and wire, and spit it out. Maybe they've migrated elsewhere, or maybe—just maybe, mind you—they have bigger brains than fishermen.

The trip was by no means a loss. We (the men, anyway) enjoyed ourselves thoroughly, because it's fun for deskbound sailors to get a deck beneath their feet once in a while. We got sunburned and found our sea legs in a rough sea. I relearned something about oceanography all of us in the business need to be continually reminded of. Although we had a pretty good array of talent aboard, with a hundred years of book learning and scientific work between us, at sea your reputation hangs on old-fashioned seamanship. We all know how to design sea hardware, how to manage men, and how to write grandiose proposals for funds—but on this trip, the chiefs were all Indians together.

Fundamentals of seamanship counted most, as they probably do on most voyages. Can your helmsman pick up a speck of a buoy a mile away in a 20-knot wind—or keep station on its tiny light at night, neither losing it nor running it down? Can your skipper come alongside a buoy in the dark in a state-5 sea and pick it up in the ship's lee without getting its line in the screws? Can your crewmen heave a grapnel properly, quickly make up a tight thimble, or bend a stopper line onto running wire in seconds? We could—and we're a bit proud of it.

So, we returned home, monsterless, more than ever determined to return before long with better gear, new bait. We have new plans for the old monsters, so watch for a flash from *Oceaneer* off Baja one of these days that will say: MET MONSTER, MASTERED SAME.

THE BIGGEST SEA BEASTS

HERE are the measurements, collected from many sources, on the hugest monsters in the oceans:

The Great(est) White Sharks

A 17-foot-2-inch great white shark (*Carcharodon carcharias*) was caught off Montauk Point, Long Island, New York, by a group of anglers including International Oceanographic Foundation member Harvey Fersten. Mr. Fersten and his friends were shark fishing, catching porbeagle sharks on rod and reel from the 42-foot Montauk charter boat *Crickett II,* when the huge head of a white shark rose vertically five feet out of the water beside the boat. After failing to tempt the fish with a baited hook, they harpooned it and were towed by the giant for over four hours. The monstrous man-eater shark, a female, had a 13-foot girth and an estimated weight of 4,500 pounds. Unfortunately, its stomach contents were not examined.—*Sea Secrets,* December, 1964.

Several Foundation members have questioned the estimated weight of 4,500 pounds given for the great white shark caught by member Harvey Fersten. Some readers believed the weight to be inaccurate, as they would not expect a 17-foot-2-inch shark to weigh that much.

The great white shark is an exceedingly heavy fish, and, because the species is fairly rare, there are few reports of verified weights. One study was made in the Pacific, off Washington, however, and published in *Opeia* in 1942. It listed one 8-foot white weighing 342 pounds; those in the 12-foot range weighed between 800 and 1,000 pounds; and those in the 13-foot range weighed between 2,000 and 2,400 pounds. There is a great deal of variation between individual sharks, however, and these differences seem to increase with size. A 15-foot-2-inch white caught off Australia weighed only 1,720 pounds, while a 13-foot-3-inch specimen taken in South Africa weighed 2,176 pounds.

Atlantic specimens apparently run just as heavy. The largest white shark ever weighed was taken off the north coast of Cuba during the heyday of the shark-liver industry about fifteen years ago. It was 21 feet long and weighed 7,100 pounds, and had a liver that weighed 1,005 pounds! This catch was reported by Dr. Luis Howell Rivero.—*Sea Secrets,* February, 1965.

Biggest Without a Backbone

The giant squid holds nature's record for suction power. It is the largest invertebrate (backboneless animal) on earth, spanning sometimes 60 feet from the tip of its snake-like tentacles to the edge of the mantle. In one specimen the tenatacles measured 37 feet, and it is possible that there exist in the deep oceans squids spanning 100 feet.

Each of the ten tentacles, almost solid muscle and thick as a man's leg, are armed with numerous suckers, measuring about 2 inches across. They are rimmed with fine hooklike teeth for gripping slippery skin. Some species (*Onychoteuthis*) have a sharp, strong hook in the center of each sucker. The hooks are plunged deeply into the flesh of the prey to aid the suckers in holding fast.

The suckers work on the vacuum principle. When the sucker grips, its center is raised by a muscular piston, and the consequent vacuum holds it in place. Instances are known of the arms of small cephalopods being torn apart before the suckers released their hold. . . .

But, exaggerations of fiction apart, the strength of a giant squid is tremendous. Captain John D. Craig, a deep-sea diver, puts the suction power of each sucker at 19 pounds per square inch. And as squids have some two thousand suckers, the total suction power is enormous.—Frank W. Lane in *Nature Parade.*

A Recent Giant Squid

I quoted a personal communication from Dr. (Robert) Clarke, telling me that of the 112 squids which he had taken from sperm stomachs in the Azores, the largest measured only 8 feet (i.e. body and arms, but excluding the long tentacles) while the average length was just on 3 feet. Since then (1956: A giant squid swallowed by a sperm whale. Challenger Soc. Abstr., 3, VIII, 31) he has, also at the Azores, recovered from the stomach of a 47-foot sperm whale a complete and intact giant squid, *Architeuthis sp.,* measuring 34 feet 5 inches from the tail to the tip of the tentacles, or 16 feet 3 inches excluding the long tentacles; it is interesting to know that these whales can swallow so large a mouthful whole.—Sir Alister Hardy, *The Open Sea.*

The Largest Mammal, and Biggest Baby

The blue whale is the largest mammal existing today, and probably the largest that has ever lived. Blue whales are found from the polar to the temperate seas, and occasionally even at the equator. The migrational routes followed by these whales depend largely upon the seasonal locations of their food supply. In winter, when the water surfaces grow colder and food is scarce or inaccessible because of field ice and ice floes, the blue whales move to warmer waters. There the young are born.

Whales are mammals and exhibit all the characteristics of true mammals. They are backboned, warm-blooded, bear traces of hair (along the margins of the lips), and suckle their young with milk. The blue whale calf at birth may be as much as 26 feet long. It is nursed for about seven months and is weaned when it has attained a length of about 50 feet. Full grown, it may attain a length of 100 feet and weigh 150 tons. These measurements are comparable to those of the Pacific-type steam passenger locomotive to be exhibited in the Smithsonian's Museum of History and Technology. . . . The throat of the blue whale is so narrow that it can swallow nothing larger than small fish. Because of this, its diet normally consists of tremendous masses of small crustaceans, collectively known as krill. The external folds or grooves along the throat and abdomen are elastic and can be greatly expanded to increase the size of the mouth, so that the quantitites of krill may be taken in. When the mouth is full, the whale closes its jaws, and its huge tongue, weighing as much as 4 tons, forces water out through the baleen sieve, leaving the krill to be swallowed. As much as a ton of krill has been found in the stomach of a blue whale, and this is probably not a full day's quota of food.—*Blue Whale,* Smithsonian Institution Information Leaflet 357.

The heart of the blue whale weighs 1,000 pounds and generates something like 10 horsepower while pumping the whale's 8 tons of blood through its circulatory system.—*Chemistry,* January, 1964.

The Half-Ton Bluefin

Recently reported was the battle between Halifax fishermen Joseph and Dennis Dempsey and a 985-pound bluefin tuna.

The monster struck at a handline set beside their herring boat while they were engaged in net hauling in their 28-foot boat. Both brothers grabbed the hemp handline while the tuna towed them around in circles for more than an hour and a half near the entrance to Halifax harbor.

After finally hauling in the giant bluefin, the weight was registered as 985 pounds, seven pounds more than the world's record tuna caught on rod and reel, but it cannot be recorded in the books because it was captured on a handline. The record of angler Duncan M. Hodgson of Montreal, Canada, set in 1950 at St. Ann's Bay, Nova Scotia, still stands.—*Sea Secrets,* December, 1963.

A Giant Jellyfish

Prof. Louis Agassiz, one of the best known of the early American biologists, measured a specimen (probably the jellyfish *Cyanea capillata*) found off the Massachusetts coast, and its bell was 7½ feet in diameter. Its tentacles were more than 120 feet long! Others with bells 12 feet across have been reported. There is no animal known, either living or extinct, with appendages or body as long as the tentacles of the largest of the jellyfishes.—Osmond P. Breland in *The Illustrated Library of the Natural Sciences,* edited by Edward M. Weyer.

The Great Seal

Of all the seals in the oceans, the elephant seal, *Murounga angustirostris* is the largest, the heaviest, and the most homely of them all! Because of the value of its oil, this blubbery beast with a snout like an elephant's trunk was almost exterminated during the nineteenth century, but through conservation measures and the cessation of commercial hunting, the species has recovered during the last thirty years. At present the elephant seals number more than ten thousand.

The name "elephant seal" derives from the large proboscis or trunk with which the male makes a great to-do purely for protection and bluff. Male seals are called "bulls," the females are "cows," their offspring are "pups," and the whole family is a "harem." The exclusive function of the bull's phenomenal snout is the part it plays in a spectacular vocalizing which precedes most combats and is often so effective that a fight is unnecessary. . . . The elephant seal feeds mostly on slow-moving fish that inhabit deep water. Sharks, squids, rays, skates, and dogfish are the sea animals it eats. The ability of the seal to dive is shown by some of the food items found in its stomach: ratfish, for example, never live in less than three hundred feet of water, and some of the other foods of the seal live as deep as seven hundred feet. All of the seal's food is small, since its teeth are not fitted for chewing. Spikelike and without grinding surfaces, the teeth are set far apart, so the animal must bolt its food whole and struggling.

Bulls may grow as long as 15 feet and weigh over 4,000 pounds. The southern species living in the Antarctic is larger, more than 16 feet long and weighing about 5,000 pounds. The girth of some of these beasts measures from 15 to 18 feet around. Females are much smaller, 8 to 10 feet long and about one third the weight of the male.—Frank G. Ashbrook in *Sea Frontiers,* February, 1962.

The Manta Ray

Largest of the rays is the manta, known also as the devilfish, the vampire ray, and the sea bat. It is as broad as it is long and measures about 20 feet across the disk. Its big gaping mouth gives it a rather stupid and yet alarming appearance. One would think that such a monster, weighing over 3,000 pounds [the weight of a large rhinoceros] would be content with a life on the sea bottom, like so many of its smaller relatives, and this is the life it undoubtedly lived in the past. But a 3,000-pound body needs a lot of nourishment, so for this and no doubt other reasons the manta brought its huge bulk to the surface and took to swimming about. It had no tail to help it (it only possesses one of the small ratlike appendages), so had to use its "wings," beating solemnly through the water like some squat, legendary bird. It soon learned to swim gracefully and easily in the upper regions of the sea, a feat accomplished by no other tailless creature of that size.—John Crompton in *The Living Sea.*

The Stupendous Crab

The Paris Museum of Natural History, writes Pouchet, recently received the remains of the largest crab ever known. Each of its pincers measured 1 meter 20 centimeters in length (a meter is equal to 39.3707904 inches, or 3 feet 4 inches nearly). The space between two feet, when extended, was upward of 2 meters 60 centimeters. It was caught in Japan, on the eastern coast of Niphon, between the 34th and 35th degree of north latitude, by M. de Sieboldt. It belongs to the species of Spiny Spider Crab (*Maia aquinada*); animals of no great beauty, even when they are not larger than a child's head. It was known, of course, that they were found of larger dimensions in the Chinese seas, but it was not suspected they ever attained such proportions as those we have just described. The crab we speak of was undoubtedly an individual of great age.—Armand Landrin in *The Monsters of the Deep* (1875).

Big Ones on Rod and Reel

A black marlin was, in fact, the largest game fish ever taken on a rod and reel. It was caught off Cabo Blanco, Peru, by Alfred C. Glassell, Jr., of Houston, Texas, on August 4, 1953. You can see it (an estimated 2½ million persons each year do) in the Hall of Life in the Sea on the first floor of the Museum of Natural History at the Smithsonian Institution, Washington, D. C. It weighed 1,560 pounds and measured 14 feet 6 inches in length and 6 feet 9 inches in girth. It took Mr. Glassell 1 hour 45 minutes to bring the marlin alongside his boat. The marlin meanwhile made 49 jumps clear of the water. Movies made as Mr. Glassell caught the black marlin were dubbed into the film *The Old Man and the Sea.*

Two world's record sharks caught on rod and reel were bigger than Mr. Glassell's black marlin and are the only rod-and-reel catches listed by the International Game Fish Association that were bigger. A 2,664-pound white shark, a man-eater, was caught by Alfred Dean off Ceduna, South Australia, on April 21, 1959. It was 16 feet 10 inches long and 9 feet 6 inches around. A 1,780-pound tiger shark was caught by Walter Maxwell near Cherry Grove, South Carolina, on June 14, 1964. It was 13 feet 10½ inches long and 8 feet 7 inches in girth.—Gardner Soule in *The Ocean Adventure.*

The 8-Foot Long Chelonian

The leathery turtle (*Dermochelys coriacea*) is by far the largest of the turtles and is, in fact, the largest living chelonian (a term comprising turtles and tortoises). It may measure nearly eight feet in length and weigh over half a ton. . . . It is easily recognized by the seven longitudinal ridges on the shell, which differs from that of all other turtles in consisting not of a few symmetrically arranged shields but of a great number of closely set small bones covered with smooth leathery skin.

The leathery turtle has always been considered to be rare, but in 1952 it was discovered that large numbers of them come ashore every year to lay their eggs on the coast of Trengganu, north of Dungun (in Malaysia). The breeding habits are similar to those of the green turtle, but the eggs are larger, as big as billiard balls. The tracks made by these turtles in the sand, as they laboriously make their way up and down the shore, are easily recognizable, as their width, representing the span of the front flippers, is about seven feet.—M. W. F. Tweedie in *Malayan Animal Life*.

The Giants of the Deep Waters

By contrast with the deep-sea fishes, in several groups of invertebrates (animals without backbones) it is the largest individuals that inhabit the deep sea. For example, living in the depths there is an orange-red ostracod (a small bivalved relative of the shrimp) that grows as big as a cherry. Since most ostracods are tiny—even microscopic—this fellow is a veritable giant and bears the name *Gigantocypris agassizi.* The biggest sea urchins found anywhere are in the deep waters, their leathery bodies being a foot thick. A giant crab, orange in color and 6 feet across from the tip of one leg to another, inhabits the deep western Pacific. Isopods on land include the pill bugs encountered in damp ground, and these are little fellows about ¼ of an inch long. The isopods in the ocean are usually in this range of size too, so the deep-sea species, *Bathynomus doederleini* and *Bathynomus giganteus,* look decidedly outsized at 6 to 8 inches. The hydras are ordinarily insignificant-looking creatures, perhaps a few inches high, resembling flowers more than the animals that they really are. The grandly named imperial wax flower hydra, of the deep sea off Japan, has a stature—some 8 feet—to go with its appellation. Some sea pens, colonial animals whose size is ordinarily a foot or so, grow to about 8 feet in the great depths.—C. P. Idyll in *Abyss*.

The Hugest Fish

Question: What is the largest fish in the world? B.L., Port Washington, New York. *Answer:* If we include sharks, the largest is the whale shark, *Rhineodon typus.* This shark reaches a length of 45 feet and has credibly been reported to exceed 60 feet. The weight of a 38-foot specimen, taken in Florida, was estimated at 26,600 pounds. The second- and third-largest are also sharks: the basking shark and the white shark, respectively. The basking shark, *Cetorhinus maxiumus,* reaches about 40 to 45 feet. It is, of course, difficult to get accurate weights on such large animals, but one that was about 30 feet long weighed 8,600 pounds. The white shark, *Carcharodon carcharias,* has been credited with reaching a length of 40 feet, but the largest actually measured was about 30 feet, and individuals in excess of 20 feet seem rare. Again, weights are difficult to come by, but one about 21 feet long weighed about 7,100 pounds.

Among the bony fishes, the heaviest are perhaps the sturgeons, and one specimen caught in 1922 in Russia weighed about 2,700 pounds. Another individual captured in the Volga Basin in the last century weighed 3,000 pounds. Such large sturgeons have not been recorded in recent years. Sturgeon, of course, have been subjected to considerable fishing pressure, primarily for caviar.

The blue marlin is known to exceed 2,000 pounds, and a number of other fishes, including the black marlin, the bluefin tuna, and a whole series of sturgeons, approach 2,000 pounds.—*Sea Secrets,* April, 1965.

The Biggest Shell in the Sea

On a beautiful October day I was paddling over a coral reef off the jungle-clothed coast of Celebes, Dutch East Indies. . . . I saw, half embedded, what looked like a giant shell, wide open. It was a shell, sure enough—the biggest clam in all the world. . . . This particular clam was only 4 feet under the surface. I jabbed my paddle deep into the innocent looking mass. The jaws snapped shut and held the paddle in a viselike grip. It was impossible to get it out; I had to break it off. As near as I could estimate, this clam was about three feet across. In the Museum (American Museum of Natural History) we have on exhibition a pair of shells that are three feet in diameter and weigh 579½ pounds. Off the coast of Australia it is reported that they reach a length of 6 feet and a weight of nearly a ton. . . . *Tridacna gigas* is the name because of three fingerlike points of the shell.—Roy Chapman Andrews in *This Amazing Planet*.

The 6-Foot-Wide Mouth

The biggest shark I ever saw was the giant whale shark that was captured in the Bahamas. Its total weight was between 20,000 and 30,000 pounds, and its mouth was nearly 6 feet wide! The monstrous creature was towed in from the Gulf Stream, and photographer Ralph Bowden and I took underwater movies of it while it was still alive. It was so huge that just to swim from one end of it to the other took considerable effort because there was a strong current that day. I found it easier to crawl rather than swim along the giant creature's body, and this worked fine until I discovered that I was bleeding badly. The creature's skin was as rough as sandpaper and it had scraped my flesh bare in many places, which I hadn't noticed because of the excitement. This was very painful and was aggravated by the mucus or slime from the whale's skin. To add to the discomfort, there were numerous sharks cruising a short distance away, but, fortunately, none of them came close, probably because we had several boats anchored in the near vicinity. We took turns swimming around the giant fish to show on film the comparison in size between a human and the monstrous fish, and when one of us would swim off toward the gigantic tail, we would appear very tiny, almost like ants climbing on an elephant. We climaxed the movie with a close-up shot of the creature's tremendous mouth, which was opening and closing rhythmically, and I swam up to the giant head and peered into the cavernous maw. I had placed one arm on the lower jaw and held my other arm above me so that I could feel the upper jaw when it came down and then could pull my head out in time. It made a good movie, and although I was wearing full aqualung equipment, I could easily have swum down inside the creature's gullet with room to spare.—Robert P. L. Straughan, *Sharks, Morays, and Treasure.*

For Contrast:

The smallest fish in the world is a tiny goby, *Mistichthys luzonnensis,* found in fresh- to brackish-water lakes in Luzon, Philippines. It seldom exceeds one half inch at adulthood, yet is so abundant it supports a fishery.—*Sea Secrets,* January, 1962.

SECTION IX

THE LEGEND OF ATLANTIS
Are We Writing an End to Plato's Tale?

What a light shot through my mind! Atlantis, the ancient Meropus of Theopompus, the Atlantic of Plato. . . . I had it there now before my eyes.
—Professor Pierre Arronax speaks in Jules Verne's 20,000 Leagues Under the Sea.

LONG-LOST ATLANTIS—
HAVE WE FOUND IT?

SINCE the days of Plato (about 422 B.C. to 348 B.C.) men have heard of and wondered about a civilization that sank beneath the sea—and that some day might be found again. They called it Atlantis. Now Atlantis may have been found. This is by J. W. Mavor, Jr., a research specialist in the Department of Applied Oceanography at the Woods Hole Oceanographic Institution. Mavor helped develop the deep-diving submarine *Alvin*. This article has been reprinted from *Oceanus*, the Woods Hole quarterly magazine for November, 1966:

The Island of Thera, 100 kilometers north of Crete in the Aegean Sea, erupted with tremendous violence between 1500 and 1450 B.C. At the end of this period a large part of the island collapsed into the sea, creating enormous tidal waves which caused floods and coastal damage as far away as Egypt. The roar of the explosion may have been heard as far away as Scandinavia.

Standing on the edge of the collapsed volcanic cone (*caldera*) of Thera, a sheer drop 400 meters above the sea, one can see the surrounding islands of Anaphe, Amorgos, Sikinos, Ios, and Pholegandros, and, in the winter, Crete. The enormity of the cataclysm is brought home with frightening clarity. Around the rim of the *caldera,* some ten kilometers in diameter, the forty-meter-thick white volcanic ash layer of the Minoan eruption is visible, contrasting with the layers of black and red lava beneath.

Prof. A. G. Galanopoulos, who is director of the seismic laboratory at the University of Athens, proposed in 1960 that Thera was the metropolis of Plato's Atlantis, the smaller of two islands making up the royal lands. The other, the royal state, was Crete. Other settlements on the Aegean islands, and along the eastern Mediterrean coasts, were ruled from these two islands. Galanopoulos has presented considerable evidence to support his theory. Moreover, Mellis and Ninkovich and Heezen have reported the analyses of deep-sea cores which indicate the widespread effects of the great volcanic explosion.

The Minoan civilization in its Palace Period from 1900–1450 B.C. is known from excavations of the Cretan palaces. Written letters and artifacts of the surrounding cultures appear to relate to the Minoans and to the collapse of their civilization. The records include Plato's dialogues *Timaeus* and *Critias,* the Tel-el-Amarna [tablets] of Egypt, the excavations at Tell-el-Qadi in Palestine, the tradition of the flood of Deucalion, the Hittite legend of Ullikummi, and the Etruscan excavations in Italy. Also pertinent are the Old Testament books of Judges, Exodus, Amos, Jeremiah, Zephaniah, and Joshua, and the inscriptions of Tel-el-Yahudiya. References in Egypt include the Hermitage papyrus, the Ipiwer papyrus, and the inscription at Speos Artemidos. J. G. Bennett has discussed the Egyptian sources showing that the Thera cataclysm was destructive in Egypt.

PRELIMINARY SURVEY

Late in 1965, from August 26 through September 10, we made a preliminary survey to discover further evidence to support Professor Galanopoulos' suggestions that Thera is the site of "long lost Atlantis." Two items of Plato's story were considered major areas of interest: (1) a comparison of the physical description of the island; (2) a search for remnants of the Atlantean civilization. Critias described the metropolis of Atlantis as a circular island 100 or 105 stadia in diameter. Inside this circle were three naturally formed ring-shaped harbors with a connecting channel between and to the sea. White, black, and red building blocks were said to be quarried from the raised banks of the harbors. On the center island, five stadia in diameter, were a hot spring and a cold spring. To verify this description, it is necessary to reconstruct the topography of the island prior to the collapse of 1450 B.C.

We were fortunate in that the R. V. *Chain* (an oceanographic ship from Woods Hole) was on a geophysical cruise in the eastern Mediterranean, with Mr. E. F. K. Zarudski as chief scientist on board. Due to his interest in Thera, our survey party was transported on the *Chain* from Athens to the island. The ship then spent one day at Thera to make a seismic sparker profile through the *caldera* and around the island. Although we have to await complete analysis of the records, the seismic profile indicated a radial cross-section of the collapsed portion of the island underwater and a deep, filled basin within the *caldera* which could have been a preeruption waterway. An examination of the cliff strata and underwater bottom profiles made by the survey party, using Professor Edgerton's short-ping sediment profiler, indicated a complex volcano having many lava plugs or tubes. It does not appear that the island was a single cone before the eruption but several intersecting cones. It may well have had a *caldera* of smaller size than the present one. The cyclic behavior of the volcanic activity (building up and collapsing) reported by Ninkovich and Heezen supports this thesis. The Minoan eruption of fine white ash does not appear to have come from a central single vent, since it varies in both thickness and size over the island.

The present island group is smaller than the metropolis of Atlantis was reported to be. There is evidence that land slumping took place on the island periphery either during or after the eruption. The survey indicated a 2-to-4-kilometer larger pre-eruption outline which fits Plato's 100-stadia diameter exactly.

Plato described a *caldera* with volcanic islands inside the collapsed cone. The lava, pumice, and tuff of Thera which are cut from the cliffs and used for building blocks are white, black, and red. Hot springs occur on the central volcanic cone, and a single cold spring occurs presently on the lime stone mountain, Mount Elias, a 600-meter sheer outcrop.

SEARCH EVIDENCE

The second major area of interest was the search for evidence that Thera was the religious center of the Minoan or Atlantean civilization and that temples and palaces are to be found. No evidence has yet been found of large Minoan temples. Certainly, any ruins on the central part of the collapsed island have been destroyed beyond recovery. In 1879 [Ferdinand, André] Fouqué reported three excavations on separate parts of the island. A fourth was found by Galanopoulos in 1956. These ruins were all discovered at the bottom of the top white and rose pumice layers and were well preserved, buried as at Pompeii. Minoan artifacts including pottery, gold jewelry, copper tools, and skeletons were found. The habitations seemed to be farms. Most discoveries were made during mining operations, when the pumice was dug from the cliffs and conveyed to ships for use in cement. The modern practice of blasting and bulldozing is constantly destroying Minoan ruins. In spite of this, wood and pottery were observed during the current survey in the red weathered lava earth just under the rose pumice. Wood samples were taken for carbon-14 dating. In one pumice mine, evidence of a fresh-water lake or marsh was found. From the thickness and composition of the earthy Minoan surface in two locations, it appears that there were wooded regions on the island. Plato mentions spring-fed ponds and excellent soil.

FOSSIL MONKEY

Previous to the present survey, E. Loring found a fossil monkey head on the beach at Kamari. This fossil, found in the pumice and lava formed during the eruption of Thera, was inspected by Professor Poulianos, a leading anthropologist, who identified it as *Cercopithecus callitrichus,* or West African green monkey. Such animals are known to have been brought to Crete by ship for the amusement of royalty. This implies the presence of royalty on the island, and one might speculate that adequate quarters comparable to the Cretan palaces were available.

At the summit of Messavouno, a 350-meter-high spur of Mount Elias, lie the extensive ruins of ancient Thíra, settled since Phoenician times in 1100 B.C. Each succeeding people rebuilt with the stones of the preceding culture, there being no sedimentation to establish the strata upon which archaeologists depend for relative dating. Inscriptions, architecture, and design are the guides here. On the site of this great ruin, all the white pumice layer has weathered away, leaving bare limestone. While no Minoan antiquities have been found at this site, an ancient Greek stone inscription reading ΕΥΜΝΛΟΣ exists. According to Plato, Εγνηλος, which means "rich in sheep," was the twin brother of Atlas, King of the islands of Atlantis. Εγνηλος was given as his lot an island nearest the Pillars of Hercules. Galanopoulos has suggested that the Egyptian manuscript of the story of Atlantis did not mention the Pillars of Hercules, and that this place, known as the present-day Straits of Gibraltar, was an embellishment added by Plato. Plato was presented with a description of the geographical location of Atlantis, which clearly places it in the Aegean Sea. However, he was faced with dimensions far too large to place it in the Mediterranean. Furthermore, he did not know of the eruption of Thera. Faced with this dilemma and being a logical person, he placed Atlantis in the

Ocean Stream beyond Gibraltar. The name Atlantis in its Greek meaning, daughter of Atlas, may have been part of the original story, or it may have been invented by Plato. The narrow passage identified by Plato as Gibraltar was more likely one of the many straits in the Aegean, such as Dhiavlos Elaphonesos at the southeastern corner of the Peleponnesus. The island of Melos, west of Thera, may be the ancient domain of King Μηλος. The location of Atlantis on the Mid-Atlantic Ridge of the Atlantic Ocean, considered by many people as the most likely location, is based solely on a few brief sentences of Plato, whereas an eastern Mediterranean location is clearly indicated by many other parts of the text. Radioisotope measurements of sediment of the Mid-Atlantic Ridge suggest no major changes for the past 73,000 years. Geophysical studies in the central Atlantic Ocean Basin indicated no major changes over a period of 280,000 years.

FACTOR OF 10

One of the more significant pieces of evidence supporting the Minoan-Atlantis theory concerns the numbers used in Plato's story. Atlantis is clearly said to be a Bronze Age civilization. The Bronze Age in Europe and the Near East is dated from 2000 to 1000 B.C. Plato dates the destruction of Atlantis at 9000 years before the time of Solon in 590 B.C. Plato certainly did not describe a mesolithic culture, as this date implies, so there must be an error. Let us assume that there is a factor-of-10 error in the date, that in translation or recording, 100 was read as 1000. Such an error is easily made. The date of the destruction then comes out 1490 B.C. To make this more believable, there must be a consistent error throughout Plato's story and a substantial number of instances. This is the case. The royal state is described as an oblong region 3,000 by 2,000 stadia. Reducing this to 300 by 200 is just the size of the Neocene Basin of Crete, which is described perfectly in other terms. Moreover, a ditch or river is described surrounding the plain, 10,000 stadia long. This would be 1,100 miles. The periphery of the plain of Messara in Crete is about 110 miles. The royal state is presented as one of the 10 kingdoms of Atlantis, the others being possibly in Libya, Tyrrhenia, etc. The army of this kingdom is organized in relation to each lot of land, about one square mile, furnishing so many chariots, archers, javelin throwers, etc. The number of lots is given as 60,000, and when reduced to 6,000 results in a more reasonable number of soldiers, which probably still is exaggerated. The navy of 1,200 ships is said to require 200 sailors per ship. From "frying pan" drawings, seals, and wreck excavation, we know that a typical Minoan vessel did not require a complement of over thirty men.

EXAGGERATIONS

In picturing the cultures of prehistoric times, it is important to scale down one's impression from the inevitable exaggerations that occur in historical reporting. The people of Minoan times may have been less in number than today's population even though the land was more fertile. The geographical extent of Athens proper is given precisely and covers a small portion of Attica. The army was said to be drawn from the surrounding people. The war between Athens and Atlantis, won by Athens, was most likely a land engagement which took place on the shores of Attica. In the opening paragraph of this article it was said, referring to the Athenians, that "all your warlike men in a body sank into the earth." This was likely an earthquake associated with the collapse of Thera. Professor Galanopoulos has shown by studying seismic records that Attica has not been subject to large seismological disturbances in historical times. Only the earthquakes and floods accompanying the collapse of Thera would create such an opening of the earth. Plato also reported that the Acropolis in Athens had a fountain spring which was extinguished by the earthquake. Evidence of such a spring has been found.

ACTIVE DIGS

Active Minoan digs are currently underway on the island of Kea near Attica and at two recently discovered palaces on Crete, Zakros and Arkhanes. It is hoped that Thera can be added to this list in the near future. Needless to say, we are anxious to return.

A word should be said about possible underwater ruins at Thera. Several sites have been reported. They were examined acoustically and, where the water depth permitted, by swimmers. No diving equipment was used. On the *caldera* rim the bottom is very rough, covered with large rocks and deeply faulted. At three locations, formations which appeared man-made from surface, looked natural on close inspection. Off the southern and eastern beaches a stratum two to six meters under the sand was found, which became irregular near shore. This could be a ruin or a naturally formed concrete geologically known as beachrock, which was found above the bottom in some places. Our conclusion is that the work should be pursued with more powerful equipment and facilities for diving. Both in archaeological and geological points of view, Thera would be a most interesting place for a deep submersible capable of working to a depth of 700 meters.

SECTION X

THE OCEAN DENIZENS
We Learn Some Amazing Things about Animals

The far vaster, unseen—and till recently, unapproachable—area of the deep sea has its own fauna, an assemblage representing nearly all branches of the animal kingdom.
—C. P. Idyll in Abyss.

EVERY FISH MAKES A NOISE

From Naval Research Reviews, *March, 1964:*

More Than seventeen years of continuous research on fish and other marine organisms have convinced a University of Rhode Island scientist that through an understanding of fish "talk" and through related knowledge, fishermen can be helped to increase their catches in the sea. The help would be given by means of fixed, unmanned, underwater listening devices similar to those the Navy now uses to track enemy submarines. If fish of commercial interest were to swim near these posts and "talk," the sounds would be picked up and rebroadcast to fishermen in the area. Also a possibility is the broadcasting of man-made sounds underwater to attract some marine animals, to frighten others away, and even to herd fish or contain them in selected areas.

The scientist who has suggested these fishing methods is Marie Poland Fish of the URI Graduate School of Oceanography and the director of the world's largest underwater bioacoustic library. Mrs. Fish's broad knowledge of undersea sounds was gained in part through studies carried out under the oldest continuous biological contract held with the Office of Naval Research. Each year she has accumulated hundreds of miles of audio tape. When a new sound is discovered and analyzed thoroughly, it becomes part of the Reference File of Biological

Sounds, maintained since 1954 at the request of the Navy. Although this library contains sounds recorded by researchers all over the world, about 98 percent of the material was compiled by Mrs. Fish and her associates.

The evidence that fish "talk" is quite conclusive to the bioacoustic librarians. Usually, the animal sounds are associated with "colony life." For example, if you capture one fish of a school, a characteristic sound will be produced by others present, and the entire group will flee. The "talk" is also associated with such activities as breeding and competitive feeding, and, in the case of nocturnal fish, with carrying out their activities in the dark. Some marine animals may have quite extensive vocabularies; for example, studies of sounds made by white whales held in captivity have revealed a wide repertoire of recognizably different types of sounds that, used singly or in combination, have specific meanings.

The value of the knowledge gained through investigations of marine animal sounds can be indicated by a few examples:

1. Sonarmen need to be able to distinguish between sounds made by submarines and by animals so as to identify correctly sound-producing objects underwater. Sounds identified incorrectly could lead to such mistakes as sinking a whale because it was thought to be an enemy submarine.
2. Knowlege of bioacoustics also figures prominently in the design of torpedoes and mines that are activated by sound.
3. The research has also proved worthwhile in other unexpected ways; for instance, when one of the Texas towers toppled into the Atlantic with part of its crew aboard, Mrs. Fish was able to tell salvagers that the noises heard were from nearby whales, not survivors trapped in the underwater wreckage.

Mrs. Fish's research on marine animal sounds began with a review of more than 1,500 submarine war-patrol reports, including underwater sound logs and recordings, if available. Later it involved the auditioning of about 400 of the sound-producing organisms in the western North Atlantic Ocean, ranging from shrimp and crabs to porpoises, whales, sea lions, sea cows, and many kinds of fish. Every animal studied was found to have a characteristic sound "signature."

The next step was to determine what mechanisms various organisms use to produce sounds. Fish have neither vocal cords nor ears, as we commonly think of them, but various parts of their anatomies serve in a similar capacity. For instance, many species have air bladders with which they control their depth in the water. Some fish squeeze this organ with imbedded muscles to make a variety of noises. Other sounds are produced by long muscular "strings" attached to the bladder that can be made to vibrate. In both instances the air bladder operates as a sounding board. Still other species snap their fins, scrape their "gill teeth" together, or manipulate other parts of their anatomy.

Vast as is Mrs. Fish's underwater bioacoustics library, it is far from complete, for there are thousands of animals in the sea whose sounds have not yet been recorded and analyzed. The work is still going forward, and it will probably continue to do so for a long time.

CRABS TURN DARKER AT LOW TIDE

IN THE PALM BEACH *Post-Times,* Margaret Biggerstaff, an oceanographic consultant, writes of some of the amazing things marine animals do—apparently in response to something like an alarm clock, or biological clock, built inside and into them:

Have You ever seen any of the tiny "fiddler crabs?" These are outstanding in the group of sea animals who can "tell time." They abound on the beaches of New England, and have been the subject of much investigation by Dr. Frank A. Brown of Northwestern University, who spends his summers at the oceanographic center of Woods Hole, Massachusetts.

Just before dawn, Dr. Brown observed, they turn dark in color so they will be safer to run on the dark sand of the beaches on which they live. But at night, when the sand is lighter than the darkness of the night, they change again, this time to a pearly gray that blends in perfectly with the sand.

The question arose in Dr. Brown's mind, "Is this color change due to a response to sunlight or a lack of it?" So he put a number of the fiddler crabs into a photographic darkroom, under a steady temperature, and found that they still changed color at dawn and at dusk, thus telling time as well as a man-made clock.

Crabs are also perfect tide charts, turning darkest at low tide. If low tide occurs during the daylight hours, when the crabs are already dark (as we have explained), they will become even darker, proving there are two factors of control, not just one. They show approximately a 12½-hour change for the sun cycle and approximately a 6½-hour change for the tide cycle. In tide, they are obeying a moon, or lunar, cycle, for the moon is a main controller of the earthly tides. Even in a closed room they will change color according to the actual high and low tide charts of the beaches where they once lived.

Dr. Brown took back to Chicago with him some of the fiddler crabs from two widely separated Massachusetts beaches, whose tides were entirely different. But they obeyed the tide chart from their own beaches, changing color accordingly, although they were hundreds of miles from home.

Alton L. Blakeslee, science reporter for the Associated Press, following an interview with Dr. Brown, writes:

"Is this biological clock something that is built in, running at constant speed according to the metabolism of the speed of their life cycles?

"Or is it governed by physical forces connected with the earth's rotation, perhaps by some force which man does not yet know can affect these living things?

"Some kind of harmonics or vibrations definitely seem to affect these biological clocks, found also in earthworms, salamanders, fruit flies, and even potatoes, as all of these things, and many more, have given evidence of having these built-in clocks. (The lowly potato, for example, shows daily and lunar rhythms of oxygen consumption.)

"Rhythms and cycles are observed in many kinds of human behavior, even in economic cycles. Mental patients are reported to show swings of improvement or worsening with phases of the moon. Is it really the moon affecting them? Do the rhythms in human behavior have any connection with biological clocks of some kind? If so, how do they operate; how are they to be controlled?"

In his experiments Dr. Brown subjected the fiddler crabs to different drastic temperature changes. An astonishing thing happened. He chilled them to near freezing for six hours, then warmed them up again. The chilling stopped their "clocks"—for, when warmed up again, they began to follow their regular cycles of change—but now they were nearly six hours slow.

Oysters show a similar line of rhythm, opening their shells most at high tide. New Haven, Connecticut, oysters shipped to Illinois, opened for a couple of weeks at the time of high tide in the New Haven area. Later they slipped out of the pattern of the New Haven tidal time and became influenced by the lunar time in Illinois.

These are some of the fascinating stories coming out of the oceanographic research laboratories. It is not impossible to think that the studies of the built-in clocks of these creatures of the sea can, some day, give us a better understanding of mankind —including ourselves.

WHY THE TUNA NEVER STOPS SWIMMING

THE ONLY laboratory in the world where living tuna are successfully kept in captivity for study of their behavior is the Kewalo facility of the Bureau of Commercial Fisheries (BCF) Biological Laboratory in Honolulu. This is from its 1964–65 Progress Report:

Visitors Watching the tuna continuously circling the tanks are likely to ask two questions: "Do they always swim in the same direction?" and "Don't they ever stop swimming?" The answer to both questions is "No." The fish do change their direction of swimming. And never do they cease to swim, although normally they swim only slowly.

For swimming, to the tuna, is far more than a method of getting from one place to another. It is as vital to the fish as breathing is to a man. If the tuna stopped swimming, it would suffocate. And since the density of its firm body is slightly greater than that of seawater, the fish would also sink.

The Kewalo facility allows exact studies of the swimming speed of tunas as it is related to the needs for ventilation of the gills and the maintenance of hydrostatic equilibrium.

John J. Magnuson has found that the little tunny circles the tank at 0.75 m.p.s. [meter per second] (or about 1.5 miles per hour) both day and night. When the fish were deprived of food for several days, their speed declined to 0.55 m.p.s. (about 1.1 m.p.h.). The little tunny feeds by day. If the search for food played a predominant role in establishing swimming speed, one would expect the fish to swim slower by night; and certainly one would expect that the creature starved for several days and questing for food would swim faster than the satiated one. The little tunny, however, showed neither behavior. Whether the minimum speeds reached were chiefly related to a single function—gill ventilation or hydrodynamic lift—Magnuson is not yet sure. For some tunas, there is evidence that the requirements for gill ventilation are somewhat less than those for hydrodynamic lift, which means that the fish would sink before it would suffocate.

Although tunas respond to sound, there is only the slightest evidence that they themselves produce sound. That fish make sounds men can hear was demonstrated to science 101 years ago. (Fishermen had known it for untold millennia.) Since the advent of sensitive hydrophones, scientists have learned that the sea is quite a noisy place. Many laboratories possess tape recordings of the hissings, grunts, squeaks, and moans that contribute to the totality of audible sound in the ocean. The living sources of some of these have been identified. The carangid *Trachurus trachurus* Linnaeus, for example, is known to make "sounds like those produced by running the fingers along the teeth of a comb."

THE FASTEST FISH

So far as this capability has been measured, the tuna seems to be one of the fastest fish. It ranks with the cheetah, the eagle, and the dragonfly as among the swiftest creatures of their kind on earth. Most of the time, however, in tanks at least, the tunas swim rather slowly. Rates reported from studies at sea vary widely.

The presence of underwater viewing ports on the *Charles H. Gilbert* has enabled our Laboratory scientist Heeny S. H. Yuen to make quantitative studies of the swimming speeds of yellowfin and skipjack tunas in the ocean. The procedure for finding these speeds is ingenious: The fish are photographed with a 16-mm camera; from calculations that take into account the speed of the camera, the ship's forward movement, and its roll, Yuen is then able to measure successive images on the film in such a way as to arrive at a realistic estimate of the actual speed of a fish that may have appeared within the viewing range of the camera no more than half a second.

In this manner, he has made 510 measurements of the swimming speed of feeding skipjack tuna from four schools and 33 measurements of yellowfin from a single school. These results were then treated statistically to determine the validity of some of the relations suggested by the data.

The swimming speeds of the yellowfin tuna so measured were from 1.6 to 5.4 m.p.s. (3.2 to 10.9 m.p.h.). These results fall between those reported for yellowfin swimming at a depth of about 350 feet (2 m.p.h.) and struggling at the end of a fishing line (40.8 m.p.h.).

The swimming speeds of the skipjack tuna (0.3 to 6.9 m.p.s., or 0.6 to 13.9 m.p.h.) are much lower than those found by other researchers (about 10 m.p.s. sec., or 20.2 m.p.h.). The reason for this difference is unknown.

Both species swam faster (covered more body lengths) at the tailbeat rates measured than did the few other kinds of fish studied by earlier workers.

Although the observations just described tell us how fast individual fish swim, they say nothing about the speed of schools as units. What these speeds are, whether the fish school at night, when visual contact may be lost, what depths they may prefer—these are unknown factors at present. They may not remain so. The *Townsend Cromwell* will take to sea for the first tests of a new sonar system.

Unknown to the fish, long beams of unheard sound will play upon creatures almost a mile away from the ship and far below it. The echoes of these beams, received by sensitive electronic equipment aboard the vessel, will give scientists a new dimension to their picture of life in the open ocean.

The sonar will be a continuous-transmission, frequency-modulated equipment operating in two ranges of frequencies. This sophisticated gear was chosen instead of the more conventional pulsed sonar because it allows a target to be kept under constant surveillance. Its use lessens the probability of "losing" a target. The equipment will have a range of about 1,000 feet on individual tunas and perhaps 5,000 feet on a target of suitable strength—for example, a school. It will be capable of high resolution, distinguishing between fishes 7 inches apart at 300 feet.

And a still more exciting prospect looms ahead—the possibility of the construction of a nuclear submarine specially designed for fishery-oceanography research, the first nuclear submarine to be used for nonmilitary purposes. All the advance planning for this addition to the nation's research capability has been done at our Laboratory. Obviously, the submarine will have enormous possibilities for enlarging man's knowledge of the behavior of creatures in the sea.

The new sonar and the research submarine—these are exceedingly complex instruments for research. They make demands on many types of technical skills and cost a great deal of money. They are characteristic of much of the conduct of science of the latter half of the twentieth century. But complexity and great cost are not necessarily the sole hallmarks of progress. The past months have seen some good science done at our Laboratory with a piece of equipment that was technologically feasible at least two thousand years ago when Alexander the Great made his celebrated descent in a diving bell to the floor of the Mediterranean.

A LOG WITH A VIEW

Fishes collect around logs and other flotsam at sea. This habit is commonly exploited in sport fishing, and some small commercial fisheries have been based upon it. A few years ago, Reginald M. Gooding built what is essentially "a log with a view," a small raft equipped with a many-windowed caisson beneath the waterline. Tested first off the island of Hawaii, the raft *Nenue* proved seaworthy. The information she provided was found worth collecting. Early in 1964, the *Nenue* was shipped aboard the *Charles H. Gilbert* to equatorial waters. There she undertook two drifts, one of eight days, the other nine. During daylight, she was manned at all times by two observers. Among them, Gooding, Magnuson, and Randolph K. C. Chang spent 276 hours observing the behavior of fishes under the dazzling canopy of the sea surface.

What did they find? When the raft was first put in the water, no fish were to be seen. Within ten minutes the first of them arrived, little rudder fish that are cousins of the Hawaiian nenue for which the raft is named. Dolphin fish, known as mahimahi in Hawaii, appeared. They mingled with triggerfish, close relatives of the Hawaiian humuhumunukunukuapuaa, and many others. Within a short time, numerous fishes had been sighted. By the end of the longer drifts, almost a thousand fishes and some other creatures were swimming within sight. Many of the same species are present in both the Hawaiian and equatorial localities. The length of these creatures ranged from a few inches to several feet. The observations on these drifts constitute the most exhaustive study yet made on an underwater community in the open sea.

THE BARNACLES THAT HITCHHIKE

By Waldo L. Schmitt, research associate at the Smithsonian Institution, in Crustaceans:

Barnacles of the genus *Chelonibia* are found on the shells of sea turtles, a location for which they are structurally well adapted. Others are found attached only to whales. The late Mr. Ira Cornwall observed that these species accommodated themselves most wonderfully to the 10,000-mile voyages indulged in by their mighty hosts, during which the whales journey from their breeding ground in the equatorial seas to their summer feeding grounds in the shadow of the Poles. To cope with the extremes of environment confronting the animals in the course of the whales' migration—especially the sojourn in tropic seas—certain of the whale barnacles of the genus *Coronula* possess the largest and most highly developed gills, or branchiae, of any cirripeds known. As Mr. Cornwall explained, "It is well known that the warm water of the tropical seas contains less oxygen than the cooler water of the northern and southern oceans; also, the increase of temperature causes an increase of the rate of metabolism, and a consequent greater demand for oxygen. The combination of these two factors would explain the great development of the branchiae of the barnacles."

And how differently do the several species of whale barnacles attach themselves to their host! *Coronula reginae,* with very few exceptions, is found on the lips and the front edge of the flippers; *Coronula diadema,* in heavy masses on the throat and corrugated belly. *Coronula reginae* first embeds itself below the surface of the skin, with only the hood projecting above it. As the shell grows, the skin is forced back and eventually about a third of the shell is exposed. Another barnacle, also found on whales, is so attached to the flippers and flukes that its opening faces backward when the whale is in motion. This barnacle has been reported as occurring on porpoises also. The rarest of the whale barnacles in American collections is a small, tubular, storied-looking affair, *Tubicinella major.* It is found on the upper jaw, on the forehead, and over the eye of the southern right whale. *Stomatolepas,* as the name indicates, is found embedded in the mucous membrane of the gullet of sea turtles. *Platylepas* lives embedded in the skin of turtles and in that of manatees, sea snakes, and fishes as well.

THE MOST UNUSUAL SEAFOOD CHOWDERS

By Waldo L. Schmitt in Crustaceans:

Barnacles have their uses as well as their drawbacks from man's point of view. In Chile, where a common species grows to a prodigious size (for a barnacle)—nine inches in length and several inches across—the meat of this shrimp relative is an important article of food. It is considered quite a delicacy and is much sought after as an ingredient in soups and chowders. The flavor—all its own—of this barnacle soup, as I can attest, is equal to that of the best clam chowder, while the flesh is more palatable than clam meat.

SECTION XI

THE OCEANOGRAPHERS
Men Aboard the Challenger *Pointed the Way*

The Challenger *laid down the broad general foundations for the modern science of oceanography.*
—Sir John Murray in The Ocean.

GREAT VOYAGE: THE *CHALLENGER*

MEN have been sailing the surface of the sea throughout their recorded history; they have been seriously looking beneath the surface of the sea for less than 150 years. So brand new is the idea of exploring the depths that the cruise of Great Britain's *Challenger,* from 1872 to 1876, is regarded as the voyage that established oceanography. As this is written, the voyage of the *Challenger* was ninety years ago—or the space of time that would be covered by the lives of only two middle-aged men. Here the *UNESCO COURIER* in its November, 1954, issue describes the *Challenger*'s trip:

On December 21, 1872, the 2,300-ton wooden corvette H.M.S. *Challenger* sailed out of Portsmouth, England, to explore "conditions of the Deep Sea throughout all the Great Oceanic Basins." During 3½ years she sailed and steamed nearly 70,000 nautical miles around the globe, and made observations by soundings at 362 stations scattered over the 140 million square miles of the ocean floor. When she returned to England in May, 1876, she had sounded the depths of every ocean except the Arctic and had laid the foundation for the modern science of oceanography.

The scientific expedition, coming only forty years after the famous voyage of Darwin aboard the *Beagle* (1831–36), aroused considerable public attention. It proved beyond question that life existed at great depths in the sea . . . charted the first systematic plot of ocean currents and temperatures, showed that the temperature in each zone was fairly constant in all seasons, and charted what is still today our basic map of the world under the seas.

Before the *Challenger,* only a few isolated soundings had been taken of the ocean depths, and it was generally believed that nothing could live in the cold, black waters of the deep sea. Even the British biologist Edward Forbes, one of the first men to take a scientific interest in the ocean depths, held the belief that no life existed below 1,500 feet. A century ago he wrote: "As we descend deeper and deeper into this region, the inhabitants become more and more modified, and fewer and fewer, indicating our approach to an abyss where life is either extinguished or exhibits but a few sparks to mark its lingering presence."

But Forbes urged more exploration of "this vast deep-sea region" to settle the question definitely, and his own pioneer work in the Aegean Sea led the way for the *Challenger* expedition. In 1818 worms were brought up by an Arctic expedition from 1,000 fathoms; in 1860, a cable in the Mediterranean bed at 1,200 fathoms was found encrusted with corals and other animals.

Then came the voyage of the *Challenger.* "From bottoms lying under miles of water," writes Rachel L. Carson in her now famous *The Sea Around Us,* "from silent deeps carpeted with red clay ooze, and from all the lightless intermediate depths, net haul after net haul of strange and fantastic creatures came up and were spilled out on the decks. Poring over the weird beings thus brought up for the first time into the light of day, beings no man had ever seen before, the *Challenger* scientists realized that life existed even on the deepest floor of the abyss."

The *Challenger* was fitted with everything that could be carried in the way of appliances for scientific research at the time. Its equipment included sounding instruments, water bottles, undersea thermometers, 144 miles of sounding rope, and 12.5 miles of sounding wire; sinkers, nets, dredges, and "spirits of wine" for preserving specimens. A fully equipped zoological laboratory was set up on board. The Royal Society drew up a complete scheme of instructions for the voyage, captained by George Nares and led by Charles Wyville Thomson.

For a year the *Challenger,* fitted with auxiliary steam power in addition to her sails, explored the Atlantic depths, crossing from the Canary Islands to the West Indies, skirting the American side as far north as Nova Scotia, then recrossing the Atlantic to the Azores. She then sailed to the Brazilian coast and crossed the southern Atlantic to the Cape of Good Hope. From there, the *Challenger* headed into the southernmost part of the Indian Ocean and was the first steamship to cross the Antarctic Circle. After reaching the ice pack, she was caught in a dense snowstorm and crashed into an iceberg (losing the jib boom and other rigging, later recovered). The *Challenger* then proceeded to Australia, Fiji, the Philippines, Japan, China, and the Sandwich Islands (Hawaii).

On March 23, 1875, off the Marianas Islands, the expedition made its deepest sounding—26,850 feet. With a little luck, the *Challenger* might have discovered the deepest known place in the ocean, the Marianas Trench, some 200 miles southwest of Guam. It was a second H.M.S. *Challenger* that obtained a sounding of 35,640 feet in October, 1951, 200 feet deeper than the Mindanao Trench off the Philippines reported by a German cruiser in 1927.

After sailing due south to the Tropic of Capricorn, the *Challenger* expedition took an easterly course to Valparaiso, Chile, made its way into the South Atlantic again through the Straits of Magellan, and ended its remarkable voyage in England on May 24, 1876.

The narrative of the expedition has been told in popular form in Moseley's *A Naturalist on the* Challenger. The complete account of the scientific results of the voyage was published over a period of ten years in fifty volumes, the first of which contains an interesting "Narrative of the Cruise."

THE DAY WHEN OCEANOGRAPHY BEGAN

THE LATE Capt. E. John (Jack) Long had a rare combination of abilities. He was a graduate of both the U.S. Naval Academy and the Columbia Graduate School of Journalism. As both a sailor and a writer, he was an outstanding reporter on oceanography. This is from his *New Worlds of Oceanography:*

What We May Date as the "formal beginning of oceanography" was on December 30, 1872, when the H.M.S. *Challenger* made its first "station" (halt at sea where observations are recorded) after leaving Portsmouth on a cruise that was to last four years and circumnavigate the globe. At this point the latitude was 41° 57′ N., the longitude was 9° 42′ W., and the depth was 1,125 fathoms. According to Joel W. Hedgpeth (Pacific Marine Station, California): "Nothing very remarkable was discovered, as the dredge did not work quite right and came up half empty—but with enough ice-cold bottom mud nevertheless to chill a bottle of champagne we drank to the success of the expedition!"

It was about this time, too, that another aspect of oceanography began to emerge, both in Europe and in America. These were seaside laboratories, where fresh specimens could be examined and studied, and aquariums, where living forms could be kept. In later years aquariums became entertainment features, rivaling zoos in attracting the general public. Imported tropical fish and mammals such as seals and porpoises have added amusement features.

NAPLES AND PENIKESE

The first seaside laboratory was opened in 1872 at Naples, Italy. A year later, Louis Agassiz, founder of the Museum of Comparative Zoology at Harvard in 1859, set up a small summer laboratory on Penikese Island, off Cape Cod. It was soon abandoned, but the nearby Marine Biological Laboratory of Woods Hole, founded in 1888, is a direct descendant. Three years earlier, however, the first of the permanent establishments that have made Woods Hole the largest oceanographic center in the world was constructed by the Woods Hole Fisheries Station. Known locally as "The Fisheries," the station later became the Bureau of Commercial Fisheries Biological Laboratory, now a part of the Department of the Interior. Its new aquarium attracts some 200,000 visitors to Woods Hole annually.

England founded its first seaside laboratory, known as the Marine Biological Association of the United Kingdom, at Plymouth in 1888. It operates a public aquarium as well as research functions. The first laboratory on the Pacific Coast was the Hopkins Biological Station of Stanford University, established at Pacific Grove in 1892. The famous Marine Biological Association of San Diego, at La Jolla, was endowed by members of the Scripps family in 1905. It became part of the University of California in 1912 as the Scripps Institution for Biological Research. It was redesignated in 1925 as the Scripps Institution of Oceanography.

A HOST OF NEW LABORATORIES

Shortly afterward (1930) the famous Woods Hole Oceanographic Institution was born, and a host of marine laboratories followed about the same period or shortly later. Included among others were the Oceanographic Laboratories of the University of Washington (1930); the Bingham Oceanographic Foundation, at Yale (1930); the Tidal Institute (England) was combined with the Liverpool Observatory (1929); Lamont Geological Observatory, Columbia University (1949); University of Miami Marine Laboratory (1947); Marine Laboratory, Duke University (1938); Department of Oceanography, Texas A. & M. University (1949), and a score of others of equal standing, both in the United States and abroad.

Throughout the period between World Wars I and II, oceanography was slowly but surely coming of age, through laboratories ashore, research ships at sea, various governmental agencies, and private commercial firms. While the name "oceanography" had not yet come into general use, an ancient term "oceanology" was sometimes used. More often, the word "hydrography" covered the ground, but not too well, because it was sometimes confused with "hydraulics," a common engineering term. Those who included oceanography among the "Earth Sciences" (as it is today) confused those who did not understand that "Earth" with a capital "E" is not the same as "land." So the growing pains went on.

SECTION XII

EYEWITNESSES IN THE DEPTHS

Men in the Sea Have Unique Experiences

Most of our world is covered by ocean, containing billions of living things, large and small.
—"Guide to Marine Studios," Marineland, Florida.

THE JUNGLE BENEATH THE NEAREST SEA

TO 150 FEET DOWN

Just Off the Shore, when men step down into the sea beyond the low tide line, they enter some of the great undersea forests made up of great seaweeds: "The long-stalked kelps," the late Rachel Carson called them in *The Edge of the Sea,* "that sway in dusky forests just below the level of the spring tides."

In some "great submarine jungles of the Pacific," Miss Carson wrote, "the kelps rise like giant forest trees, 150 feet from the floor of the sea to the surface." Kelp, a brown or brownish seaweed, has the ability (not understood by science) of concentrating in itself one of the scarcest nonmetallic elements in the sea: iodine. There is about one gram of iodine to 20 tons of ocean water; kelp concentrates it at as much as one gram of iodine to 200 grams of dry seaweed. It is from the ashes of burned kelp, from the fossils of kelp, or from salt beds (particularly in Chile) that men have got their iodine. Kelp may have another use in medicine. In its July–August, 1966, issue, *Sea Frontiers* reported that it might reduce bone cancer.

Continues Rachel Carson in *The Edge of the Sea:*

On all rocky coasts, this laminarian (giant kelp) zone just below low water has been one of the least-known regions of the sea. . . . The area is obviously difficult to explore, with heavy seas breaking there most of the time. Such an area on the west coast of Scotland was, however, explored by helmet divers working with the British biologist, J. A. Kitching. Below the zone occupied by *Alaria* and the horsetail kelp, from about two fathoms below low water and beyond, the divers moved through a dense forest of the larger laminarias. From the vertical stipes (stalks or trunks), an immense canopy of fronds was spread above their heads. Although the sun shone brightly at the surface, the divers were almost in darkness as they pushed through this forest. Between three and six fathoms below low water of the spring tides the forest opened out, so that the men could walk between the plants without great difficulty. There the light was stronger, and through misty water they could see this more open "park" extending farther down the sloping floor of the sea. Among the holdfasts and stipes of the laminarias, as among the roots and trunks of a terrestrial forest, was a dense undergrowth, here formed of various red algae. And as small rodents and other creatures have their dens and runways under the forest trees, so a varied and abundant fauna lived on and among the holdfasts of the great seaweeds.

John S. Colman, Director of Marine Biological Station at Erin, Isle of Man, writes in *The Sea and Its Mysteries:*

The Animals in a single holdfast (root system) of the kelp include barnacles, nematode worms, hydroids, small mollusks, polyp compound ascidians, mites, oligochaete worms (related to earthworms, they have no distinct heads), amphipods, and many species of polychaete worms (their distinct heads have eyes and tentacles, and they have short, stumpy limbs). From below the tide to a depth of about 3 fathoms, or 18 feet, there may be in the kelp forests some half million animals on each square yard of sea floor, not counting microscopic animals such as protozoa!

University of California News Release, March 1, 1965:

A forest of giant kelp of a species which grows only in deep waters around two islands off the southern California coast is being tended by scuba-equipped undersea foresters.

Dr. Bruce Parker, University of California at Los Angeles botanist, has staked out a claim in the submarine forest which is located just off Catalina Island. Scuba (self-contained underwater breathing apparatus) divers from UCLA's Diving Board, under the direction of Glen Egstrom, are helping in a scientific study of the kelp. Two plots have been staked out and marked with tile on which is printed, "UCLA Botany Department."

The species belongs to a group of seaweed known as elk kelp, so named for the antlerlike shape of its branches. This particular species, known as *Pelagophycus giganteus,* is found only off Catalina and San Clemente Islands, and apparently nowhere else in the world.

This variety of kelp is one of the deepest seaweeds, growing at depths of 50 to over 130 feet. The name *Pelagophycus* is from the Latin *pelagic,* meaning on the bottom, and *phycus*—seaweed. At these depths there is little light for photosynthesis, but apparently just enough.

One of the unique features of the Catalina species of elk kelp is the large bladder which keeps the giant seaweed off the bottom. It contains the deadly gas carbon monoxide, which is not a common plant product.

Divers are helping to conduct a year-around study of growth and development of the elk kelp. They return every few weeks to collect data from two plots of kelp located at a 75-foot depth.

Another species of elk kelp grows just offshore at San Diego. Now a possible third species at Santa Cruz Island is being studied by Dr. Parker.

Some of the San Diego kelp was recently transplanted among the Catalina kelp. Apparently fish which feed on the elk kelp found this transplanted species to their liking. They stripped the stalks bare, and the plants died within weeks. Perhaps the kelp from other pastures looked "greener," Dr. Parker says.

Creatures that lurk in this kelp forest include sea bass and halibut.

The Late William Beebe, while with the New York Zoological Society (the Bronx Zoo), studied kelp in the Gulf of California. He wrote of it in *Zaca Venture:*

Not Only in size but in real complexity of organization of structure the giant kelp stands at the head of all marine plant life. There has never been in the sea any development of flowers or seeds, real leaves, roots or bark, but the kelp presents most interesting parallelisms of some of these. . . . The holdfast of the giant kelp is a mass of interlaced, tangled, rootlike fingers, tightly clasped about a stone. From this arises one or several stems from which, at intervals, spring series of fronds, either double or single, looking, on the whole, like a giant fern frond made of soft, pliable rubber. The short base stalk of each leaf is swollen into a pear-shaped float.

Within certain limits the kelp varies considerably in color. The young fronds and floats are as pale as tawny olive, or, in the sunlight, honey yellow; the adult growths are brownish olive, while sunlight shining through them turns them to greenish gold. The very young and small fronds are flat and smooth, but all older leaves are ribbed and reticulated in raised ridges and alternating depressions, irregularly waves. . . .

In sheer length of growth the giant kelp exceeds the height of the tallest redwood trees, and only the lianas of the tropical jungles far outgrow them. Extreme and improbable lengths of 900 and 1,000 feet have been reported, but 600 seems to be an authentic measurement of an Antarctic plant, according to Wells and Huxley. All that I saw were only a fraction of this length. . . .

The delicate patches of grayish white Bryozoa were by far the commonest form of animal life on my kelp. They should be named "Lichenozoa" instead, for on the kelp they present to human eyes far more the appearance of lichens than moss. . . . Bryozoa are puzzling creatures, being in some ways as closely related to worms as they are to mollusks. With a more than respectable ancestral lineage of 450 million years, they are still very abundant today. On the kelp leaves they formed flat incrustations, round, oblong, or irregular. Under the microscope they were exceedingly beautiful and varied. I found five species on a single small leaf, each with its individual ground plan and elevation, each with characteristic calcareous ornamentation. Some looked like sculptured, petrified lacework, and others were plume- or featherlike, resembling frost crystals on a windowpane. . . .

A kelp leaf was occasionally thickly covered with hundreds of small snail-like shells all glued fast on one side. These were coiled worms with the rather pleasant name *Spirorbis.* Small compressed crustaceans crept or swam over the surface, varying in color from pale to deep green, the dominant form of this group being an olive-green isopod. Thousands, of all sizes, were found on a single plant, all creeping slowly about and relying upon their amazing resemblance to the color of the fronds to escape detection. . . .

About fifty miles farther south, nearer Clarion, the *Zaca* was slowed up and a big mass of floating kelp pulled aboard. Several good-sized fish dropped out and the fronds were, as usual, alive with hundreds upon hundreds of large green isopods, besides a dozen or more small crabs and many naked mollusks. All these creatures were part and parcel of their seaweed home, blending in color, texture, and pattern, their individual outlines lost in the lights and shadows of the fronds and floats.

THE GREAT BARRIER REEF

"THE GREAT Barrier Reef of Australia is the most stupendous structure which living creatures have built upon our earth," Hans Hass, the Austrian scuba diver, writes in his *We Come from the Sea,* "an estimate of the cubic contents of the reef, which is 2,000 kilometers (1,242 miles) long, in many places 150 kilometers (93 miles) wide, and, on the outer edge, forms a rampart that drops precipitously to a depth of over 2,000 meters (6,562 feet) . . . if we take these figures, then we shall see that the Great Barrier Reef has a volume of 8 million times greater than that of the Pyramid of Cheops at Giza, 100,000 times greater than that of the Great Wall of China, and 2,000 times greater than the whole mass of the City of New York." In the spring, 1963, *POSH,* published by the P & O Lines, the world's largest shipping line, Australia's David Anderson, who has sailed through the Great Barrier Reef many times, writes:

TO 150 FEET DEEP

All nature is a wonderland which invites our awe; but every now and then, as though in collaboration with the late Robert Ripley, she pulls out all the stops. She has done so with the Australian Great Barrier Reef.

Throughout the warm oceans of the world, the polyp, a sea animal related to sea anemones and jellyfish, has raised thousands of atolls. With their limy skeletons polyps have built Zanzibar Island and Pemba off the east coast of Africa; they have raised thousands of atolls throughout the Pacific and Indian Oceans; off the coast of northern Australia they have built a kingdom. Here the limy skeletons of countless trillions of tiny polyps (each no bigger than a pin's head) have built through tens of millions of years, a great coral breakwater nearly 1,300 miles long. Veering 10 to 150 miles out from the Queensland coast, it runs from Cape York to just above Brisbane, Queensland's capital. It follows the line of the continental shelf and locks in its multicolored walls over 80,000 square miles of blue water. As the continental shelf sank slowly, the little coral insects continually built upward and in places the Reef is 450 feet deep.

The Great Barrier Reef is the biggest in the world. But nature has not been content to stop there; not only are the many kinds of coral of a heart-tugging beauty, but all ocean and beach life is on an exaggerated scale. Sea creatures which elsewhere are small, grow here to an immense size; some which are drab elsewhere, here are as gorgeous as butterflies. Starfish are often a foot across, anemones are enormous, sea urchins are giants; the clams are five and even six feet long and weigh a quarter of a ton; the octopuses are six feet across. Here are fish that *walk* on land and sea snakes with the worst bite in the world. On the islands themselves, the same superlative and extravagant scale is maintained: butterflies and moths with wing spans of eight inches are as big as birds; beetles are jeweled; spiders are as big as bats; fireflies are several inches long; and flies and mosquitoes take on the same Munchausen quality.

Against the great coral breakwater thump the great rollers of the Pacific, whipped along by the southeast trade winds for nine months of the year. But on the western side it is generally calm—sometimes the water is so still that the surface is as still and clear as plate glass. I can still recall the first shock of surprise on my first visit to the Reef many years ago. The seas and the clear skies were very blue, as though they had been made with the old-fashioned washing blue that our grandmothers used to use, and the little foam our launch kicked up fell back with a vivid cauliflower whiteness. Here within the huge coral wall is what Australians call the "Grand Canal" along which shipping sails to and from the Far Eastern ports. Within the 80,000 square miles of coral-locked water are many thousands of shoals, reefs, cays, atolls, and "high" islands. The "high" islands are the tops of old mountains that were once part of the Australian continent. The Reef is a living, growing thing. Here are reefs awash which will gather the sea's debris and in time become islands; the sand will become soil and will support life; coconuts, pandanus, mangroves, pisonias, and casuarinas will eventually take root here. Here are reeferies which so far grow only coarse grass. The older are ones which have become atolls 15 feet high, with their vegetation 70 feet high. Around all are armlets of coral which enclose lagoons of calm water. A few of the older cays are large—50 and even 150 acres in extent. The "high" islands are bigger still—Hinchinbrook Island, in Whitsunday Passage, north of Mackay, is 30 miles long. The "high" islands have a tropical vegetation like that of the nearby mainland, of tall hooppines, magnolias, coconut trees, pandanus palms, brilliant flame trees, wild plums, and the gray feathery-topped eucalyptus.

For me (and many others) the greatest lure of the Reef is that it is primeval. It is as it was a million years ago. There is so much of it, and so few people, it is doubtful if man can ever spoil it—that 80,000 square miles of water is as large as Idaho or Minnesota.

For many, the coral is the major attraction. Here, too, nature has exerted herself in the most exotic and extravagant ways; she has chosen a technicolored palette and has got away with it. Drift over a coral garden in a boat with a glass bottom—or better still, put on an aqualung and merge yourself in the coral kingdom. Here are some enormous coral heads: They rise like cliffs 100 feet from the bottom; others are like giant toadstools and grow from a small base to an expanse possibly 200 feet across. Here, too, is a great blue lace expanse of table coral; here in the reef wall, staghorn corals grow like so many trophies garnered by an underwater hunter—but the stags are bizarre because the "horns" are blue-tipped; here are ebony clusters of brain coral and jet black niggerheads; there are drowned cities—towers, battlements, churches, cathedrals, and eastern temples. The colors are vivid and daring: all shades of pink, red, green, brown, sapphire blue, royal blue, Roman purple, orange, and cornflower blue. They are all here in delicate and exotic shapes.

Among the coral grow the flowers of the reef, the anemones which are the homes of small orange-and-white clown fish which can swim safely among the flickering pale tentacles so deadly to other fish. When threatened, the decoy clown fish scuttle inside their anemone host, which proceeds to entrap the pursuer. Afterward anemone and clown fish sup together! Other fish are as brilliant as the coral itself—some small, some huge. Here are tiny fish with eyes like sapphires and turquoise scales; pearly emperors with red bow ties; multibanded parrot fish, sergeant fish with three stripes, red emperor, blue-spotted grouper. And at the bottom of the "garden" are gay-colored sea slugs, sea urchins, slim starfish with slow-moving limbs, crayfish gay as Renaissance courtiers, crabs, and giant clams with kris-shaped lips.

Ripleyism even extends to bottom fishing in Barrier Reef waters; fishermen confidently expect to catch 300 or 400 pounds of fish in a few hours, and it is not unknown for three fishermen, using hand lines, to catch over half a ton of fish in a single night.

You won't find the walking fish in the coral gardens; you must look for them on the mudflats where they come ashore to hunt for insects. These are the mudskippers or kangaroo fish, members of the goby family, with well-developed muscles on their pectoral fins, which they use to lever themselves across the flats. They have faces like frogs, grow up to 12 inches, and breathe through their tails as well as through their gills: They have very useful tails which can take in oxygen from the air. Here again nature has exerted herself; the mudskippers will drown if you keep them submerged without access to air!

If bottom fishermen are well provided for, nature has been equally lavish for fishermen who seek light big-game fish, such as tuna, kingfish, trevally, barracuda, Spanish mackerel. Underwater spearfishermen too make big hauls—groupers grow to 500 pounds or more. And the multicolored banded sea snakes? Well, they pack much more venom to the ounce than any other snake in the world—ten times as much as a cobra—but, fortunately, they are usually wary of underwater swimmers.

Green hawksbill and loggerhead turtles are abundant in these waters; and here is another Munchausen touch, for turtle-riding is a sport on the Reef islands. The first European who told of this feat was ridiculed. This was, of course, Louis de Rougemont. He would laugh ironically today if he could see the not very inspiring spectacle of giant turtles, weighing several hundredweight, carrying tourists on the beaches of the Barrier resorts.

Here in these waters, too, are dugongs, the pig-faced and snouted originals of all the mermaid myths; they are gentle, warm-blooded creatures which graze on the sea grasses and are distant relatives of your own manatees.

This great marine wonderland is also the home of millions of seabirds—fierce whistling sea eagles, raucous gulls, stately pelicans, pert noddies, and indomitable terns and petrels. These last have migratory cycles of thousands of miles over the Pacific and return, generally on the same day each year, to start once more the raising of a family. And on Reef islands a million petrels blot out the sky and settle noisily on the beach on the same October day each year.

Ageless time and the eternal truths are never very far away on this great, primeval Barrier Reef. In the building of this great wall by tiny polyps is symbolized man's slow accumulation of culture. The Reef was probably building before man had built his first hut and made his first tool. And whatever man chooses to do with his own life on the planet, the coral polyps will continue to live and die and build.

SECTION XIII

PUZZLES OF OCEAN LIFE
There Are Fish and Monsters We Can't Catch

The marine animals and plants have been neither exhaustively surveyed nor fully described. There must be many species, and even some higher orders in classification, which zoologists and botanists have missed.

—Lionel A. Walford, Living Resources of the Sea.

WE PREDICT THE FISHING

From "Progress in 1964–65" at the Bureau of Commercial Fisheries Biological Laboratory, Honolulu:

The Name "skipjack" has been applied to several species of fishes that jump above or play at the surface of the water. The tuna that is called skipjack is found and fished in all the world's oceans except the Arctic. There are names for it in at least twenty tongues. In 1963, the skipjack tuna outranked in weight all other tunas caught in the Pacific. The skipjack is a short-lived fish and has a dark-blue back and a silvery belly. It attains a length of about 30 inches. There are at least three cogent reasons for the study of the skipjack: the commercial importance of the present fishery; the much greater potential commercial importance of the species; and the growing possibility that elucidation of some of the mechanisms that link the skipjack and its environment in the central Pacific may give results that could be applicable to fishery problems throughout the world.

THE AKU FISHERY

The Hawaiians have a name for the skipjack tuna that is halfway between a cough and a sneeze—"aku." The aku catch is by far the state's largest, accounting for 69 percent of the total landings of 5,874 tons (about the average annual catch) in 1963, according to the Hawaii Division of Fish and Game. The skipjacks are caught in Hawaiian waters every month in the year, but the fishery depends heavily upon the larger fish that are most often in evidence during the summer.

The Hawaiian aku fishery is conducted by the sampan fleet, the size of which has been dwindling with the years, although catches have not paralleled this trend. Fishing is done by pole and line. Usually schools are located by observing bird flocks. The schools are chummed with live bait, by preference the nehu or anchovy (*Stolephorus purpureus*). Landings have varied from 29,000 pounds in January, traditionally one of the poorest months, to more than 3 million pounds at the height of the season in July, according to Richard N. Uchida, our Laboratory scientist who has made a definitive statistical study of the 1952–62 catch.

As predictably as tourists flock to the famous beaches of Waikiki in summer does the skipjack catch rise in the warmer months. Both tourists and tunas are a source of income to the State of Hawaii. (But tourism is a $200-million-a-year business; the fishing industry brings in about $1 million to the fishermen.) The arrival of both tourists and tunas in Hawaii is predictable. Unpredictable are the numbers in which either will turn up. May, 1965, was a phenomenal month for the skipjack fleet. In May the fishermen had a month such as normally occurs only at the peak of the season, July. In fact, this May's catch was estimated to exceed that of most Julys'. Fishing almost within sight of Waikiki, the sampans came home night after night heavily loaded with aku. And the captains of the Laboratory's research vessels reported that the fleet was only nibbling on the population; schools were abundant offshore for many miles to sea.

The unusual catch in May could be attributed to two causes. First, it may have represented the passage through the fishery of a year-class of great strength. Year-classes of almost legendary abundance are well documented in many fisheries. Like comets and great men, they appear so briefly and infrequently as to be remembered long afterward. The much-studied 1939 year-class of sardines off the West Coast provides an instance, as does the classical 1904 year-class of Norwegian herring. Second, the May catch might have reflected the response of the skipjack to some change in the ocean environment. These two possibilities are not mutually exclusive, of course.

AKU FORECASTS

The Hawaiian Islands lie near the boundary between two water types. It is a boundary that, like the front line in a stalemated war, shifts back and forth. Thus the islands are bathed by water of relatively high salinity during part of the year, by less-saline water during the rest. Normally, but not always, the more-saline water prevails during the fall and winter, the less-saline during the late spring and summer.

Good fishing seasons for the skipjack tuna are often characterized by a flow of less-saline water about the islands. This circumstance is interesting but of little predictive value to the fishermen, for by the time the less-saline waters arrive off Hawaii's shores, the fish are there too. Our Laboratory scientists have noted, however, what appears to be another characteristic of good fishing years: the seasonal warming of the sea surface starts early.

Using the time of intitial warming, as measured at Koko Head, the southernmost point of the island of Oahu, and information on the changes in salinity near the islands, oceanographer Gunter Seckel for the past six years has issued an "aku forecast" in April. The season has usually borne out the forecast. The forecast for 1965 called for an "average or above average" catch.

These forecasts are of more use to the scientists than to the fishermen. "Below average," for example, a term as exact as the scientists are yet prepared to use, could mean anything from rather poor to catastrophic, a big difference to a man trying to make his living from the fishery. To the scientists they provide clues to the natural processes that may account for the variations in the skipjack catch, and these clues are being followed up.

The phenomenal catch in May provided a dramatic illustration. The salinity value of 34.8 0/00 (parts per thousand) has been empirically selected as that separating "favorable" from "unfavorable" waters. When the salinity at Koko Head dropped below this value and stayed there, the estimated skipjack catch rose abruptly, and although landings declined in June, they remained well above previous levels. The estimated monthly take of skipjack tuna from January through April was between 300,000 and 800,000 pounds per month. Then, in May, the catch increased to an estimated 3.5 million pounds and in June was 2.3 million pounds. For the first four months of the year average salinities at Koko Head were about 34.99 0/00, dropping to 34.65 0/00 in May and June.

On the basis of previously established criteria, the waters changed from what is designated as an unfavorable type in April to a favorable type in May. From the weekly landings and the biweekly salinity samples one can see that the change must have occurred about May 5. The salinity was 34.99 0/00 on May 4, dropped to 34.68 0/00 on May 7, and 34.53 0/00 on May 11. For the 7-day period ending on May 3, the estimated Oahu landings were 130,000 pounds, for the 7-day period ending May 10, they were 510,000 pounds.

This correlation supports the hypothesis that water type is important in the distribution of skipjack. It should be emphasized, however, that the correlation is between type of water, of which the salinity is merely an index, and skipjack catch—not between salinity itself and skipjack catch. The decline in the catch rate in June, when salinity remained low, shows that other factors also affect the availability of skipjack.

WHERE ARE THE MISSING TUNA?

IF there are old fish in the sea, there must be young—somewhere. From "Progress in 1964–65" at the Bureau of Commercial Fisheries, Biological Laboratory, Honolulu:

The Central Pacific is fished by the Hawaiian fleet and the Japanese. The Hawaiian fleet is rarely out of sight of land. It takes about 7,000 tons of tuna a year. The Japanese fleet ignores the islands to reap a harvest overwhelmingly larger than that taken by the Hawaiians.

Several lines of evidence suggest that the Japanese fleet is not exhausting the protein riches of the Central Pacific: There are still far less potentially harvestable fish caught than uncaught. The most plentiful tuna larvae in the area are those of the skipjack tuna. Because the skipjacks apparently spawn no more frequently or plentifully than the other tunas, the presence of these larvae point to the existence in the central Pacific of an immense population essentially untouched by the Japanese longline fleet and only sampled by the Hawaiian vessels. The bigeye and yellowfin tunas taken on the Japanese longlines are large and old; somewhere in the area there must be not only more of these fishes but also larger populations of the smaller and younger fish, that now are not taken at all.

Speaking at the Governor's Conference on Science and Technology, State of Hawaii, in January, 1965, John C. Marr, BCF Area Director, Hawaii, said, "It has been estimated that these resources could yield an annual catch of perhaps 200,000 tons. We know that the resources exist, we know the general—but not the specific—details of their geographical distribution, we know that they generally occur beneath the surface, and we suspect that they occur in schools. We do not know where major concentrations occur; if such exist, we do not know their depth distribution and how this may vary, and we do not know certainly that the fish occur in schools."

Much of the work of our Laboratory is shaped toward solving the problems in measuring, locating, and harvesting this great hidden resource.

THE ANTARCTIC MYSTERY OF THE FISH GRAVEYARD

From the United States Antarctic Research Program, National Science Foundation:

McMurdo Station, Antarctica, February 17, 1964. A scientist here has exploded an old theory and thus deepened the mystery of the stranded Antarctic fish.

One of the first Antarctic explorers more than fifty years ago discovered 4-foot-long dead fish, and invertebrates such as "glass" sponges (sponge balls with delicate spicules), and coral scattered on top of the thick ice that covers southwestern McMurdo Sound. The remains were largely intact and remarkably well preserved, except that some fish were headless. There was no obvious cause for the appearance of marine bottom life on the ice surface in uninhabited Antarctica.

However, the explorer—Frank Debenham, of the second Scott Expedition—knew that the ice comes from a freshwater glacier flowing out over the sea from a coastal mountain valley. He theorized that seawater froze beneath the floating glacier, or ice shelf, all the way down to the floor of the sound, trapping bottom-dwelling animals. Over hundreds of years sun and wind wasted away the top of the shelf—as evidenced by a highly eroded surface and summer melt pools—but seawater kept freezing below the buoyant ice to replace the loss, Debenham said.

The animal remains could gradually work up through the ice in this way until they reached the surface, he said. According to the speculation, at this point the original freshwater ice would have all disappeared, leaving a shelf made entirely of frozen seawater.

Three years ago United States scientists discovered a large concentration of marine bottom life near the easternmost of the Dailey Island group which protrudes through the ice shelf. They found the same kinds of remains that Debenham had observed, as well as groups of clamlike shellfish and heads of fish which they estimated must have had bodies about five feet long. They interpreted their findings as supporting Debenham's hypothesis.

Now glaciologist Anthony J. Gow has cored completely through the shelf near the island and discovered by laboratory analysis of the ice-core crystal structure that the shelf is freshwater ice from top to bottom, and not sea ice, as required by the theory. Nor did he find any animal remains in the cores, as might be expected from the theory. His measurements show that the ice varies from 20 to 50 feet in the area.

Gow and assistants George Hendrickson and Robert Rowland camped on the ice shelf for six days to conduct the studies. Hendrickson and Rowland departed last month; Gow was there three months and is now on his way home.

Not only has Gow left the enigma without explanation, but he has added other pieces to the puzzle. He discovered a layer of fresh water sandwiched between ice-shelf bottom and seawater, but could not determine its thickness or temperature.

He said that the layer might somehow be due to shelf-bottom melting, although Antarctic ocean waters are normally three degrees below the melting point of fresh water; or may result from melt water running off the surface and down cracks and fissures that split the shelf in many places. The occurrence is unusual and possibly unique, he commented.

Gow's research provided two possible leads toward a solution to the problem of the animal remains. He discovered that some of the cores, though composed of freshwater ice, do not appear to have glacial crystal structure. This odd situation may be caused by freezing of the freshwater layer underneath the shelf, and gradual buildup of a freshwater but nonglacial shelf in a manner similar to Debenham's process, he explained.

Gow said he found that the invertebrate remains were most concentrated in areas of surface moraine, suggesting that perhaps both moraine and animals arrived in the same way. Moraine is material picked up by the bottom of a glacier as it flows over the land. Scientists do not know exactly how it gets from bottom to top, but think it undergoes very slow churning within the glacier.

Both the island and the moraine in front are composed of volcanic rock, and dirt was found throughout the core taken at this spot, indicating that perhaps the moraine—and with it the invertebrates—may have possibly come from the submerged edge of the island, according to Gow.

Gow's work on the ice shelf is one phase of a long-term, large-scale study of Antarctic glaciology being done as part of the United States Antarctic Research Program (USARP). USARP is funded and coordinated by the National Science Foundation, an independent agency of the Federal Government. Gow is a civilian scientist with the U.S. Army Cold Regions Research and Engineering Laboratory and works under direction of Dr. James A. Bender.

According to Gow, "Whatever mechanism is responsible for the presence of marine remains on the ice must be extremely delicate—fragile glass sponges remain intact, clamlike shells are still hinged together, and coral stays attached to rock. Only the fish have been marred.

"Another unusual aspect of the fish is that they are all of the same family. Most fish caught by biologists in this area are less than one foot long, so I would expect to find some of these smaller fish on top of the ice, but there are none. Seals bring up big fish, and sometimes leave their catch to look for more, so this might explain the presence of damaged fish, but would not account for the other animals. Another solution for the fish alone is that they swim up cracks in the ice and become trapped.

"Perhaps there is one explanation for the fish and another for the invertebrates, which might be fossils picked up by the glacier as it passed over an old shoreline before it reached the sea. It has been suggested that they might even have floated up from the ocean bottom to the underside of the shelf on filaments of ice, which are known sometimes to form around them, but each explanation has objections.

"A survey of temperatures, salinities, thicknesses, depths, and flow rates should be made of the shelf and underlying waters not only to help explain the mystery of the animal remains, but also because of the glaciological importance of the ice shelf."

Gow first came to Antarctica during the International Geophysical Year of 1957–58 and has been down every austral summer but one since. He participated in the project that drilled a 1,013-foot hole, 6 inches in diameter, in the Continental Icecap at Byrd Station the first year.

His periodic remeasurements of the hole have provided information on rates and patterns of ice flow, since ice flows like thick molasses, only much slower. These measurements have also given evidence that Antarctica was a few tenths of a degree colder two thousand years ago—the age of the ice at the bottom of the hole—but that the composition of the atmosphere, which formed still-existing air bubbles, was the same. (These surely must be the oldest bubbles in the world.)

Work on other pits and holes in the icecap has shown that the temperature at a depth of 30 feet is equal to the average air temperature, meaning that temperature records do not have to be kept for a year in an icecapped region to determine the annual average. Gow is also working on methods to trace wind and storm patterns over the continent by analysis of chemical properties of surface snow.

He said that the icecap is a good collection site for micrometeorites and for keeping track of radioactive and industrial chemical fallout, because unlike any other area of the world it is virtually free of natural or man-made contamination.

Gow has been working for several years on chemical and

physical properties of Antarctic ice, annual accumulation and flow factors; collecting core samples for storage and later analysis in the United States; and developing new techniques to extract more information about the earth, its history, and its climate from the frozen records surrounding the South Pole.

A later paper—by Anthony Gow, W. F. Weeks, G. Hendrickson and R. Rowland—had this explanation of the fish and invertebrate remains found: That the fish, left by deep-diving seals (after being partly eaten) were frozen into fresh water under the ice. The fish in time were forced to the surface of the ice. The invertebrates were frozen in with the moraine at the time the moraine was formed. The paper appeared in the *Journal of Glaciology,* Vol. 5, No. 42, October, 1965.

SOLVED: THE MYSTERY OF THE TRACKS ON THE BOTTOM OF THE SEA

From the Columbia University News Office, October 11, 1965:

Oceanographers have finally cracked the mystery of the strange animal burrows and tracks on the ocean floor that have long been a puzzle to science.

The oceanographers, one from Columbia University and the other from the University of Cambridge in England, said deep-sea cameras have caught the source of some of the tracks—a "giant" [three feet long] enteropneust or acorn worm.

One photograph, taken in the Pacific at 15,534 feet, or nearly three miles, is believed to be the first deep-ocean record of an acorn worm since the famed English oceanographic ship *Challenger* dredged up three similar but damaged specimens from the bottom of the Atlantic in 1873.

Bruce C. Heezen, associate professor of geology and a member of the Lamont Geological Observatory staff at Columbia, and Donald W. Bourne of the Department of Zoology at Cambridge and of the Woods Hole Oceanographic Institution, Woods Hole, Massachusetts, reported on their findings in *Science,* a publication of the American Association for the Advancement of Science (October 1, 1965). Their research was supported in part by the Office of Naval Research and the National Science Foundation.

The scientists said that the mysterious tracks have perplexed both the experts of deep-sea photography and paleontology. The tracks and burrows can often be found in the photographs, but the problem had been to find the animals that made them, they added.

One kind of track, in the form of large coiled or "spiral" patterns of from about 1 foot to 6-feet in diameter, sometimes appear in deep-ocean photographs taken in most oceans.

"The patterns begin and end abruptly," said the Columbia and Cambridge oceanographers. "We have never discovered traces leading toward their centers or away from their outer ends."

The *Science* article explained that in some areas the tracks "are quite plentiful." On a voyage of the *Vema,* one of Columbia's oceanographic vessels, between Wellington, New Zealand, and Tahiti, a camera recorded them at nearly every ocean-bottom area that was studied and in depths greater than two miles.

Later, the U.S.N.S. *Eltanin,* a National Science Foundation oceanographic ship which usually carries scientists from Columbia and other institutions on its cruises, photographed the tracks at sixty bottom areas in the southwest Pacific and the Scotia Sea, the scientists said.

"Still more 'spirals,' about twenty, have been found in pictures from the North Atlantic, Indian Ocean, and North Pacific," they added. "But in our survey they have appeared most often in pictures from the high southern latitudes; the southern South Pacific seems a particularly good place for them."

It was at one of these South Pacific sites (29° 40′ S., 176°

43′ W.) that the scientists photographed very clearly not only a track but the animal responsible.

"To find an enteropneust that makes any sort of track is remarkable, for they are generally thought only to live protected in burrows or, for example, among rocks or the holdfasts of seaweeds," said Drs. Heezen and Bourne.

The oceanographers said that a description of the acorn worm was made after the *Challenger* dredged three damaged ones from the Atlantic bottom off West Africa ninety-two years ago.

One of those fresh specimens, it was said, was "probably of considerable length" and was "distinguished by very lively colors."

HOW DID THE SALMON DO IT?

From Sea Secrets, *October, 1965:*

A SALMON THAT CAME HOME

The Bureau of Commercial Fisheries reports a remarkable story of a California salmon which accomplished one of the most phenomenal migrations ever recorded.

Early in 1964, the salmon (then 1½ years old) was taken from its tank in the hatchery at Orick, California, marked by removal of a fin, and placed in a stream some miles distant. This year, the fish made its way back to the hatchery from the Pacific through one of the most difficult obstacle courses ever constructed.

The fish swam up two creeks, through a culvert under U.S. Highway 101, and into a 4-inch drain pipe with a 90-degree turn. Then the fish had to leap through a 2½-foot-high pipe and over a 2-foot-high wire net. At one point, the salmon had a choice of five pipes, four of which were dead ends, but it chose the right one and returned to its hatchery tank.

SECTION XIV

THE RIVERS IN THE SEA
Scientists Tackle the Gulf Stream—and Others

There is a river in the ocean. In the severest droughts it never fails and in the mightiest floods it never overflows. . . . The Gulf of Mexico is its fountain, and its mouth is the Arctic Ocean.
—Matthew Fontaine Maury on the Gulf Stream.

CAN WE EXPLAIN THE DEEP-SEA RIVERS?

65 TO 325 FEET DOWN

"In the Deep Ocean Basins," writes Sir Alister Hardy in *The Open Sea,* "we may even find currents at different levels flowing in opposite directions."

We found in the 1950's, beneath the westward-flowing South Equatorial Current in the Pacific Ocean, an enormous, eastward-flowing current we knew nothing about. "It is," says Sydney Chapman in *IGY: Year of Discovery,* "one of the great oceanographic discoveries of our time, comparable with the discovery of jet streams in the upper atmosphere."

"Just think," said Roger Revelle of Harvard, formerly director of the Scripps Institution, "a river in the ocean of this size and its very existence was not known a few years ago!"

C. P. Idyll reports in *Abyss:*

This Current, perhaps the second largest in the Pacific after the Kuroshio Current, carries over half as much water as the Gulf Stream, at nearly as fast a rate. It seems incredible that a current transporting 40 million tons of water a second—as massive as thousands of Mississippi Rivers—could escape the notice of men for so long. The current came to light in a curious manner. Scientists of the U.S. Fish and Wildlife Service, probing waters for tuna at the equator south of the Hawaiian Islands, had set their gear for a depth of about 165 feet in an area where the surface waters flowed westward under the influence of the South Equatorial Current. They were astounded to see the buoys head unmistakably to the east! Apparently there was an easterly current only 100 feet or so below the surface. The next year the Fish and Wildlife Service sent one of its oceanographers, Townsend Cromwell, to the equatorial Pacific to make a careful study of this unexpected current. His work brought to light its remarkable characteristics.

Subsequent work by a group of scientists from the Scripps Institution of Oceanography headed by Dr. John A. Knauss has shown the Cromwell Current to be one of the major components of the Pacific current system. It is at least 3,500 miles long. It extends eastward to the Galapagos Islands; in the west it has been identified at 150 degrees west (about the latitude of Tahiti). There are hints that it exists at latitude 160 degrees east, near the Solomon Islands, and Japanese oceanographers have turned up currents on the far side of the ocean that may well be the other end of the Cromwell Current, giving it a total length of 8,000 miles.

A remarkable feature of the Cromwell Current is its shallowness. . . . At 140 degrees west longitude, the top of the current is about 65 feet below the surface and its core 325 feet deep. The current slows down below the core; by 1,640 feet what movement remains is in the opposite direction. This thin ribbon of water is about 250 miles wide—1,500 times as wide as deep—extending 2 degrees on each side of the equator.

Most remarkable of all, perhaps, is the constancy of the current. Over the whole length that has so far been charted, it extends a steady 125 miles on either side of the equator, with its center exactly on the equator. Its speed of about 2½ to 3 knots and its volume apparently vary surprisingly little. There seems to be little doubt that this constancy of behavior is associated with the position of the current precisely on the equator.

Sea Secrets for April, 1963, continues the story:

J. A. Knauss of Scripps Institution of Oceanography has discovered the "lost" eastern portion of the Cromwell Current (the current was named for its discoverer, Townsend Cromwell) in the Pacific Ocean. He has found that the current veers north of the Galapagos Islands, becoming weaker and much deeper, and then returns to the equator farther east.

Discovered only in 1951, the Cromwell Current differs from all other ocean currents—for example, the Gulf Stream—in that it consists of water no different in temperature or biological content from that on either side. It is a large, shallow stream flowing east beneath the equator from the western Pacific to the Galapagos Islands. There—until Knauss' location of the missing part—the current previously seemed to vanish.

What the great ocean currents mean to men is told by Robert C. Cowen in *Frontiers of the Sea.* Their significance is great indeed:

Seven tenths of our planet's surface is never at rest. Quite apart from the phenomena of tides and waves, the interlocking water masses of the oceans are forever on the move. Sometimes they are in a hurry, as when the Gulf Stream pours past Miami like a millrace. Sometimes they barely creep along, as in the case of the cold bottom currents that may take decades, even centuries, to complete their journey. But somehow, over no one knows how long a time, any given droplet of seawater will find its way to almost every part of the sea's domain.

This constant movement of the waters, this restless stirring which we classify as great current systems, is one of the most characteristic features of the sea. It mixes the oceans so thoroughly that, in spite of the local salinity variations that continually develop, the general composition of their dissolved salts is everywhere the same. It helps even out the unequal distribution of the sun's heating and regulates the weather. . . .

It is one of the principal mechanisms by which the oceans help maintain the earth's heat balance and regulate the climate. Geophysicists will never understand the overall workings of weather and climate until they have a true picture of these deep-water movements. . . .

It creates vertical upwelling currents that bring nutrient minerals from the depths. These fertilize rich plant growths in many areas, which in turn are the mainstay of the world's great fisheries.

Because the ocean circulation is so basic, it is one of the first things oceanographers must understand to build a comprehensive science of the seas. Yet they have scarcely begun to unravel its puzzle.

DOES THE GULF STREAM HAVE A PULSE?

WHAT MAKES ITS HEART BEAT?

To oceanographers, the Gulf Stream is an enigma, the National Geographic Society's Matt C. McDade says (in a News Bulletin, March 12, 1963). Serious study of the Gulf Stream began as recently as 1844, and intensive research with modern scientific tools suggests that it contains deeper mysteries than were suspected. One recent expedition discovered, for instance, that off Florida, the stream seems to have a pulse which makes the water flow in repeated thrusts like blood in an artery.

A RIVER—OR A WALL?

Some oceanographers no longer think of the Gulf Stream as a great river snaking across the North Atlantic. They regard it, rather, as a barrier separating cold Arctic waters from the warm Sargasso Sea.

"The intensity of flow of the stream, the stream's direction, and its temperature are not primary climatic factors in determining the climate of Europe," writes Henry Stommel, of Woods Hole Oceanographic Institution, in his comprehensive book *The Gulf Stream*. "But the role which it plays in determining the northern boundaries and average temperature structure of the Sargasso Sea must be of critical importance."

The Sargasso, according to this theory, acts as a huge hot-water tank for Europe. Dispersal of its comforting warmth is controlled, to a large extent, by the speed of the Gulf Stream.

Paradoxically, Europe would become colder—not hotter—if the Gulf Stream should begin to flow faster. The effect would be not to carry more warmth but to tighten the barrier about the Sargasso. . . .

THE WORLD'S SWIFTEST CURRENT

The fastest current ever found in open sea—almost eleven miles an hour—was measured off Florida in the Gulf Stream. In contrast, a normal current lazes along at a pace of half a mile to a mile, and as a rule the Gulf Stream seldom exceeds four to five miles an hour. . . .

In 1770, Benjamin Franklin gathered data about the Gulf Stream for British authorities who could not understand why their packets to New York were taking two or three weeks longer than American merchants ships putting into Rhode Island ports.

Not much was really known about the Gulf Stream, however, until the middle of the nineteenth century. In 1844, the first major study of it was begun by Franklin's great-grandson, Alexander D. Bache, for the United States Coast and Geodetic Survey.

The first textbook of modern oceanography, published by

Matthew F. Maury in 1855, began with this paragraph: "There is a river in the ocean. In the severest droughts it never fails and in the mightiest floods it never overflows. . . . The Gulf of Mexico is its fountain, and its mouth is the Arctic Ocean."

In time, oceanographers learned that the Gulf Stream is misnamed. Some of the currents feeding the stream surge through the Gulf of Mexico, but they mix hardly at all with its waters.

Study of a fast-moving, fluctuating river in open sea remains difficult. New ideas and instruments have inspired a number of major efforts in recent years by organizations such as the Coast and Geodetic Survey, Woods Hole, the Navy Hydrographic Office, the University of Miami Marine Laboratory, and the National Geographic Society.

It was Henry Stommel, of Woods Hole, who discovered that a massive deep current flows beneath the Gulf Stream in an opposite direction. This phenomenon, when understood, could revolutionize present concepts of ocean-circulation systems.

American oil tankers, equipped with loran, took part in a year-long survey which found that the stream twists and bends hundreds of miles in mysterious tune to seasons and tides. It flows faster in summer than in winter. This survey also determined that giant waves, or "meanders," move ponderously in the same direction as the stream.

The pulsating nature of the Gulf Stream in the Florida Straits was detected during a ten-year study of its teeming animal and plant life carried out by the Marine Laboratory and National Geographic.

Fish use the stream as a subway. Millions of eels take it from their birthplace southwest of Bermuda to North America and Europe. Incredibly, the America-bound eels know exactly where to get off.

WE LEARN THE GULF STREAM ACTS "LIKE A LIVING THING"

By Raymond Wilcove, U.S. Coast and Geodetic Survey:

A Study of the Gulf Stream by United States oceanographers has shed new light on this mysterious "ocean river."

Data obtained are providing scientists with material upon which more definite conclusions regarding the nature of the Gulf Stream may ultimately be reached.

The ambitious undertaking, in which fifteen governmental and private groups are participating, is being coordinated by Dr. Harris B. Stewart, Jr., director of the Institute for Oceanography, a component of the U.S. Department of Commerce's Environmental Science Services Administration (ESSA).

Participants include ships, planes, and scientists of ESSA's Institute for Oceanography, Coast and Geodetic Survey, and Weather Bureau; Naval Oceanographic Office; Office of Naval Research; Coast Guard; Interior Department's Bureau of Sport Fisheries and Wildlife, and Bureau of Commercial Fisheries; University of Miami; Duke University; Columbia University's Lamont Geological Observatory; University of Rhode Island; Massachusetts Institute of Technology; Woods Hole (Massachusetts) Oceanographic Institution; New York University; and Lerner Marine Laboratory, Bimini, Bahamas.

Stewart said that while no formal reports have yet been made, preliminary findings disclosed the following:

1. The Gulf Stream expands and contracts like a living thing, but with an apparent irregularity that so far defies prediction.
2. The stream fluctuates like an undulating body. During the initial three-month period of the study (September

through November, 1965), the position of the stream fluctuated as much as 250 miles, changing at times 15 to 20 miles a day. From September to October, a fluctuation of 200 miles was measured; from October to November, about 100 miles. The studies revealed that the stream's course varied more and more the farther it went from the North American coast.

This extensive fluctuation was observed about 800 miles out to sea from Cape Hatteras, North Carolina, where the giant stream veers northeast toward Europe after flowing up the United States coast from the Straits of Florida.

3. In this area, the stream was found to migrate in northerly and southerly directions. After leaving Cape Hatteras, the stream proceeded north to about the same latitude as New York City, then veered south about 150 miles to the latitude of Washington, D.C., then north again some 210 miles to the latitude of Boston, then south once more approximately 150 miles to the latitude of Philadelphia.
4. These sharp fluctuations in the stream's course are known as meanders. The meander which fluctuated between Washington and Boston was observed in October. By November, the stream had apparently straightened out considerably, for the October meander was no longer so pronounced.
5. From time to time, part of a meander will break off, forming an eddy. The eddies remain unconnected with the stream until they disappear. One eddy 60 miles in diameter was discovered in September south of the stream (none has yet been found to the north). It whirled counterclockwise around its 180-mile circumference at a speed of about ⅓ revolution per day.

How long eddies retain their identity before they disappear is still unknown. The eddy found in September was still in existence in November.

Eddies are not easily seen, because of their size and relative slowness of motion. During the winter, an effort will be made to track an eddy using aircraft.

6. The stream is detected most readily after it leaves Cape Hatteras at a depth of about 600 feet, where the temperature changes rapidly across the stream. The maximum surface current appears to lie above the region where the temperature at this depth is 15 degrees Centigrade (59 degrees Fahrenheit). Oceanographers call it the 15-degree isotherm and regard it as the main velocity axis of the stream. The 15-degree isotherm indicates the location of the "cold wall" forming the edge of the stream.

   Ships participating in the study observe the stream's course by following the 15-degree isotherm. They do so by towing a 500-pound heat-sensing instrument known as a V-fin at the 600-foot depth. As the temperature is recorded aboard ship, the vessel turns left when the water gets warmer than 15 degrees and right when it becomes colder.

7. There is evidence that the stream extends to the bottom of the sea, even after it leaves the relatively shallow water (about 2,400 feet) over the Blake Plateau and proceeds northeastward over the deep sea. The Blake Plateau is a flat underwater shelf off the South Carolina coast.

One oceanographer theorized that the stream assumes a champagne-glass shape (minus the bottom) as it leaves the Blake Plateau. It is broader on the top and then narrows toward the bottom. He based this hypothesis on bottom-current measurements and mathematical computations.

Indicative of the scientific onslaught on the secrets of the Gulf Stream, the center of speculation for more than four hundred years, is the extensive mileage chalked up by just one of the participating ships. During the initial three months of the project, the Coast and Geodetic Survey ship *Explorer* clocked 9,288 miles during three two-week trips.

Facilities included in the program are the Coast and Geodetic Survey ships *Explorer* and *Peirce;* Navy, Coast Guard and ESSA aircraft; the Woods Hole Oceanographic Institution ship *Crawford;* the *Eastward* of the Duke University Marine Laboratory; the *Kyma* of New York University; the *Stormy Petrel* of the University of Miami; and the *Trident* of the University of Rhode Island.

The study, which will continue, is being concentrated in these areas: off Miami, Florida; between the Straits of Florida and Cape Hatteras off Charleston, South Carolina; and in the North Atlantic from Cape Hatteras out into the ocean to the area south of Nova Scotia.

When the study is completed, scientists will have a much better understanding of the great stream which, when it leaves the Straits of Florida, is like a mighty river discharging 100 billion tons of water each hour. It has been calculated that the Gulf Stream flow is 22 times as large as all the rivers of the world.

SECTION XV

THE OCEAN'S NEWLY FOUND ANIMALS

We Discover Some Unknown Creatures

Of all the unknown animals that have been discovered in recent years, the strangest is a tiny, worm-like creature, with a brain but no mouth, that has been named the pogonophore.
—Gardner Soule in The Maybe Monsters.

MEN HAUL UP A STRANGE NEW ANIMAL

From the September, 1964, Oceanus, *the magazine of the Woods Hole Oceanographic Institution:*

The Naturalists and biologists of the eighteenth and nineteenth century had a grand time. On land and in the sea new animals and plants had to be described and placed in their proper order. This was not only great fun, but naming organisms also provided an opportunity to honor royalty, patrons of the sciences, and colleagues. Scientists, being only too human, engaged in endless squabbles to determine if it was right to erect a new phylum, class, or order.

By the end of the nineteenth century the land animals were pretty well described and the cream was skimmed off the top of sea organisms, although new species and even genera still are found every year. For instance, since 1931 at least thirty new marine organisms have been named after members of our staff at Woods Hole, while in 1955 our Dr. H. Sanders discovered a new subclass, the Cephalocarida.

Now comes a new phylum! Pogonophora, the animal in Professor Zenkevitch's article below. Here is an animal without a mouth, gut, or anus! It is found worldwide in the sediment, mostly below 2,000 meters. It is enormously abundant in places. In the 1920's, Pogonophora were shoveled overboard by the ton from the R.R.S. *Discovery II* when deep net hauls were found to be clogged with masses of "fibres." Some of the leading biologists of the day muttered: "Another batch of those disgusting 'gubbins.' " Now Professor A. V. Ivanov has published a book *, translated from the Russian by D. B. Carlisle, describing this new invertebrate group of high systematic rank. A great zoological curiosity!

POGONOPHORES ARE SMALL, DEEP-SEA WORMS

In the September, 1964, *Oceanus,* Russia's Prof. L. Zenkevitch describes Pogonophora. The editor of *Oceanus* describes Professor Zenkevitch as "a corresponding member of the U.S.S.R. Academy of Sciences. He is chairman of the National Oceanographic Committee of the U.S.S.R. and Vice President of the Special Committee on Oceanic Research (SCOR)."

Most Interesting results have been obtained by Artemi Ivanov, Professor of Leningrad University, who has taken part in many expeditions on the *Vitiaz.* He has discovered a new group of animals, pogonophora, and reconstructed a whole link in the evolution of the animal world.

These unusual organisms, encased in thick, skinny tubes, resemble small worms. They are typical and common representatives of great ocean depths and, to a lesser degree, of its average depths. Only in cold zones, such as the sea of Okhotsk and the Barents Sea, where some deep-water inhabitants rise to the upper zones, pogonophora are sometimes found in shallow depths.

* A. V. Ivanov, *Pogonophora,* Academic Press Ltd., London; Consultant Bureau, New York 1963.

Professor Ivanov has definitely proved that these organisms are an independent group of Deuterostomata, close to the type of chordates. His system of Pogonophora includes two orders, five families, and about twenty genera. He has made up a map of their geographic distribution in all the oceans.

NO MOUTH!

The total absence of digestive organs, mouth, and anal opening is a remarkable feature of pogonophora. They feed through special big cells forming part of their tentacles. These cells absorb nutritive substances from the environment by water filtration along the tentacles. Ivanov has studied the early stages of development in the tubes inhabited by pogonophora and established their similarity to chordate animals.

Professor Ivanov has been awarded a Lenin Prize for his discovery, undoubtedly the most important event in zoology in the last half century.

THE UNKNOWN FISH WITH THE MONOCLE

"ICHTHYOLOGISTS, fish scientists," says Jane Wood, "get more excited over a new species of fish than do bobby-soxers over a new crooner." Jane Wood knows. She works with the Miami, Florida, Seaquarium, whose 10,000 exhibits—constantly replenished by collecting trips by undersea hunters—make the Seaquarium one of the world's largest museums of the sea.

Here is her story, written especially by her for this anthology, about one Miami Seaquarium sea-bottom hunter and how he brought back alive one of the rarest fish in the sea:

40 FEET BELOW

One June afternoon of 1958, Phil Case went overboard after lunch to settle his meal with a soothing aqualung exploration of a rocky bottom in 40 feet of water.

Phil was on a Miami Seaquarium expedition to the Bahama reefs.

Up he came—like a jack-in-the-box.

Up he popped to tell Capt. William Gray, the Seaquarium's No. 1 collector of specimens, that down below was a fish he had never seen.

"Get it," commanded the Captain, handing Case a dip net.

Next, the dip net rose above the warm reef waters. The net, held aloft above the surface by a hand, was like King Arthur's sword Excalibur. It contained a fish an inch long.

The significance of the fish was lost at first on ichthyologist Craig Phillips, today Director of the National Aquarium, Washington, D.C., and then with the Miami Seaquarium.

First, Phillips thought it was a new kind of damselfish. Then he saw that because of the presence of a curved spine on the gill cover it had to be some sort of an angelfish, the like of which he had never seen.

"That thing is exceedingly rare," said Phillips, now all alert.

"There are more below!" said Case.

They were pygmy angelfish.

Thirteen of the little fish were the final haul, dip-netted up from the Bahama waters. They were up to 2 or 3 inches long. Their heads and breasts were bright orange. The rest of them was a glowing—almost phosphorescent—blue. Around the eyes they wore glowing blue monocles.

For years some remained alive. They became acclimated to the Miami Seaquarium tank and added their brilliant colors to those of other small tropical fish in the clear tank water.

The fish, when they died, received honored preservation in

museums around the nation. The museums begged for specimens of the little monocled mystery.

Men saw the first pygmy angelfish in 1908. Louis Mowbray, now curator of the Bermuda aquarium, caught a new fish in 90 fathoms of water on the Argos Reef, off Bermuda, in a deep trawl. It was dead when he got it.

He sent the preserved specimen to the Chicago Natural History Museum, where it remained a mystery fish from 1908 to 1951.

In 1951, Dr. Loren Woods studied the preserved specimen, and described it as a new species, *Centropyge argi*. Other pygmy angelfish of the same genus were known from the Pacific, but no others had ever been found in Atlantic waters.

Then, in 1952, ichthyologists were electrified by the find of a second pygmy angelfish—dead—in the stomach of a snapper caught in 40 fathoms of water on the Campeche Bank off Mexico by ichthyologist Stuart Springer.

From 1908 to 1958, the ichthyologists had hunted for a living specimen of this rare little fish. Then Phil Case found thirteen in one hour.

At the Miami Seaquarium, the pygmy angelfish—also called by Seaquarium people the cherub fish—acted as though people were as unknown to it as it is to people. It swam around, for all the world peering out in surprise, right through its monocle, at some of the first men and women it had ever seen.

ON THE DEEP-SEA FLOOR WE CAPTURE OLDEST SPECIES

From the Columbia University news office, January 13, 1959:

Four Paleozoic *Neopilina,* small snail-like creatures whose ancestors were among the first animals to leave a clear fossil record on earth and which until recently were believed to have been extinct for 300 million years, in the autumn of 1958 were brought up alive from the depths of the Pacific Ocean by Columbia University scientists.

The tiny *Neopilina* was hailed as the oldest living representative of the primitive ancestors of a "really successful animal group."

The important scientific find was reported in a message to Dr. Maurice Ewing, director of Columbia's Lamont Geological Observatory from the University's research vessel *Vema.*

FOUR PALEOZOIC NEOPILINA ALIVE WHEN SAMPLED FROM THE NORTH END OF THE MILNE-EDWARDS TRENCH, the message said.

The radiogram added: WORZEL BRINGING SPECIMEN AND PHOTOGRAPHS OF ENVIRONMENT.

Worzel was Dr. J. Lamar Worzel, chief scientist aboard the *Vema.*

The specimens were caught in deep-sea nets at a depth of more than 18,000 feet (more than 3 miles) in the trench 200 miles west of Lima, Peru. The deep-sea nets used by the *Vema* were developed by Dr. Robert J. Menzies, director of marine biology at Lamont. (Dr. Menzies today is director of the Marine Laboratory of Duke University, North Carolina.) The nylon net is about 9 feet long, a little more than 3 feet wide, and has a steel frame which bites into the ocean bed. The nylon bag, with ½-millimeter mesh, is shaped like a butterfly, and the apparatus is fixed to the end of a steel cable. Photographs of the ocean-bottom environment of the creatures were taken with underwater cameras developed at the Lamont Observatory and included in the *Vema*'s equipment.

Dr. John Imbrie, associate professor of Geology at Columbia, described the small creatures as about 1½ inches long, with a conical shell that resembles a miniature dunce cap.

"This type of animal happens to be important biologically," Dr. Imbrie said, "because it is a representative of a group known as the Monoplacophora, called 'monoplacs,' a primitive group of snail-like creatures that began their history 500 million years ago and until recently were thought to have become extinct 300 million years ago.

"In their heyday they lived in shallow water along the shores and they are the ancestors of snails and chitons, coat-of-mail snails that cling to rocks on the seashore and are quite common today. The snails and chitons made their appearance about 450 million years ago. It might be said that the 'monoplacs' have been replaced by their more advanced descendants.

"All living things (man included) are a link to the past in the sense that our ancestry goes back to the beginnings of life on earth.

"But, in the sense that *Neopilina* is a living animal which has changed very little from ancestors 500 million years ago, *Neopilina* is one of the two oldest living animal links to the past.

"The other candidate for this post is *Lingula,* an obscure shell-bearing animal, called a brachiopod, which lives today in shallow waters of Japan, as it has been doing for nearly 500 million years.

"*Lingula,* however, is less interesting because the brachiopod group, of which it is a member, never evolved into anything very complex or advanced.

"*Neopilina*'s ancestors, however, gave rise to the large and familiar group of animals known today as snails, as well as the chitons, and possibly clams as well. It is, therefore, the oldest living representative of primitive ancestors of a really successful animal group."

Hailing the *Vema*'s "catch," Dr. Imbrie said that snails were among the first animals that left a clear fossil record on earth.

"In the pre-Cambrian era over half a billion years ago, animals and simple plants lived in the seas. They left tracks and trails, but they had no skeletons, and we have no direct knowledge of what they looked like.

"In the Cambrian period about 500 million years ago a few shellfish appeared, and for the first time we had living in the seas animals possessing skeletons which could be preserved.

"These primitive creatures began putting on armor—shells—in that period, and as one species developed shells for its own survival, other species did the same thing. It was like 'keeping up with the Joneses.' "

Dr. Imbrie said that in the millions of years intervening since the group was common, the monoplacs apparently retreated from the shores to the ocean floor more than 10,000 feet down, straining nourishment from the mud for their existence.

"This find by the *Vema,*" he said, "will provide biologists with good fresh material for study."

The temperature at the depth from which the specimens were taken is close to the freezing point, so the little animals experienced a temperature change of around 60 degrees when they were brought to the surface.

Dr. Imbrie said the change from the extreme pressures at the *Neopilina*'s 18,000-foot habitat to the surface pressures should have no effect on the specimens. They have no air sacs, and do not "explode" when brought to the surface.

A MAN IMAGINED *NEOPILINA* BEFORE WE KNEW IT EXISTED

THE VERY FIRST neopilina of all had been seen by men only six years before the Columbia University expedition. The stunning impact of the discovery was described in *Abyss* by C. P. Idyll of the Institute of Marine Science, University of Miami:

Paleontologists and evolutionists delight in going through the exercise of reconstructing the appearance of the ancestors of modern animals. The reconstruction of such a "missing link" was attempted in 1952 by the biologist Brooks Knight in the case of the mollusks. These are the snails, the clams, the octopuses, and their various allies, the most primitive of which are the chitons, which cling to the rocks of the seashores of the world. Knight's ancestral mollusk resembled a chiton, with an oval shell, a fleshy foot, simple gills, and a radula, or toothed tongue. Imagine the amazement of the biologists when out of the abyssal deep sea there came, later in 1952, a creature so like the theoretical mollusk that Knight could almost have had the actual animal in front of him when he created his model!

This epochal capture was made by the *Galathea* at the very end of her cruise, off the coast of Mexico in the Pacific. From a deep dredge, fishing on dark, muddy clay in 11,878 feet of water, she brought up ten live specimens (and three extra shells) of a limpetlike creature thought to have been extinct since the Devonian Period, 350 million years ago. This archaic mollusk, neither clam nor snail but more primitive than either, is a member of a group called the Monoplacophora. It was named *Neopilina galathea* in honor of the ship. The shell of this relic mollusk was spoon-shaped. The biggest individual was 1½ inches long, 1¼ inches wide, and ½ inch high. The oval shell, thin and fragile, semitransparent and pale yellowish white, rose to a little peak, with the point tilted over. Inside, the shell had a very thin, lustrous layer of mother-of-pearl. The greater part of the body was taken up by a large, almost circular foot of a bluish color, with a diffuse pink central area. Five pairs of primitive gills surrounded the foot. In front of the foot was a small triangular area that has no counterpart in other living mollusks. Around the mouth were fleshy structures; these probably help to collect the bottom deposits that are the food of *Neopilina*. Radiolarians are their favorite food, judging from the gut contents of the creatures captured off Mexico.

SECTION XVI

SUNKEN TREASURE
The Sea Around Us Is Full of It

On the sea floor there is an ample supply of sunken treasure.
—M. Scott Carpenter, astronaut and aquanaut, speaking at Texas A. & M. University.

TWO THOUSAND SUNKEN TREASURE SHIPS?

IN the Palm Beach (Florida) *Sunday Times* of October 13, 1965, Mrs. Margaret Biggerstaff, an oceanographic consultant, quotes from Charles Harnett's *Operation Lodestone:*

Sometime Between 1497 and 1501, commercial relations were established between Spain and the West Indies. With this establishment a flood of ships sailed from Europe to the Caribbean; the preponderance were Spanish, with a smattering of British, Dutch, and French privateers that preyed on the richly laden trade and treasure ships of Spain.

Prior to 1560, the principal trade route from Spain to the Indies followed a course from Cádiz, Spain, to Cartagena, Colombia, and Veracruz, Mexico, via Puerto Rico. At the latter port the fleet would separate into two components, one landing at Cartagena, the other at Veracruz. After unloading their cargoes of grain, provisions, arms, ammunition, clothing, horses, cattle, glass, paper, cutlery, textiles, watches, clocks, quicksilver, shoes, books, pictures, wines and fruits, the fleets would load aboard immense quantitites of gold, silver, precious stones, indigo, cacao, tobacco, sugar, hides, and some East Indian goods brought by the annual Manila galleon to Mexico from the Far East. Once loaded, each fleet sailed independently to Havana and, meeting there, joined for protection for the return journey to Spain through the reef-and-pirate-infested channels of the South Bahamas.

During those sixty years of commerce, so many of Spain's ships were lost in the Old Bahama Channel that reason dictated that a safer course be chosen for the returning fleets. The new route decided upon carried the forty-odd ships of the combined fleet from Havana northward into the Straits of Florida and continued parallel to the peninsula's east coast until, at approximately the latitude of St. Augustine, they turned eastward into the Atlantic and followed a course to Spain via Bermuda.

Thus, the straits of Florida, or New Bahama Channel, as it was called, served as the major trade route for the heavily loaded Spanish vessels from 1560 through the culmination of Spain's heyday in the New World in the late eighteenth century.

Conservative estimates place the number of Spanish ships, alone, that perished along the Florida coast as well over 2,000. Some 1,000 have already been located by museum experts, and charted for future exploration. Of these shipwrecks, certain examples stand out in the early histories, more often because of the value of the cargoes lost than for the number of ships or lives claimed by the sea.

These early wrecks . . . which carried especially fabulous cargoes, would have great significance.

THE SUBMARINE CITY OF PORT ROYAL

THERE Is a handbook that tells you just how to go look for sunken Spanish galleons and other treasure ships: how to dive, what to look for, how to preserve the pieces of eight or cannonballs you find. It is *History Under the Sea* by Mendel Peterson, the chairman of the Department of Armed Forces History at the Smithsonian Institution, Washington, D. C. Here Mr. Peterson tells of two productive sites of sunken relics:

Around the Edges of the world's seas or on islands, ruins of cities may be found beneath the water. Generally such ruins have sunk beneath the sea through a gradual subsidence of the earth's surface, but in the case of Port Royal, Jamaica, a great earthquake dumped much of the city into the sea in a few moments. This disaster, one of the greatest natural disasters of the Western Hemisphere, occurred June 7, 1692, between 11:30 A.M. and 12 noon.

In 1655 the Lord Protector of England, Oliver Cromwell, sent an expedition under the command of Admiral Penn (father of the proprietor of Pennsylvania) and General Venables to capture a base in the West Indies from which to threaten the treasure route from the Indies to Spain. The troops attacked Santo Domingo but were poorly organized and an inferior Spanish force repulsed them. Rather than return home as failures, the commanders decided to attack the island of Jamaica, which they knew to be only lightly defended. In this they were successful, capturing the capital, St. Jago de la Vega (now called Spanish Town), and routing the few Spanish troops which attempted to defend it. Realizing that their intrusion would arouse the enemy to reprisals, the English selected the tip of the peninsula which forms the southern shore of the present harbor of Kingston as the site of their settlement. Using the natural defenses of the place to an advantage, they planted three forts around the end to cover attack by sea, Forts Charles, James, and Carlysle, and cut off the land approaches with a palisade across the peninsula. Later the seaward approaches were reinforced with a water battery stretching down the beach from Fort Charles and commanding the channel leading into the harbor. This became known as Morgan's line after Governor Henry Morgan, the reformed buccaneer. It is a tribute to the efficiency of these works that they were never attacked by an enemy, the highest accolade that can be bestowed upon a fortification.

Port Royal thrived and became the center of operations against the Spanish in the West Indies and along the Spanish Main. The town became the capital of the buccaneers at the height of their power, and the treasures of the Indies flowed over the docks. This great wealth attracted merchants, tavern keepers, and prostitutes to the town, and the place became known as the "wickedest city on earth." Any merchant who could get a place on the waterfront was virtually assured of a fortune from trade with the buccaneers, and property values rose to equal those of London. Because of the high price of land and the limited area of the town, merchants built houses of three stories along the docks. Unknown to them, they were built on a shelving beach of sand, gravel, and rotten mangrove trees. When the great earthquake struck, the tremendous weight of the brick houses and the unstable nature of the ground caused two thirds of the town to slide into the harbor. In two or three minutes the city was submerged or shaken down and 2,000 of the 5,000 population were destroyed. Only parts of Fort Charles remained standing. Forts James and Carlysle were tumbled into the harbor.

Today the old city of Port Royal is only a layer of rubble under the harbor, or the beach on the harbor side of the peninsula which has been built up since the time of the earthquake. The layer of rubble is covered with sand, broken coral, mud, and debris which has settled over it. Some writers, with more imagination than accuracy, have pictured the city as standing under the water, permitting a diver to enter the buildings and even to find a church steeple standing with the bell in it! Actually, only the foundations of some buildings and parts of Fort James and Carlysle still stand, and these are covered by silt.

In 1956 the site was explored by Mr. and Mrs. Edwin A.

Link, with Mr. Peterson participating, to determine its condition and to make plans for a future expedition to the area. The conditions described above were found, and Mr. Link set about to design special equipment to move the tremendous quantities of silt which shrouded the remains. At the same time he designed a new salvage vessel equipped to handle any problem which might present itself at this or other underwater sites. The result is the new *Sea Diver,* the finest vessel of its type engaging in exploring historic underwater sites. The ship can support six to eight divers at once, has all types of electronic gear for searching under water, can lift loads weighing up to 6 tons, and offers comfortable air-conditioned rooms to the divers after an exhausting day under water. The ship has special gear to assure ease of maneuvering and anchoring over sites to be explored. Special water jets in the bow, invented by Mr. Link, add to the ease of handling the 164-ton vessel.

Soon after the *Sea Diver*'s shakedown cruise, early in the summer of 1959 an expedition sponsored by Mr. Link, the National Geographic Society, and the Smithsonian Institution assembled at Port Royal for an assault on the mud and coral which shrouded the remains of the historic town. After a survey of the site it was decided to begin the digging behind Fort James, where old charts indicated the presence of several brick buildings and one end of the King's warehouse. The few days were spent in cutting exploratory trenches in the overburden of 4 to 5 feet of mud, sand, coral, and debris. After several days during which several test trenches were dug, the airlift [a tube that sucks up mud, sand, and small objects] began to uncover clay pipes, broken pottery, bricks, roof tiles, and other evidence of a building. The site proved to be a brick building which had contained a fireplace. The homes of Port Royal normally did not have fireplaces, since heat in that tropic climate was not required. Cooking was done in small cookhouses separate from the dwelling. The location of the fireplace led us to believe that we were in a cookhouse, and the uncovering of cooking utensils, pewter spoons, plates, and platters confirmed this. The site has been identified as a cookhouse located in back of Fort James and perhaps belonging to the dwelling of a Mr. Littleton identified by a pre-earthquake chart of the lots of the town.

During the operations on this site, Mr. Link suggested that a team of divers go over the area with his underwater detector. This device, which indicates an electrical conductor, can in effect see through several feet of mud or sand and has led to the discovery of much material which would otherwise have been overlooked. The team took it down and a few minutes later came up to get the airlift moved to a spot where they had detected the presence of metal under the mud. After a very short period of pumping mud, the divers uncovered a bent and battered brass pot and brought it to the surface. When Mr. Link cleaned the sand and mud from the interior, he found in it animal bones which later were identified as those of a cow and a turtle, and he observed dark-red brick from the interior of a fireplace. We know that the earthquake struck just before noon, and the evidence here indicates that a beef-and-turtle stew was cooking in the fireplace when the chimney collapsed, crushing the pot with its contents still in it.

The quantitites of building materials which were recovered, including flat clay roof tile, bricks, plaster fragments, pieces of wattle and plaster showing impressions of it, confirmed pre-earthquake descriptions of the buildings of the old town. Exploration in two other sites near that of Littleton's house produced a collection of iron artifacts, including a steelyard with weights, tools such as axes, and fittings for ship's rigging. Perhaps the most unusual object from this site was an unused yard for a small ship some twenty feet long. This was found lying along the side of a foundation of the building. These finds indicated the site of a supply house, perhaps that of a ship's chandler.

The site of Fort James, which we had investigated in 1956,

was not neglected on this expedition. We had reason to believe that the interior of the fort might yield some interesting weapons. A team from the Navy contingent, which was cooperating with us, was sent to look over the area and after several hours of diving and digging came up with two interesting shot. One of these was half a bar shot with hemispherical ball, the other a solid lead shot for a swivel. Since authentic projectiles of the seventeenth century are quite scarce, these specimens were most welcome.

The Navy team, consisting of six expert underwater demolition men and a submarine surgeon, did yeoman service under water. Their knowledge of search techniques was most valuable, since the water over Port Royal is in reality liquid mud when the silt on the bottom is stirred up by the salvage operations.*

The largest object recovered was a 24-pounder iron tube which was found at Fort James in 1956 and now lifted from the water near the shipyard dock where it had been placed to preserve it. This was the largest gun in the defenses of Port Royal and served to defend the harbor against attack by large enemy warships carrying guns of similar size. The tube weighed 5,000 pounds. It was probably cast between 1660 and 1690. It bore the crowned rose normally appearing on English tubes until the reign of the Hanoverians and the weight mark according to the English system.

While working on the site of the "chandler's" house, there was turned up a wrought-iron, breech-loading swivel gun. This piece proved to be a type made in the last of the fifteenth century and during the sixteenth century. This type of piece was not being made when Port Royal thrived, and it was probably at least a century and a half old when the earthquake struck the town. It

* The team in charge of Lt. C. D. Grundy consisted of A. J. Banawsky, W. L. Collins, W. T. Farrell, C. E. Nowell, and D. E. Peck. Lt. Comdr. Charles Aguadro USN submarine surgeon and expert diver, was on hand to administer any emergency care the divers might require; fortunately, no injuries occurred during the entire operation.

may have been held as a curio from the old Spanish fortifications but could have been in the stores as a usable weapon since several of its breech blocks were found with it. It is known that similar pieces were used for very long periods. These swivels were stone throwers. They were simply loaded with a handful of gravel which formed scatter shot when the piece was fired. They were usually carried on the poop and forecastles of ships and used to resist boarders, although they were used also in land fortifications against attack by foot troops.

In the last month of the operations an object of utmost importance turned up. This was a watch with a brass case and silver dial. Inside it was signed "Paul Blondel." The face of the watch was covered with the normal coral-sand crust stained with iron oxide. Mr. Link had an X-ray plate made which revealed distinct lines where the steel hands had been. These showed the time when the watch stopped to have been seventeen minutes to twelve. Later in the Victoria and Albert Museum, London, Mr. Link learned that the watch had been made before 1686 by a French watchmaker working in the Netherlands. He was told that the case was originally covered with fine leather held in place with silver studs, some of which remained. Thus the time of the earthquake was recorded on the timepiece of one of the victims!

The expedition recovered hundreds of objects; however, only a very small portion of the submerged city could be explored in the time available. There remains today beneath the water and mud of Port Royal the most important remnants of seventeenth-century English America to be found anywhere. Here is a cross-section of the material culture of an important city of the New World which has furnished and will continue to furnish historians with a graphic picture of life in late seventeenth-century America.*

* See *Exploring the Drowned City of Port Royal,* by Marion Clayton Link. In *National Geographic* magazine, Vol. 117, No. 2, pp. 151–183, February, 1960.

THE TUCKER TREASURE

From History Under the Sea *by Mendel Peterson:*

A Young Diver named Teddy Tucker was exploring a reef off the western end of Bermuda in 1950, when he discovered six encrusted cannon in a coral pocket. Tucker lifted the guns from the water and sold them to the government of Bermuda. His work kept him from revisiting the site for five years, but late in the summer of 1955 he returned to the spot and began a careful search of the sand in the bottom of the pocket. He discovered portions of the ribs and keel of a moderate-size vessel preserved beneath the sand in the hold. After a few days' search he turned up a gold bar weighing 32 ounces. During the next week or so Tucker discovered a magnificent emerald-studded cross, two cakes of gold, two sections of gold bar, and pearl-studded gold buttons. This treasure is the most important to be discovered in the Western Hemisphere in modern times. Not only did the site yield treasure of gold and gems but, more importantly for the historians, it produced a collection of artifacts which has been called the most significant Tudor period find of this century, for the wreck is now known to have occurred about the year 1595. The collection from it included navigating instruments, fittings from the ship's rigging, pewter, tools, and silver and ceramic utensils. The wreck also yielded weapons and other artifacts of the Carib Indians which are of the utmost rarity and interest. Today, this priceless collection is exhibited in The Aquarium Museum in The Flatts Village, Bermuda. This find is spectacular, and there is every reason to believe that other and perhaps more fantastic finds will be made in the wreck-studded waters of Bermuda.

SECTION XVII

"THINGS EAT ON YOU"
Squid May Hurt—Octopuses Rarely Do

In the May, 1966, Navy League magazine Navy, *Lester Bell quotes Rear Admiral Odale D. (Muddy) Waters, on the ocean's depths vs. space: "There are also things that eat on you. They haven't found that, at least not in space."*

THE FIGHT WITH THE GIANT SQUID

TWENTY THOUSAND LEAGUES UNDER THE SEA by Jules Verne, from which this is taken, appeared almost exactly a hundred years ago. It was science fiction. But Verne based much of *Twenty Thousand Leagues* on known facts. His description of the squid, which he calls a cuttlefish, is in many details accurate. The squid does have two long tentacles in addition to the eight arms Verne mentions. There have been no man-versus-squid fights like this that I know of in modern times. But such a battle or two between the squid, which may reach 60 feet in length, and men in small sailing ships were reported in ancient days:

Ned hurried to the window.

"What a horrible beast!" he cried.

I looked in my turn, and could not repress a gesture of disgust. Before my eyes was a horrible monster, worthy to figure in the legends of the marvelous. It was an immense cuttlefish, being eight yards long. It swam crossways in the direction of the *Nautilus* with great speed, watching us with its enormous staring green eyes. Its eight arms, or rather feet, fixed to its head, that have given the name of cephalopod to these animals, were twice as long as its body, and were twisted like the Furies' hair. One could see the 250 air holes on the inner side of the tentacles. The monster's mouth, a horned beak like a parrot's, opened and shut vertically. Its tongue, a horned substance, furnished with several rows of pointed teeth, came out quivering from this veritable pair of shears. What a freak of nature, a bird's beak on a mollusk! Its spindlelike body formed a fleshy mass that might weigh 4,000 to 5,000 pounds; the varying color, changing with great rapidity, according to the irritation of the animal, passed successively from livid gray to reddish brown. What irritated this mollusk? No doubt the presence of the *Nautilus,* more formidable than itself, and on which its suckers or its jaws had no hold. Yet, what monsters these polyps are! What vitality the Creator has given them! What vigour in their movements! And they possess three hearts! Chance had brought us in presence of this cuttlefish, and I did not wish to lose the opportunity of carefully studying this specimen of cephalopod. I overcame the horror that inspired me; and, taking a pencil, began to draw it.

"Perhaps this is the same which the *Alector* saw," said Conseil.

"No," replied the Canadian; "for this is whole, and the other had lost its tail."

"That is no reason," I replied. "The arms and tails of these animals are reformed by redintegration; and, in seven years, the tail of Bouguer's cuttlefish has no doubt had time to grow."

By this time other polyps appeared at the port light. I counted seven. They formed a procession after the *Nautilus,* and I heard their beaks gnashing against the iron hull. I continued my work. These monsters kept in the water with such precision that they seemed immovable. Suddenly the *Nautilus* stopped. A shock made it tremble in every plate.

"Have we struck anything?" I asked.

"In any case," replied the Canadian, "we shall be free, for we are floating."

The *Nautilus* was floating, no doubt, but it did not move. A minute passed. Captain Nemo, followed by his lieutenant, entered the drawing room. I had not seen him for some time. He seemed dull. Without noticing or speaking to us, he went to the panel, looked at the polyps, and said something to his lieutenant. The latter went out. Soon the panels were shut. The ceiling was lighted. I went toward the Captain.

"A curious collection of polyps?" I said.

"Yes, indeed, Mr. Naturalist," he replied, "and we are going to fight them, man to beast."

I looked at him. I thought I had not heard aright.

"Man to beast?" I repeated.

"Yes, sir. The screw is stopped. I think that the horny jaws of one of the cuttlefish is entangled in the blades. That is what prevents our moving."

"What are you going to do?"

"Rise to the surface, and slaughter this vermin."

"A difficult enterprise."

"Yes, indeed. The electric bullets are powerless against the soft flesh, where they do not find resistance enough to go off. But we shall attack them with the hatchet."

"And the harpoon, sir," said the Canadian, "if you do not refuse my help."

"I will accept it, Master Land."

"We will follow you," I said, and following Captain Nemo, we went toward the central staircase.

There, about ten men with boarding hatchets were ready for the attack. Conseil and I took two hatchets; Ned Land seized a harpoon. The *Nautilus* had then risen to the surface. One of the sailors, posted on the top ladder step, unscrewed the bolts of the panels. But hardly were the screws loosed when the panel rose with great violence, evidently drawn by the suckers of a polyp's arm. Immediately one of these arms slid like a serpent down the opening, and twenty others were above. With one blow of the ax, Captain Nemo cut this formidable tentacle, that slid wriggling down the ladder. Just as we were pressing one on the other to reach the platform, two other arms, lashing the air, came down on the seaman placed before Captain Nemo, and lifted him up with irresistible power. Captain Nemo uttered a cry, and rushed out. We hurried after him.

What a scene! The unhappy man, seized by the tentacle and fixed to the suckers, was balanced in the air at the caprice of this enormous trunk. He rattled in his throat, he was stifled, he cried, "Help! Help!" these words, *spoken in French,* startled me! I had a fellow countryman on board, perhaps several! That heartrending cry! I shall hear it all my life. The unfortunate man was lost. Who could rescue him from that powerful pressure? However, Captain Nemo had rushed to the polyp, and with one blow of the ax had cut through one arm. His lieutenant struggled furiously against the other monsters that crept on the flanks of the *Nautilus.* The crew fought with their axes. The Canadian, Conseil, and I buried our weapons in the fleshy masses; a strong smell of musk penetrated the atmosphere. It was horrible!

For one instant, I thought the unhappy man, entangled with the polyp, would be torn from its powerful suction. Seven of the eight arms had been cut off. One only wriggled in the air, brandishing the victim like a feather. But just as Captain Nemo and his lieutenant threw themselves on it, the animal ejected a stream of black liquid. We were blinded with it. When the cloud dispersed, the cuttlefish had disappeared, and my unfortunate countryman with it. Ten or twelve polyps now invaded the platform and sides of the *Nautilus.* We rolled pell-mell into the midst of this nest of serpents, that wriggled on the platform in the waves of blood and ink. It seemed as though these slimy tentacles sprang up like the hydra's heads. Ned Land's harpoon, at each stroke, was plunged into the staring eyes of the cuttlefish. But my bold companion was suddenly overturned by the tentacles of a monster he had not been able to avoid.

Ah, how my heart beat with emotion and horror! The formidable beak of a cuttlefish was open over Ned Land. The unhappy man would be cut in two. I rushed to his succor. But Captain

Nemo was before me; his ax disappeared between the two enormous jaws, and, miraculously saved, the Canadian, rising, plunged his harpoon deep into the triple heart of the polyp.

"I owed myself this revenge!" said the Captain to the Canadian.

Ned bowed without replying. The combat had lasted a quarter of an hour. The monsters, vanquished and mutilated, left us at last, and disappeared under the waves. Captain Nemo, covered with blood, nearly exhausted, gazed upon the sea that had swallowed up one of his companions, and great tears gathered in his eyes.

MAN VERSUS OCTOPUS: OR, CHILD'S PLAY

SIR ARTHUR GRIMBLE, a British official at Tarawa, Gilbert Islands, in the South Pacific, tells in *We Chose the Islands* how he himself became bait that an octopus grabbed:

The Very Quality of the octopus that most horrifies the imagination—its relentless tenacity—becomes its undoing when hungry man steps into the picture. The Gilbertese happen to value certain parts of it as food, and their method of fighting it is coolly based upon the one fact that its arms never change their grip. They hunt for it in pairs. One man acts as the bait, his partner as the killer. First, they swim, eyes under, at low tide just off the reef, and search the crannies of the submarine cliff for sight of any tentacle that may flicker out for a catch. When they have placed their quarry, they land on the reef for the next stage. The human bait starts the real game. He dives and tempts the lurking brute by swimming a few strokes in front of its cranny, at first a little beyond striking range. Then he turns and makes straight for the cranny, to give himself into the embrace of those waiting arms. Sometimes nothing happens. The beast will not always respond to the lure. But usually it strikes.

The partner on the reef above stares down through the pellucid water, waiting for his moment. His teeth are his only weapon. His killing efficiency depends on his avoiding every one of those strangling arms. He must wait until his partner's body has been drawn right up to the entrance of the cleft. The monster inside is groping then with its horny mouth against the victim's flesh, and sees nothing beyond it. That point is reached in a matter of no more than thirty seconds after the decoy has plunged. The killer dives, lays hold of his pinioned friend at arm's length, and jerks him away from the cleft; the octopus is torn adrift from the anchorage of its proximal suckers, and clamps itself the more fiercely to its prey. In the same second, the human bait gives a kick which brings him, with quarry annexed, to the surface. He turns on his back, still holding his breath for better buoyancy, and this exposes the body of the beast for the kill. The killer closes in, grasps the evil head from behind, and wrenches it away from its meal. Turning the face up toward himself, he plunges his teeth between the bulging eyes, and bites down and in with all his strength. That is the end of it. It dies on the instant; the suckers release their hold; the arms fall way; the two fishers paddle with whoops of delighted laughter to the reef, where they string the catch to a pole before going to rout out the next one.

Any two boys of seventeen, any day of the week, will go out and get you half a dozen octopus like that for the mere fun of it. Here lies the whole point of this story. The hunt is, in the most literal sense, nothing but child's play to the Gilbertese.

As I was standing one day at the end of a jetty in Tarawa lagoon, I saw two boys from the near village shouldering a string of octopus slung on a pole between them. I started to wade out in their direction, but before I hailed them they had stopped, planted the carrying-pole upright in a fissure and, leaving it there, swam off the edge for a while with faces submerged, evidently searching for something under water. I had been only a few months at Tarawa, and that was my first near view of an octopus hunt. I watched every stage of it, from the dive of the human bait to the landing of the dead catch. When it was over, I went up to them. I could hardly believe that in those few seconds, with no more than a frivolous-looking splash or two on the surface, they could have found, caught, and killed the creature they were now stringing up before my eyes. They explained the amusing simplicity of the thing.

"There's only one trick the decoy-man must never forget," they said, "and that's not difficult to remember. If he is not wearing the water spectacles of the Men of Matang, he must cover his eyes with a hand as he comes close to the kika (octopus), or the suckers might blind him." It appeared that the ultimate fate of the eyes was not the thing to worry about; the immediate point was that the sudden pain of a sucker clamping itself to an eyeball might cause the bait to expel his breath and inhale sea water; that would spoil his buoyancy, and he would fail then to give his friend the best chance of a kill.

Then they began whispering together. I knew in a curdling flash what they were saying to each other. Before they turned to speak to me again, a horrified conviction was upon me. My damnable curiosity had led me into a trap from which there was no escape. They were going to propose that I should take a turn at being the bait myself, just to see how delightfully easy it was. And that is precisely what they did. It did not even occur to them that I might not leap at the offer. I was already known as a young Man of Matang who liked swimming, and fishing, and laughing with the villagers; I had just shown an interest in this particular form of hunting; naturally, I should enjoy the fun of it as much as they did. Without even waiting for my answer, they gleefully ducked off the edge of the reef to look for another octopus—a fine fat one—*mine*. Left standing there alone, I had another of those visions. . . .

It was dusk in the village. The fishers were home, I saw the cooking fires glowing orange-red between the brown lodges.

There was laughter and shouted talk as the women prepared the evening meal. But the laughter was hard with scorn. "What?" they were saying. "Afraid of a kika? The young Man of Matang? Why, even our boys are not afraid of a kika!" A curtain went down and rose again on the residency; the Old Man was talking. "A leader? You? The man who funked a schoolboy game? We don't leave your sort in charge of districts." The scene flashed to my uncles. "Returned empty," they said. "We always knew you hadn't got it in you. Returned empty. . . ."

Of course it was all overdrawn, but one fact was beyond doubt. The Gilbertese reserved all their most ribald humor for physical cowardice. No man gets himself passed for a leader anywhere by becoming the butt of that kind of wit. I decided I would rather face the octopus.

I was dressed in khaki slacks, canvas shoes, and a short-armed singlet. I took off the shoes and made up my mind to shed the singlet if told to do so; but I was wildly determined to stick to my trousers throughout. Dead or alive, said a voice within me, an official minus his pants is a preposterous object, and I felt I could not face that extra horror. However, nobody asked me to remove anything.

I hope I did not look as yellow as I felt when I stood to take the plunge; I have never been so sick with funk before or since. "Remember, one hand for your eyes," said someone from a thousand miles off, and I dived.

I do not suppose it is really true that the eyes of an octopus shine in the dark; besides, it was clear daylight only six feet down in the limpid water; but I could have sworn the brute's eyes burned at me as I turned in toward his cranny. That dark glow—whatever may have been its origin—was the last thing I saw as I blacked out with my left hand and rose into his clutches. Then I remember chiefly a dreadful sliminess with a herculean power behind it. Something whipped round my left forearm and the back of my neck, binding the two together. In that same flash, another something slapped itself high on my forehead, and I felt it crawling down inside the back of my singlet. My impulse was to tear at it with my right hand, but I felt the whole of that arm pinioned to my ribs. In most emergencies the mind works with crystal-clear impersonality. This was not even an emergency, for I knew myself perfectly safe. But my boyhood nightmare was upon me. When I felt the swift constriction of those disgusting arms jerk my head and shoulders in toward the reef, my mind went blank of every thought save the beastliness of contact with that squat head. A mouth began to nuzzle below my throat, at the junction of the collar bones. I forgot there was anyone to save me. Yet something still directed me to hold my breath.

I was awakened from my cowardly trance by a quick, strong pull on my shoulders, back from the cranny. The cables around me tightened painfully, but I knew I was adrift from the reef. I gave a kick, rose to the surface, and turned on my back, with the brute sticking out of my chest like a tumor. My mouth was smothered by some flabby moving horror. The suckers felt like hot rings pulling at my skin. It was only two seconds. I suppose, from then to the attack of my deliverer, but it seemed like a century of nausea.

My friend came up between me and the reef. He pounced, pulled, bit down, and the thing was over—for everyone but me. At the sudden relaxation of the tentacles, I let out a great breath, sank, and drew in the next under water. It took the united help of both boys to get me, coughing, heaving, and pretending to join in their delighted laughter, back to the reef. I had to submit there to a kind of war dance around me, in which the dead beast was slung whizzing past my head from one to the other. I had a chance to observe then that it was not by any stretch of fancy a giant, but just plain average. That took the bulge out of my budding self-esteem. I left hurriedly for the cover of the jetty, and was sick.

THE LATEST WORD FROM THE KINGDOM OF THE OCTOPUS

HERE Is what some teutologists (octopus scientists) today say about octopuses (or octopi or octopodes; any of these plurals is correct). These questions and the answers that follow show how the octopus looks today to some of the men who are doing research on it.

What are your chances if an octopus attacks you?

You almost always get home safe after encountering an octopus. Sir Arthur Grimble's terror was pointless. This does not mean skin divers should not be cautious. It does mean octopuses are not likely to attack you and may not have the strength to harm you if they do.

How large do Atlantic Ocean octopuses grow?

From F. G. Wood, Jr., Marineland, St. Augustine, Florida: "I'm still puzzled about the size that the common Atlantic octopus attains. Robson in his Monograph of Recent Cephalopoda quotes a reference to a 25-kilogram (over 50 pounds) specimen from the Mediterranean. Henry Lee, naturalist of the Brighton Aquarium, in his 1875 book *The Octopus* quotes Victor Hugo on the size of the octopus that attacked Gilliatt. Hugo said its arms were 'nearly a meter (39 inches) long,' and Lee remarks, 'None of quite so great dimensions have, I believe, been found in the English Channel. . . .' Further on, however, he refers to apparently reliable reports of a 33-pound octopus with a spread of 3 meters taken at Nice, and others with arms 'at least 4 feet long' seen at Leghorn."

Are those the common Atlantic octopuses off the United States?

From Mr. Wood: "It appears that our common octopus is the same as, or similar to, the English one, with a maximum spread of 6 feet or so and weight of possibly 10 pounds. Those in the

Mediterranean [a different race or subspecies?] evidently get considerably larger.

"The biggest *Octopus vulgaris* we've ever seen we raised from a 2-ounce infant. It reached a maximum weight of almost 8 pounds in ten months (we weighed it regularly) and died, apparently of old age, after eleven months in captivity. Full grown it could span at least 7 feet. Its arms were therefore at least 3 feet long when extended."

How large do Pacific Ocean octopuses grow?

From the *Aquarium Newsletter,* Vancouver Public Aquarium, Canada: "One of the largest octopuses ever exhibited at the aquarium was obtained a few weeks ago at Lund, north of Powell River. The octopus, a 60- to 70-pound giant, with a tentacle spread of about 7 feet, was caught by George Huber on hook and line while he was fishing for lingcod off Savary Island. . . .

"Shortly after the arrival of the big octopus, we were informed that one having tentacles 10 feet in length [making a diameter of 20 feet] had been sighted by divers. . . ."

Kenneth Norris of the University of California at Los Angeles tells me the biggest he ever caught off the Pacific Coast was an 85-pounder with 9½-foot-long tentacles.

Are all octopuses large?

No. There are very tiny ones, 1 to 1½ inches in length of tentacles. That's their size as adults. Says Ken Norris: "These bite. A little bitty one in the Gulf of California. He has an anti-coagulant in his saliva. You keep bleeding. It hurts like the deuce. It's a very sharp searing pain, as though you'd poured acid into the wound."

I have heard that larger octopuses bite. Do they?

Mr. Wood: "Our small-tank attendant was bitten on the hand by a common octopus some years ago. He says his whole arm swelled up and was sore for days."

Why do octopuses attack men?

From G. C. Klingel in "In Defense of Octopuses" [in *The Book of Naturalists;* Knopf, New York]: "The authentic instances of octopi or squid attacking human beings or divers . . . are so rare as to be considered nonexistent in spite of a large literature to the contrary."

From Kenneth Norris: "In my opinion, they're virtually harmless."

From James W. Atz, associate curator of the New York City Aquarium at Coney Island: "I don't know of an authentic case of a man killed by an octopus."

But octopuses may grapple with you. Says Mr. Wood: "A few years ago, I encountered a small specimen clambering about a tide pool on Grand Bahama, sticking its arms into holes in search of crabs. Standing on the edge of the pool, I poked it back with my finger as it was progressing through a cut into deeper water. It had ignored me up till then, but when I touched it, it grasped my hand and did its best to pull me in with it."

Are octopuses edible?

Yes. They are eaten in the Mediterranean and Pacific regions and elsewhere. Says Maurice Ewing, head of Columbia University's Lamont laboratories: "They taste like fish—scallops, maybe." Says Ken Norris: "They have a flavor like shellfish, very good. But it's a problem to dislodge the sucker disks from the roof of the mouth."

What are the octopus' suckers like?

From Mr. Klingel in "In Defense of Octopuses:" "These suckers, which operate on much the same principle as the little rubber cups with which we attach objects to automobile windshields, are actuated by a muscular piston. The rim of the cup is fastened to an object, then the floor of the center is raised and retracted to form a vacuum. The cups, I found, would slip easily from side to side, but when I pulled directly, exercised considerable power."

How are octopuses captured?

From the *Aquarium Newsletter,* Vancouver: "The method [some skin divers have] worked out involves swimming over rocky crevices on the ocean bottom where an octopus is likely to live. If the diver is seized by a long slithery arm covered with powerful suckers, he waits until the octopus has a good grip, then takes up the octopus in his arms and swims to the surface. Thus far, the system has worked quite well."

Kenneth Norris of U.C.L.A. lowers to the bottom a doghouse-shaped box that he hopes an octopus will climb into, then he hauls the box to the deck of his boat. If an octopus is inside and won't come out, Norris tosses in a starfish. The starfish has tiny claws on its back and pinches the octopus, which thereupon emerges.

Do octopuses band together in groups or families?

From the *Aquarium Newsletter,* Vancouver: "Octopuses are interesting to observe in captivity. They are very aggressive and do not tolerate each other in the same vicinity. For this reason we seldom put them together, but . . . when we obtained two small ones [six inches in diameter] from Tacoma, we kept them together in a jar for several weeks. After a severe battle, in which a patch of skin was removed on both specimens, we decided to separate them. As in other territorial animals, their aggressiveness may space them out in the natural environment. The famous French diver, Captain Jacques-Ives Cousteau, reports having seen communities of octopus 'villas,' each of which consisted of several rocks propped together. Local divers have not observed such communities in British Columbia waters as yet, but they are looking for them. Perhaps these communities occur only at certain seasons."

To escape from an enemy, an octopus is said to eject, or squirt out, a liquid smoke screen. What is it like?

From Mr. Wood: "Re the ejection of ink, it sometimes does form a 'smoke screen' [which, incidentally, seems to deaden the sense of smell of moray eels which include octopuses in their diet, according to *The Natural History of Marine Animals* by George E. MacGinitie and N. MacGinitie, published by McGraw-Hill, 1949], but in still water it often forms a well-defined blob about the size of the octopus. The latter blanches to an inconspicuous paleness and shoots off. Cousteau and others have also remarked this. A little squid that I once tried to dip up from beside the Marineland dock did the same thing—I thought I had it in my net, but what I had was a blob of ink the size of the squid."

How many suckers does an octopus possess?

"Normally" 240 on an arm, says Frank W. Lane in *Kingdom of the Octopus*. "Surely," says Mr. Wood, "there is great variation."

Has the octopus any unusual abilities?

Mr. Wood: "An octopus can drill a hole in a clam shell (with its radula, maybe aided by a dissolving substance). It almost invariably drills the hole at the location of one of the adductor muscle attachments. Presumably the posterior salivary secretion relaxes the muscle so that the clam can be opened easily. We discovered this several years ago. More recently it was written up in *Science* by some people on the West Coast."

The radula is a file- or rasp-like scraper—a ribbon of minute sharp-pointed spines—on the top of the octopus' tongue. With it, the octopus scrapes out small particles of flesh from crabshells. Some species of octopus do not possess a radula.

Kenneth Norris, U.C.L.A., reports that Mediterranean octopuses are clever at hiding: They move or stack rocks and shells and excavate the seabed by means of their ability to jet water. Then they go inside their hole and close the door by hauling a rock or shell after them.

The octopus actually has been seen to use a tool. Albro Gaul writes in *The Wonderful World of the Seashore:* "Once I remember watching an octopus lie in wait for some time beside the closed shell of a large clam. The moment the bivalve finally opened its shell, the octopus quickly thrust a stone between the clamshells with one of its eight arms, preventing the clamshell from closing again, and laying its occupant open to the octopus' attack. This performance seemed to show not only something of the acuity of the octopus' vision, but also its intelligence in using tools for getting its food."

Many sources reported that octopuses can change color (which helps them hide from the skin diver and surprises visitors to aquariums). They can become pebbled yellow, mottled brown, white, cream white, maroon, bluish gray, light ultramarine, and a number of other colors.

Christopher Coates, former head of the New York City Aquarium, commented on the octopus' ability to flatten itself to the thickness (or thinness) of a sheet of paper and slide through a crack you can scarcely see. This ability the octopus owes to the fact that it has almost no bones; it is almost all muscle and flesh. Dr. Coates nailed an octopus into a cigar box; it slithered out. He had other octopuses in cases of half-inch wire mesh. They oozed right through the wire. There is a tale of an octopus, carried in a tightly shut wicker basket, aboard a streetcar in one of Britain's Channel Islands. The octopus, fairly large, slipped out—and sat down right in the lap of a passenger. It was some time before the excitement quieted down.

What is the great octopus mystery?

Mr. Wood has shown me newspaper articles, from the winter of 1896–97, that tell of what was supposed to be a monster octopus washed ashore near St. Augustine, Florida. Its body alone was described as 18 feet long and 5 feet of diameter. Its tentacles, which were broken off, would if proportionate have stretched 75 feet long. A scientist of the time called this mysterious creature an octopus, and not a giant squid—squids then were known, from having been washed ashore elsewhere. If anyone knows more about the mysterious Florida monster of the 1890's, either Mr. Wood or I would like to hear about it.

Is it true that octopuses are very intelligent?

Mr. Wood: "I don't think they can be compared to the higher vertebrates in this respect. They probably do stand at the pinnacle of invertebrate intelligence, and they learn with amazing rapidity. For example, in our laboratory I have observed (more than once) an octopus attempt to attack a crab floated in a beaker in its tank. In every case the octopus would approach momentarily, then release it and make no further attempts to get at the crab. This 'one-trial' learning is really rather remarkable."

Can octopuses be trained?

Yes. Their intelligence makes it possible. Says Murray Newman of the Vancouver Aquarium: "When the octopus sees his keeper above his tank, he blushes with excitement and stretches his arms up toward the surface. The tendril-like tips curl up over the side of the tank and will wrap around a finger as delicately as a baby's hand."

And Cecil Brosseau of the Point Defiance Aquarium, Tacoma, Washington, teaches his octopuses to take herring from visitors—including children.

SECTION XVIII

NAVAL SUBMARINES
Some Amazing Ships and Surprising Escapades

Control of the seas can mean peace. Control of the seas can mean victory. The United States must control the seas if it is to protect our security.
—President John F. Kennedy, aboard U.S.S. Kitty Hawk, *in June, 1963.*

THE SUBMARINE MOVES DEEPER

From Geo Marine Technology, *March 1967:*

Drastic Change once again is overtaking the U.S. Navy. It is a change which demands greatly of modern-day technology and which, before long, will require heavy investments of time, money, and energy. On the surface, at least, it is subtle and not readily obvious. However, it is just as basic to the future of the Navy's operations and the nature of its hardware, tactics, and strategies as were the changes that brought forth iron to replace wooden ships, steam to replace sails, rifles to replace smooth bores, and aircraft to replace the mighty battleship.

The submarine has been with us as an operational weapons platform now for over half a century. In World War I it had a depth capability of from 100 to 200 feet; in World War II, from 200 to 400 feet; and now, from 750 to 1,500 feet. Its submerged endurance has increased from a few hours to months. Its underwater speed has risen from 4–8 knots to 40-plus knots. Its armament has progressed from the elementary aimed torpedo sporting a high-explosive warhead and the simple deck gun to rocket-boosted torpedoes and depth charges (with either nuclear or conventional warheads) with a 30-mile range, and underwater-launched ballistic missiles with a range in excess of 2,500 nautical miles and an explosive warhead topping one megaton.

For all this impressive progress, the submarine has been limited largely to a two-dimensional environment—namely the upper 1,000 feet or so of the world ocean, scarcely enough in which to permit the modern high-speed nuclear submarine to maneuver either safely or to full advantage. Now, however, the Navy is preparing to extend its underwater operational capabilities not only to much greater depths, but throughout a much broader spectrum of naval missions. Key elements of this transition currently are the DGSS-555 Dolphin, the NR-1, the Mark-48 torpedo, and, more importantly, the whole range of activities of the Navy's Deep Submergence Program. This last is, on the face of it, concerned with the search, salvage, and/or rescue of men and objects from the ocean floor. But, with the requirements of such capabilities for advanced structures and materials, communications, navigation and control, life support, underwater "seeing," underwater work, etc., etc., a technology is emerging that before long will begin to be applied to operational deep-sea weapons platforms—whether mobile, i.e., submarines, or fixed bases. Indeed, the "next generation" of operational nuclear submarines—beginning in the late 1960's or early 1970's—will deploy to operational depths of 4,000 feet or more. Small, high-speed "interceptor" submarines may be capable of diving to 6,000 feet or better. Speeds of 60 knots will be approached or perhaps even passed. And weapons of greater sophistication and versatility will emerge.

"FASTEST, DEEPEST-DIVING, BEST-ARMED . . ."

ONE of our best-equipped nuclear ASW (Anti-Submarine Warfare) submarines is the *Dace*. Matt McDade of the National Geographic Society told about her on May 1, 1964, in one of the very few descriptions ever released of a modern ASW submarine. The article is reprinted here by permission of Frederick G. Vosburgh, vice-president and editor of the National Geographic Society:

With The Commissioning of the attack submarine U.S.S. *Dace,* four nuclear-powered ships of the *Thresher* class are now in service.

These submarines are built to hunt and destroy enemy subs. They run silent, deadly, and deep, listening to telltale echoes from their sonar pings. The Navy claims they are the fastest, deepest-diving, and best-armed craft ever delivered as operating warships to any fleet.

"Our main forte is stealth," says Commander John A. Walsh, captain of *Dace*.

Save for the winged conning tower, or sail, no protrusions disturb the black steel skin of the submarine's 278-foot-long hull. *Dace* is as smooth and lethal as a tiger shark. She is named for a slender, active fish of the carp family.

BUILT BY INGALLS

The end of April, 1964, saw *Dace* making runs into the Gulf of Mexico from the shipyard at Pascagoula, Mississippi, where she was built by the Ingalls Shipbuilding Division of Litton Industries.

On one of the runs, in addition to a crew of 12 officers and 88 enlisted men, *Dace* carried 25 guests who were privileged to see a newly assembled, first-rate crew getting the feel of a highly responsive instrument of war.

Some seventy-five miles offshore, the traditional command "Dive! Diiive!" sent *Dace* gliding down into a secret dark world beneath the shimmering sea.

For several hours, the nuclear submarine was put through a seemingly effortless underwater ballet—swift steep dives, dramatic ascents, and tight banking turns. On an even course, there was neither any sensation of movement nor vibration from the engine room in the sub's after end.

Aboard *Dace* was an invisible passenger—the specter of *Thresher.* This sister ship was lost mysteriously on a deep test dive in the Atlantic in April, 1963.

But the specter is a benign watchful spirit, not a shadow. Out of *Thresher's* sacrifice came modifications. *Dace* can expel water faster from its ballast tanks, thus surface more quickly if trouble strikes. The loss of *Thresher* also inspired new caution: iron-fisted control over the quality of every part manufactured for a new submarine; greater awareness of the problems to be encountered in penetrating deeper and deeper into the sea.

PRESSURE IS ENEMY

At 400 feet, the pressure of the sea is 176 pounds per square inch. Considering the fact that water squirts out of a kitchen faucet at the relatively puny rate of 15 psi and out of a giant fire hose at only 50 psi, one can hardly imagine the explosively fatal flooding, the thunder, and fog or mist that would result from a one-inch rent in a hull at the depths at which *Dace* is capable of operating.

Yet the atmosphere aboard *Dace* is without tension. The men even joke about the probable usefulness of the escape hatches: "These are put into the submarine for the mothers, not the sailors."

In the control center high amidships, a coxswain sits at the depth-control panel clutching a control wheel built like an aircraft's yoke. There is a cup of black coffee in a holder near his elbow. Another sailor reposes beside him at the angle control, smoking a cigarette.

Commands are given in conversational tones.

"Bob, this is good training for you. Snap 'er right in."

The submarine is sent into a breathtakingly swift rise, without warning to crew. From the mess below comes the clatter of cutlery and cups.

Even an emphatic command to put out cigarettes comes over the loudspeaker with a hint of casualness: "The smoking lamp is out now throughout the ship while they're venting the fuel tanks."

SEES BY LISTENING

Killer subs of *Dace*'s class are designed to go down into the sea and stay there for long periods, listening their way through the darkness. Equipment is shock-mounted, and the various compartments are hung from the hull, rather than fixed, so the ship will operate as silently as possible. She is outfitted with a complex, supersensitive sonar system.

"Our talent is aural," comments Commander Walsh.

More than a thousand hydrophones are packed into a sphere in *Dace*'s bow and along her sides. Sailors monitoring the sonar become so skilled they can instantly detect and differentiate the various sounds in the sea—a diesel engine, a school of fish, the purring of another sub.

In the after end of *Dace,* another world exists. Signs at a lead-floored tunnel above the nuclear reactor read: "No bunking, no loitering." This area is forbidden to unauthorized personnel.

Here, fissioning uranium in the reactor unleashes energy stored in the atoms eons ago when the stars were formed. Power surges into the twin turbines to drive the propellers. The pressurized water heated in the reactor vessel also supplies power for lights, air conditioning, the galley, sonar, navigational equipment, and atmosphere replenishment.

The nuclear Navy is attracting a new breed of submariner. Today's underwater sailors must know about nuclear power, inertial guidance, digital computers (there are three on *Dace*), and other technical marvels of the twentieth century.

Men aboard *Dace* spend a great deal of free time studying, from Captain Walsh down to the seventeen-year-old mess boy.

The youngest of *Dace*'s crewmen didn't finish high school before running away to join the Navy, but he has every intention of earning his diploma through correspondence courses. He aspires to the ship's elite nuclear crew.

Commander Walsh is a product of the Massachusetts Institute of Technology and Atomic Energy Commission, as well as the United States Naval Academy. He is a tanned, wiry, personable, highly motivated man who has spent twenty of his forty years in naval service.

CREW PLAYS CHESS

Significantly, crewmen aboard *Dace* find their favorite relaxation in chess, a game once thought suitable only for officers. No one complains that books in the ship's library are mostly technical.

Though everyday life is confining by the sheer lack of space, it is hardly Spartan. There are excellent meals, hot showers, movies, taped music in the mess and wardroom, and refrigerators to be raided.

About the only place where a crewman can really stretch out his arms is the long torpedo room with its skids and overhead rams for handling the torpedoes. *Dace* is equipped to fire the Navy's newest undersea weapon—Subroc [for Submarine Rocket]. This amazing flying torpedo will travel for a time underwater, then shoot itself into the air, disengage its rocket booster, make the trajectory prescribed in its memory system, and reenter the sea to make a kill.

Along with all its marvels, *Dace* packs an additional item of equipment that came as an incongruous surprise to her passengers on the recent visitors' cruise. While leaving and reentering her berth in the great Ingalls shipyard—the biggest south of Newport News—the submarine shunned the services of a stand-by tug to propel herself gently with a retractable outboard motor.

OUR MISSILE BASES UNDER THE SEA

"THE NATION that controls the seas," said G. V. Petrovich of the Soviet Union, "will control the world." Probably the most effective weapons at keeping the peace of the world today are the United States's nuclear submarines that carry—and can launch from under the sea—Polaris nuclear missiles. The missiles, developed under Vice Admiral William Francis Raborn, Jr. of Decatur, Texas, can travel 2,500 miles to their targets. Thus the Navy no longer is a military force that can only bombard the shore. The Navy can strike the enemy 2,500 miles inland. Almost all the military bases and cities in the world can be reached in this way. On the other hand, it is difficult for an enemy to attack our Polaris submarines. They are not kept in one place, but are distributed in the depths of the sea around the world. So the Polaris submarine fleet is not likely to be seriously damaged as was our Pacific fleet when it was caught in Pearl Harbor on December 7, 1941. The Polaris submarines are hard to find. They remain submerged for two or three months, and so cannot be visually detected. They can sometimes be found by sonar, but in any case they can move rapidly away from an enemy.

This report by General Dynamics, the builder of many Polaris submarines, is from an advertisement by that company in *United States News and World Report,* July 18, 1966:

REQUIREMENT: "Build a missile base that can be hidden under the ocean; that can keep moving so swiftly, so quietly that it cannot be found. Although it will never be used unless the United States is first attacked, build it so that it and its crew can be kept so fit, so efficient, that it can respond instantly should the order come."

ANSWER: The SSBN—Submarine Ballistic Nuclear—more commonly known as the Polaris submarine.

The nuclear-powered submarine has revolutionized naval strategy. Freed from dependence upon the atmosphere or refueling, such a ship can remain submerged for months on end. The addition of a ballistic missile that can be fired from beneath the sea creates an invulnerable deterrent against attack.

General Dynamics delivered the United States Navy's first submarine, the *Holland,* in 1900. Since then we have built 250 undersea vessels for the Navy, including the first nuclear-powered submersible, the *Nautilus.*

But the Navy's Polaris submarine, the most complex ship yet devised, has also created a revolution in shipbuilding. Questions of seaworthiness and habitability that must be factored into any ship are multiplied a thousandfold.

JIGSAW PUZZLE

The first essential in building a missile submarine is the integration of literally millions of parts, all of which must be designed to work together as a unity within the 425-foot length of the fish-shaped ship. Here are a few:

A nuclear reactor, turbines, gyroscopes, marine propulsion equipment, sixteen nuclear-tipped Polaris missiles, fire-control and navigation systems, water distillers, air purifying equipment, computers, and defensive weaponry.

Navigation and weapons control alone involve six different sonar systems, fourteen different radio systems, two or three Ship Inertial Navigation Systems, a LORAN (Long Range Aid to Navigation) system, a TRANSIT system (for contact with satellites), star-tracking facilities, and almost forty computers. All these, scattered throughout the ship, must be tied together into one central control for instant reaction. The ship must even carry its own spares, more than 30,000 different listings, each representing several sizes.

But creating a complete Polaris submarine system involves far more than a fitting job.

How do you join metals to withstand terrific pressures? How often does a man turn in his sleep? How do you keep a missile platform rock-steady in a rough sea? How do you muffle the noise of moving parts? How do you keep air fresh in a sealed environment?

STEADY AND QUIET

SSBN's are built of HY-80 steel, an alloy that can withstand stresses of up to 80,000 pounds per square inch.

But when the first ship was being built of HY-80, the metal behaved differently on outdoor building ways than it had in prior laboratory tests. The answer turned out to be one of the simpler ones. Indoor metallurgical laboratories had been warm. Outdoors, the weather got cold. Now strip heaters warm steel hull sections to a constant 200 degrees, regardless of weather, throughout the joining process.

To launch a Polaris missile successfully, the ship must be as stable a platform as solid earth, maintaining precise depth no matter how rough the sea. Making this possible was one of the toughest single design problems.

A submarine is controlled through a combination of rudders, planes (somewhat like the wings of an aircraft), and ballasting. To rise or descend, the ship must take on or force out ballast, in the form of tons of water. Ballast in various areas of a ship is continually being changed to maintain trim. An elaborate sensing and control system was developed to coordinate all parts of the complex in a perfect and delicate ballet.

In the depths, a nuclear submarine can be located mainly by sound. Anything that moves is soundproofed or cushioned. Shaft vibration of electric motors is reduced to less than one ten millionth of an inch. Hull openings, through which thousands of gallons of water must flow within seconds, are designed to minimize turbulence noise.

The millions of parts are supplied by some eleven thousand industrial companies and government agencies.

To ensure total reliability, General Dynamics makes more than fifty thousand tests—radiographic, ultrasonic, chemical, and hydrostatic—on the ship's systems, not counting those on electronics and weaponry. Even nuts and bolts must be standardized and inspected.

MAKING IT LIVABLE

Extended submerged patrol also created new questions of habitability. More than 75 percent of the total space inside a missile submarine is taken up by equipment or stores. In the remaining area some 140 men must live and work, comfortably and efficiently, for sixty days.

The submarine's galleys, not much bigger than the average suburban kitchen, are organized to store, prepare, and serve more than 800 full-course meals or snacks every day. Compact equipment distills 10,000 gallons of potable water daily. Laundries, pianos, ice-cream machines, are adapted to fit the available space.

Even sleep became a design problem. A seven-inch differential in the original space between multi-tiered bunks lets a crewman toss and turn normally to rest tired muscles.

On patrol the undersea sailor is rarely more than 150 feet from an operating nuclear reactor, yet shielding is made so effective that the submariner absorbs less total radiation than he would under normal surface conditions.

BREATHING EASY

With nuclear propulsion, engines no longer need air, but men do.

The average young adult male breathes in about 2 pounds of

oxygen each day; breathes out about $2\frac{1}{4}$ pounds of carbon dioxide. In a sealed atmosphere the air could quickly become poisonous. The first nuclear submarines still surfaced periodically to refresh the air. When sustained submersion became the rule, air regeneration became necessary.

Oxygen is electrolytically processed from water. Banks of scrubbers, precipitators, and catalytic burners remove the carbon dioxide and the three hundred or so contaminants that can build up within a nuclear submarine.

Enough air conditioning to cool a small town dissipates the heat generated by machinery and human bodies. At the end of a long patrol, the air aboard a missile submarine is far cleaner than that of the average American city.

General Dynamics delivered the *George Washington,* the first Polaris submarine, in 1959. In July, 1966, we launched the *Will Rogers,* the forty-first of these extraordinary ships that help the United States Navy guard the peace of the world.

Between the *George Washington* and the *Will Rogers,* a number of evolutions have taken place. New generations of submarine ships may be as much an advance over current models as the Polaris submarine is over the old *Holland.*

SECTION XIX

THE OCEAN WAVES
They Turn Out Even Taller than Sailor's Tales

The extreme height of storm waves is one phase of the subject [sea conditions] on which there is no evident agreement.
—U.S. Naval Institute Proceedings, August, 1934.

THE HIGHEST WAVE MEN HAVE SEEN

JUST How high do storm waves get? No one knows. When the Norwegian-American liner *Bergensfjord* crossed the Atlantic in January, 1965, waves smashed her wheelhouse windows, 65 feet above the waterline. "They were the highest waves I ever saw," said her captain, Ivan Gronbukt, who had spent thirty-nine years at sea. But while no one is certain how high waves do get, the great wave described below is the world's highest on record. By Lt. Comdr. R. P. Whitemarsh, U.S. Navy, in *United States Naval Institute Proceedings,* August, 1934. Commander Whitemarsh was serving on the *Ramapo,* a United States fleet oiler or tanker.

On February 7, 1933, a great sea wave 112 feet high was observed by personnel of the U.S.S. *Ramapo.* The weather condition in the mid-Pacific in February was unique in that it contained every element favorable to the development of extraordinarily high waves. The *Ramapo* was proceeding from Manila to San Diego in latitude 34° 30′ N. On February 3, the barometer, which had stood at 30.20, began to fall. During the seven-day period of stormy weather which followed, the ship traveled from longitude 169° E. to longitude 155° W. on an easterly course.

From the meteorological plotting chart prepared in the *Ramapo*'s aerological office, it was noted that a well-defined low (29.00), central near Dutch Harbor, Alaska, extended from the Arctic Circle to a secondary low immediately to the north of the Hawaiian Islands. On February 4, this secondary low developed and deepened to a minimum pressure below 29.10, and apparently drew much of its strength from the northern low, whose minimum pressure rose to 29.60.

This system of lows displaced the normal high-pressure area to the east of the Hawaiian Islands, whose center usually shows a pressure of 30.20. This resulted in a striking system of high-pressure areas extending along the entire coast of North America from the Arctic Ocean to the tip of Lower California.

Incidentally, such a development is characteristic of winter cold snaps in the West and Middle West, since its normal clockwise air circulation draws down the polar air mass from the arctic regions. In this case, extreme low temperatures (−40° F.) were registered in the Middle West, with blizzards and snow as far east as New York. These facts are mentioned to indicate the far-reaching influence of an extreme weather condition. The disturbance was not localized, as is the case with a typhoon, but reached all the way from Kamchatka on the Asiatic continent to New York. This permitted an unobstructed "fetch" of thousands of miles, with winds from a constant direction, all contributing to extremely high seas.

On Sunday, February 5, we crossed the 180th meridian practically in the middle of the vast Pacific Ocean. Sunday was repeated. The third low, whose presence we suspected immediately to the west, became a reality.

The barometer dropped to 29.58 to the accompaniment of winds from astern force 8 and 9. These winds lasted for four hours and resulted in a rather rough sea. This short blow is considered our entry into the real low-pressure area with which we traveled for the next four days.

By the end of the second Sunday, February 5, the barometer had slowly settled to 29.51, and winds of force 3, 4, and 5 were experienced. The wind held to the west. The system of three lows showed marked intensity, with minimum pressures below 29.00, 29.30, and 29.20, and occupied much of the North Pacific Ocean.

On February 6, the barometer dropped from 29.51 to 29.24 without any material difference in wind or sea. The wind was a strong breeze of 30 knots' velocity and caused a moderate sea.

The barometer remained at 29.24 for five hours, during which time the elements began to give evidence that something out of the ordinary was about to happen. After two hours the wind became a moderate gale, force 7 or 35 knots, and the sea at once increased to a heavy swell. These conditions were maintained for three hours without change when, for the first time, the barometer rose one hundredth to 29.25.

The result was immediately apparent. At this time the wind increased to a fresh gale of 12 knots while the sea effect was slightly increased. The following hour disclosed a whole gale of 58 knots' force and mountainous seas. This occurred at 2200 [10 P.M.] on February 6, as we began to leave the vicinity of the low center near which we had been cruising for over two days. We maintained our easterly course with the wind almost directly astern. It would have been disastrous to have steamed on any other course.

Although the ship's draft aft was 21 feet 10 inches, the propeller raced to such an extent upon the passing of the crest of a wave that it became necessary to reduce speed at 2300 [11 P.M.].

The storm reached its height between 0300 [3 A.M.] and 0900 [9 A.M.], when winds up to 68 knots in velocity were clocked with the anemometer. We occupied the bridges from 0400 to

0800 and personally verified all data. The winds came in gusts and squalls during which the greatest velocities were obtained and the highest seas were observed. This fact gives additional evidence that sea waves travel at approximately the same speed as the wind which accompanies them. It is significant that when, at 1000 on February 7, the wind dropped to force 8, the seas were simultaneously reduced from "mountainous" to "very rough."

The great system of three low centers was consolidated during the height of the storm experienced by the *Ramapo,* with extreme activity as the result. An extraordinary depth of 28.40 inches of barometric pressure was noted on February 8, 1933. The ship emerged from the low pressure area on February 9, just one week after entering it.

The weather condition may be briefly summarized. February is notoriously the most stormy month in the North Pacific Ocean. And from all reports, this was the most extensive and severe storm of the year. The *Ramapo* was in a position to experience the full force of the storm. The height of waves was materially greater than that noted when the vessel was forced to take reduced speed for three days in a typhoon near the Mariana Islands in October, 1929.

The conditions for observing the seas from the ship were ideal. We were running directly downwind and with the sea. There were no cross seas and therefore no peaks along wave crests. There was practically no rolling, and the pitching motion was easy because of the fact that the sides of the waves were materially longer than the ship. The moon was out astern and facilitated observations during the night. The sky was partly cloudy.

Probably no two seas were identical in length and height. They varied from 500 to 750 feet in length of sides, or total wave length of 1,000 to 1,500 feet, as measured by the ship itself and the seaman's eye. This is verified by motion-picture film taken during the morning watch. The *Ramapo* is 477 feet 10 inches in length. For purposes of illustration, a conservative wave length of 1,180 feet is assumed. It was noted that the ship's entire length glided down the lee slope of waves an appreciable time before the crest overtook the stern. The vessel was dwarfed in comparison with the seas.

The period of the largest sea wave was 14.8 seconds as determined by stop watch. Similarly, a wind velocity of 66 knots was taken and verified, although the average velocity for several hours was 60 knots.

Due to the extreme simplicity of the determination of the height of sea waves in this particular case, none of the factors, including wave length, period, and wind velocity, is required in the solution. These factors are of interest in checking observations and proving formulas. The height determination is by construction, wherein the ship itself measured the seas.

Among a number of separately determined observations, that of Lt. (J.G.) Frederick C. Marggraff, U.S. Navy, is employed, although one other observation similarly taken by another observer gave greater heights of sea waves. The selected observation gives a wave height of 112 feet compared with other observations of 82, 86, 107, and 119 feet, all covered by construction based on sworn affidavits of different observers.

Mr. Marggraff declares that while standing watch on the bridge between the hours of 0000 and 0400 on Tuesday, February 7, 1933, he saw seas astern at a level above the iron strap on the boom located against the mainmast crow's nest, and that at the moment of observation the horizon was hidden from view by the waves approaching from astern. Mr. Marggraff is 5 feet 11¾ inches tall. The ship was not listed, and the stern was in the trough of the sea.

This gives an exact line of sight from the bridge to the crest of the wave. This also determines the attitude of the ship with the angle of pitch. While the observer was obviously below the line of crests, the amount is indeterminate. It would reduce the observed height of the wave astern if this line were considered truly horizontal. Such an assumption is made in arriving at a height of 112 feet.

The stern of the ship had been sinking into the trough of the oncoming sea, up to the instant of observation, due in part to lack of water support aft. Water rolled aboard aft when the stern was near the crest. Nearly normal conditions of draft obtained when the stern was almost at the trough. For all practical purposes, the trough was at the waterline at the stern, 21 feet 10 inches above the keel.

The accompanying figure illustrates the attitude of the ship at the instant the height was determined. Considering the line of sight in the plane of the horizon, we measure vertically downward to the trough to obtain the wave height. The construction was from ship's plans. The height is shown to be 112 feet from this construction. The height determination depends solely upon the observed line of sight and the accuracy of these plans. . . .

Since time immemorial, seafaring men have been telling the world in their inarticulate way that storm waves attain heights

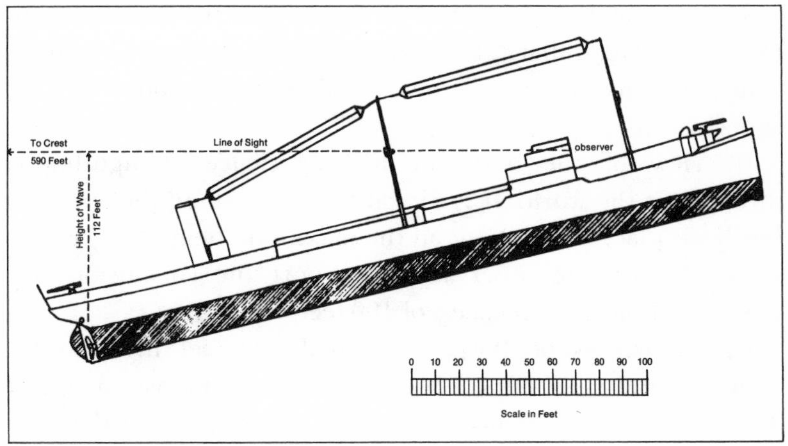

which seem incredible to the rest of mankind. In the absence of satisfactory proof in specific cases, it has been easy to doubt the accuracy of the observations.

Possibly the controversy began in 1837, when Dumont D'Urville estimated and reported a wave 100 feet high off the Cape of Good Hope. It is significant that an authority of today should consider this statement of such a dubious character that probably only seafarers would agree with it.

The privilege of viewing great storm waves of extreme height is a rare one indeed. Furthermore, we have no assurance that the highest waves of the ocean have been observed or measured. If such a wave should ever be encountered, it is probable that all hands would be chiefly concerned with the safety of the ship to the exclusion of any scientific measurement of the phenomenon.

Today the apologetic method of mariners in reporting seas in violation of the 60-foot law of science is as quoted from a *Hydrographic Bulletin:* "A measurement of one sea showed an apparent height of about 70 feet."

This particular observation was made in the North Pacific Ocean on December 31, 1932, during a typhoon in which winds of force 12, hail squalls, and a tremendous sea were experienced.

In view of the undisputable experience at lighthouses throughout the world, it is difficult to understand the apparent low limit placed by science on the maximum height of great sea waves. Lighthouse observations support the conclusion that waves reach heights in excess of 100 feet.

In the winter of 1861, a fog bell 100 feet high on the Bishop Lighthouse, Isles of Scilly, was struck by a sea wave. The breaking crest was formed well above this height and the wave struck with such force that the metal bracket four inches thick by which it was supported was broken. The bell crashed to pieces on the rocks below. The sea left sand heavily deposited on the lighthouse gallery.

Occasionally, waves go over the top of the tower of the lighthouse on Minots Ledge, Massachusetts, 75 feet above the water.

In severe storms, rocks have been thrown through the lantern glass of Tillamook Rock Lighthouse, 133 feet above the ocean. This lighthouse is situated on a rock one mile from the Oregon coast, between the 10- and 21-fathom lines and thirty miles from the 100-fathom line. This topographical condition serves to modify the extreme height of seas before they reach Tillamook. The height of 133 feet does not, therefore, represent the maximum height of offshore sea waves.

For instance, in certain localities, such as off the Malabar coast, the seas are entirely ironed out by shoal water prior to reaching land and safe anchorage is provided along an otherwise unprotected coast.

THE HIGHEST WAVE MEASURED BY INSTRUMENTS

By L. Draper, a physicist who, since 1953, has worked mainly on waves at the National Institute of Oceanography in Great Britain. Mr. Draper writes in Oceanus *of the Woods Hole Oceanographic Institution, June, 1964:*

It Is Only about thirteen years since it became possible to measure waves in the open sea from a ship with acceptable accuracy, and so provide a check on whether or not the stories of monstrous waves were to be believed. One of the British Ocean Weather Ships, operating in all weathers in the North Atlantic, has carried such a shipborne wave recorder for twelve years. As the ship is on station for about two thirds of the time, the National Insitute of Oceanography now has a long series of wave records which were taken for fifteen minutes every three hours. At first the scale of the instrument could record waves 50 feet high from crest to trough, but very soon it was found that waves higher than this were not uncommon and the scale was increased to 60 feet. This proved to be adequate for about nine years, but on September 12, 1961, *Weather Reporter* lay close to the track of the dying hurricane Betsy, and as she made her routine recording at 0900 hours, the pen dipped and touched the lower edge of the chart and then rose rapidly and "hit the stops" at the top—a wave over 60 feet high. A crest was fitted to this wave and it is estimated that the true height of the wave was not less than 67 feet from crest to trough. The period of this wave was 15 seconds, which meant that the weather ship was lifted over 60 feet in 7½ seconds and then dropped almost as far in the succeeding 7½ seconds! The probability that we actually recorded the highest wave which hit the vessel is fairly small, because the instrument is operated for only about 8 percent of the time. . . . The highest wave which was felt by the weather ship during that storm was probably about 80 feet from crest to trough. At the present time the wave which *Weather Reporter* measured is the highest one which has ever been recorded by an instrument—conservatively estimated to be 67 feet from crest to trough.

Because the proportional area of an ocean which is occupied by vessels is incredibly small, it follows that only a minute proportion of the exceptional waves which must occur each year in an area such as the North Atlantic are ever noticed by man. It therefore seems reasonable to suppose that with only one vessel equipped with a wave recorder regularly at sea in the North Atlantic, the chance that our 67 foot wave is the highest which ever occurred is small indeed. We must by no means claim that the report from the *Ramapo* was exaggerated.

HOW A MONSTER WAVE CAN OCCUR

From Naval Research Reviews, *September, 1966.*

During the early months of the 1966 tourist season, would-be travelers were shocked to learn that the ultramodern Italian passenger liner *Michelangelo* was severely damaged by a freak wave. The massive body of water smashed bridge windows 81 feet above the waterline, inundated the forward half of the ship, tore aside heavy steel flaring on the bow, and killed three people.

Dr. Richard W. James of the Naval Oceanographic Office has offered an explanation of these rare occurrences. He reports that under the influence of strong wind, the ocean's surface develops mounds and hollows in chaotic motion. Observation of waves passing a ship indicate a variety of heights running in random fashion. Waves of an average height occur almost consistently, but interspaced with them are waves that are much higher and much lower. Based on mathematical percentages, if a thousand waves pass a ship, there is one chance in twenty that a wave 2.22 times higher than the average might occur.

Since the waves encountered by the *Michelangelo* were approximately 30 feet in height, there was a mathematical possibility that the ship would encounter a wave from 52 to 66 feet high. With reported wave periods of twelve seconds, it would have taken over three hours for a thousand waves to pass. The probability would than have been one in twenty that a monster wave 66 feet high would form during that time.

NOW WE MAY MEASURE ALL THE OCEAN'S WAVES

From the Lockheed-California Company and New York University, October 31, 1966:

A system for worldwide ocean wave observation and forecasting that could enable ships to bypass hurricanes and other rough seas can be developed via a space satellite circling the earth, New York University and Lockheed-California Company scientists explain:

In this oceanic equivalent to weather prediction, the spacecraft radar-type measurements of waves would be transmitted to earth stations and fed into computers for a 24- to 48-hour forecast on sea-surface conditions anywhere on the globe.

The technical paper on global wave forecasts was presented at the U.S. Navy-sponsored Symposium on Naval Hydrodynamics in Washington, D. C., by Dr. Willard J. Pierson, Jr., and Dr. Leo

J. Tick of New York University and Dr. Ledolph Baer of the Lockheed-California Company's oceanics organization.

These very accurate advance reports on wind-generated waves could permit—

(*a*) ships to better avoid dangerous zones and to be routed across the ocean more economically;

(*b*) the Navy to plan more precisely such activities as task-force deployment, aircraft-carrier landings, maneuvers, transfer of men and equipment, and refueling at sea;

(*c*) more efficient and safer search and rescue operations;

(*d*) surer preparations for coastal recreation areas.

Knowledge of the variations in wave conditions would also aid in the design of new commercial ships and naval vessels and could play an important role in improving weather-prediction techniques because of the effect of salt particles entering the atmosphere.

The worldwide wave-grid study is being conducted by Lockheed under a contract from the U.S. Naval Oceanographic Office and New York University.

The scientists noted that the spacecraft—on a polar orbit—could make a complete survey of all oceans daily as the earth rotates, gathering information on winds (speed, direction, altitude) and waves (height, length, duration) for every ninety nautical miles. This would be the equivalent to reports from 2,800 ships spaced fairly uniformly over the oceans.

There would be some 15,000 to 20,000 observation points on a global wave-forecasting grid.

In an earlier program sponsored by the Navy, N.Y.U. and Lockheed developed a mathematical wave-forecasting technique for the North Atlantic. A similar wave-forecast grid for the North Pacific is now being prepared.

In addition to Drs. Pierson, Tick, and Baer, other scientists working on the wave-forecasting program are Louis Adamo and Mrs. Jean Hosmer of Lockheed and Tokujiro Inoue, Miss Ming Shun Chang, and Vincent Cardone of N.Y.U.

SECTION XX

THE OCEAN'S FUTURE
The Sea Holds Many Possibilities for Man

The great age of discovery certainly did not end with Columbus, Magellan, or Cook. It may well be in the future.
—Edwin A. Link in a National Geographic Society News Bulletin, June 16, 1964.

MORE SOPHISTICATED SUBMARINES

From General Dynamics, Electric Boat Division, Groton, Connecticut:

NEW BREED OF VESSEL

A hundred and thirty feet down in the Aegean Sea, a Byzantine galley had hidden its secrets for almost fifteen centuries. Then in 1964, University of Pennsylvania Museum archeologists mounted paired cameras on a new research submarine, *Asherah,* and learned more from the three-dimensional photographs obtained in one "flight" over the wreck than had been possible from weeks of scuba diving.

This was the first of dozens of undersea jobs already done by *Asherah.* The *Asherah* is the 339th—and at 17 feet long, the smallest—submarine built by General Dynamics. For comparison, the *Holland,* the very first submarine we delivered to the Navy in 1900, was 54 feet long. Over the years, we have built the prototypes of most classes of United States Navy submarines, including its nuclear-powered undersea ships.

But the true manned research submarines are really a new breed of boat. Less than a score now exist.

DEPTH AND MOBILITY

Unlike bathyscaphes, designed to drop to great depths but remain relatively immobile for passive observation, the new research submarines must have depth capability, the ability to perform useful work, and the mobility to survey extended areas at a reasonable speed.

Asherah is one of the first true research submarines. It can dive to 600 feet (World War II subs rarely dived much below 300 feet), stay submerged for ten hours, cruise at three to four knots, move in all directions. An improved sister ship, *Star II,* is made of the same HY-80 steel that goes into nuclear submarines; it has depth capability to 1,200 feet.

A larger boat we call *Star III* is built of even tougher HY-100 steel. It has a cruising depth of 2,000 feet and is equipped with an external mechanical arm that has interchangeable "hands"—a clamshell grip, a wire cutter, and a "three-finger" which can pick up a pencil or a 200-pound weight, or manipulate a valve.

The *Aluminaut,* the largest research sub so far, was built by General Dynamics for Reynolds International to prove, among other things, the feasibility of aluminum as a hull metal. The 51-foot *Aluminaut* is designed to operate at depths up to 15,000 feet, under pressures up to more than 7,000 pounds per square inch. *Aluminaut,* in early trials, has cruised as deep as 6,250 feet, and remained submerged for over 30 continuous hours. A World War II military submarine rarely remained submerged for more than 24 hours.

PROBLEMS AND NEEDS

These early research subs still have many limitations of speed, range, and submerged endurance. They require back-up by a mother ship and have to be carried or towed to a job location.

This last "limitation" can sometimes be an advantage. *Asherah* and *Star II,* for example, are small enough to be rushed by air for a rescue operation.

But subs with many special characteristics will be needed for exploring—and for exploiting—the sea.

Some vessels will have to withstand pressures up to 10,000 pounds per square inch, to allow them to penetrate into mid-ocean abysses four miles deep. Work subs for, say, mining will have to be stable enough in a buoyant environment not to be whipped about in reaction to the force of their own tools.

We have already done a study for the Bureau of Fisheries showing feasibility of a submarine to track oceanic fish. It would be 160 feet long, carry 31 persons at speeds up to 20 knots, and could cruise submerged for up to 90 days.

Right now, we don't think there will ever be one single all-purpose type of research-work submarine. Just as land vehicles range from motor scooters to 20-ton earth movers, so will most manned submersibles be designed and built for special purposes.

WEATHER FORECASTS FROM THE OCEAN

From General Dynamics:

Wouldn't it be nice if you could plan a vacation and *know* weeks ahead that the weather would be good?

Actually, 24-hour local forecasting is right almost 85 per-cent of the time. But longer-range prediction—on which can depend anything from a vacation trip to the success of a year's wheat crop—is far less certain.

Even though information from hundreds of full-time land weather stations is supplemented by measurements in the upper atmosphere and reports from weather satellites, a vital link in the chain has been missing.

Weather is essentially born or modified as a result of the inter-action of sun and air with the oceans that cover two thirds of the earth's surface.

Oceanography and meteorology can be considered two faces of

the same coin—the study of the total marine environment. And relatively little is known about it yet.

SEAGOING "WEATHER BUREAU"

What has been needed to fill the gap is an oceanographic "weather bureau."

It would have to stay in place in the deepest part of the sea, regardless of storm or current; collect environmental information from the atmosphere, the surface, and the depths; send that information regularly and correctly back to land.

And it would have to do all these jobs without human presence for long periods of time.

With a network of such sea stations seeded throughout the world, oceanic information could be integrated with that obtained from land stations and from space. Meteorologists could determine the patterns that will create the weather next week, or perhaps months hence.

Oceanographers could analyze the subsurface currents, the levels of dissolved nutrients in the water, the migratory patterns of fish to anticipate their location for commercial fishing.

And with navigation lights, fog horns, and radar beacons at known positions, such a network would provide invaluable navigation aid for ships.

MONSTER BUOYS

Today, the beginning of such a worldwide system may be at hand—an ocean data station, more commonly known as a monster buoy, developed and built by General Dynamics for the United States Navy's Office of Naval Research.

The first prototype has been undergoing sea trials since 1964, collecting and sending its information through calm and hurricane.

This ocean data system consists of a giant pie-plate-shaped buoy, 40 feet in diameter and 7½ feet deep, containing an assortment of environmental measuring devices and the electronic and power equipment to collect and transmit to shore the data acquired.

It can be "locked" in place, moored to an ocean floor as deep as 30,000 feet, by a plaited nylon cable only two inches thick. Although the buoys are presently designed to operate for a year at a time without human maintenance, the conventional propane-powered generator systems that provide electricity for the buoy's operation carry a two-year supply of fuel.

Unlike a traditional ship, which exaggerates the motion of waves, particularly in side-to-side pendulumlike rolling, the symmetrical, discus-shaped buoy hull follows the slope of the waves, reducing pitching and rolling to a minimum. Its stability keeps its omnidirectional antenna in proper position to radio information to a shore analysis station.

DEFIES HURRICANES

No one really knows just how rough the weather might get in a full-scale typhoon or hurricane—defined only as a cyclonic storm with winds of over 75 miles per hour—because of the obvious difficulty of humans' taking accurate measurements under such conditions.

The Office of Naval Research's—and General Dynamics'—ocean data station was designed to withstand winds of 160 miles per hour and waves 60 feet high.

Buoy Bravo, the first prototype, remained in place under winds of 110 miles per hour and waves 50 feet high during hurricane Betsy in 1965, with no interruption in its flow of information. Its elastic nylon mooring line permits the buoy to drift slightly and then pull back to position without dragging its "anchor" of steel chain.

Typhoons and hurricanes luckily occur only occasionally. But the intensely corrosive environment of the sea is constant. For protection, the buoy's steel hull, mast, and antennas are coated with inorganic zinc and several layers of vinyl.

A HUNDRED TESTS

An assortment of sensors can be located on the 38-foot-high mast and on the radial spokes of the discone antenna to measure wind, humidity, precipitation, radiation (from the sky and reflected back from the sea), barometric pressure, and compass bearing.

Others inside and immediately under the hull will read water temperature at the surface, wave height, period, and direction.

Clamped along the mooring line at regular intervals underwater, still others will measure temperature, pressure, and salinity and determine the structure of subsurface layers of the depths.

Inside the hull, rugged electronic components and circuitry will acquire, store, and transmit information from as many as a hundred separate sensors.

These subsystems will be packaged in containers purged with nitrogen and hermetically sealed to provide an inert, absolutely dry, environment. The buoy at sea will provide better conditions for electronic equipment than does a dust-temperature-humidity-controlled laboratory ashore.

The data-acquisition system will look at every sensor once an hour (or it can be monitored more often; individual sensors can be checked continually). Measurements will go into both a magnetic core memory with a capacity of twenty-four hours of data and a recorder that will store a full year's information.

Every six hours a ground station will interrogate the buoy, commanding it to transmit all information accumulated during the past twenty-four hours. Each discharge of data will provide an eighteen-hour overlap, giving scientists a continuous record.

The ground station will also instruct the buoy to transmit data on the particular one of its three radio channels which will assure best reception on shore of long-distance "bounce" off the ionosphere.

BENEFIT FOR ALL NATIONS

A few prototype monster buoys do not, to be sure, constitute a full-scale oceanic environmental survey. They do provide a starting point for a truly international system—one in which all nations would share, and from which all would benefit.

But now that the practicality of an ocean data station has been proved, the many elements of a total system are already being worked out: the optimum number and locations of stations to provide simultaneous coverage throughout the seas; ways to integrate at central analysis stations the ocean data with that from land and space; techniques of maintenance and replenishment for the seaborne network; development of devices to measure many kinds of subsurface phenomena.

The day when data stations will be dotted throughout the oceans for a genuine oceanographic-meteorological environmental watch could come within a decade.

MEN IN GLASS BUBBLES TO SURVEY THE DEPTHS

TO REACH the bottoms of the deepest trenches beneath the sea, six to seven miles down, as the bathyscaphe has done, we need a deep-diving ship that is (1) strong enough to withstand the enormous pressure of the water, and (2) lightweight enough to be buoyant and return to the surface. Research by the Navy and the Corning Glass Works shows that it may be made, surprisingly, of glass. This is an Associated Press report of November 10, 1965:

TO THE DEEPEST SEA FLOOR

Pasadena, California: Two men in a bubble may begin tests soon that will take them 36,000 feet down into the deepest trenches in the sea, scientists report.

The diving bubble would be made of glass, says physicist William B. McLean, developer of the sidewinder air-to-air missile. He said he chose glass because:

1. While lighter than either steel or titanium, glass is stronger under the pressure of extreme depths. "The more you compress it, the stronger it becomes."
2. Steel diving capsules with portholes have demonstrated the need for wider visibility. In the glass bubble, men could see in any direction.
3. Glass also resists saltwater corrosion. Men and instruments would be able to stay at any depth indefinitely.

McLean said the first version of the diving bubble will be 4½ feet in diameter, rather cramped quarters for two men. Instruments that don't need protection from pressure will be mounted outside, he said.

McLean said there will be no way for the men to leave the bubble until they return to the surface.

McLean, technical director of the Naval Ordnance Test Station, China Lake, California, was awarded the Rockefeller public service award of $10,000 for his achievement in weapons research.

THE HYDRONAUTS: THE NEW NAVY BREED

From the Department of the Navy, Deep Submergence Systems Project Office:

The Submarine Force, U.S. Pacific Fleet is training a new kind of submarine officer—the hydronaut. A group of officers and enlisted men at the Submarine Support Facility, Ballast Point, San Diego, attached to Submarine Squadron Three is providing the classroom training and actual experience in deep-submergence piloting and navigation, using the Navy's bathyscaphe *Trieste II*.

This group of fifteen officers and fifty enlisted men is engaged in training, evaluating and qualifying submarine officers as deep-submergence vehicle pilots and navigators, or hydronauts. To date, only ten United States naval officers have earned this distinctive title.

Hydronauts will be needed in increasing numbers as the Navy's Deep Submergence Systems Project provides the vehicles scheduled for the full spectrum of ocean work, from the continental shelf to the deep abyss.

The Deep Submergence Rescue Vehicle (a deep-diving submarine), the prototype of which is presently under construction by the Lockheed Aircraft Company, will need qualified pilots and navigators, as well as additional support personnel familiar with deep-submergence operations.

Training a hydronaut in the complicated business of piloting a vehicle and navigating it in the deep ocean calls for a packed schedule of classroom work, practical factors, orientation, simulation, and actual dives, using the bathyscaphe *Trieste II*.

Each prospective hydronaut carries a qualification notebook with him, much as he did when he was becoming qualified in submarines. He must be able to trace all systems of the deep ocean vehicle, from electrical-hydraulic to mechanical and electronic. He first studies a familiarization course, including nomenclature, history, and typical systems. He studies in the classroom, and then later in the *Trieste*. He travels to Charlottesville, Virginia, for several weeks training in the *Trieste II* Operational Trainer at the Sperry Piedmont Company Plant. He makes actual dives in *Trieste II,* and after approximately six successful dives and a thorough examination, is qualified as a pilot of deep submergence vehicles (hydronaut).

The training program, ideally, takes approximately six months, half of the time devoted to classroom work, the rest actually working with the vehicle. The hydronaut trainee may take any of the three crew positions on his preliminary dives. Normal crew for the *Trieste* consists of the pilot, copilot/navigator, and an observer.

Lt. Comdr. E. E. Henifin, officer-in-charge of *Trieste II,* said: "The three are crammed into a capsule that has about seventeen cubic feet of air space per man. I've been told that the smallest NASA space capsule had twenty-one cubic feet per man."

Eleven officers are presently undergoing training in the hydronaut program, seven of them on a maximum training schedule. The unit is also helping to develop a computerized system of navigation/ship control that will assist the pilot of the vehicle during search, and testing sensors for the projected Deep Submergence Rescue Vehicle. As the Navy procures more deep submergence vehicles, both of the rescue and search type, the hydronaut training program will move into full swing, providing pilots and navigators for the $100 million fleet of rescue and search submersibles the Navy plans to order.

FOOD FOR ALL MANKIND

THIS ARTICLE, by Charles Butler and John A. Holston, is from the October 15, 1966, issue of *Oceanology International.* Neil P. Ruzic, editor and publisher of *Oceanology International,* says of the authors: "Charles Butler and John A. Holston are long-time employes of the Bureau of Commercial Fisheries in the Department of the Interior. Butler has participated and supervised food-research programs at almost every major bureau station during the last two decades. He has been instrumental in the development of more efficient vitamin A sources, improved canned seafood, and upgraded fish proteins and oils. Butler currently heads the bureau's industrial research program. Holston has been involved in a wide range of fishery research as supervisory chemist and chief in the technology branch and deputy director of the industrial research program. He now is director of the Gloucester Technology Laboratory."

Oceans Of The World support a fishing industry that harvested 56.7 million tons of protein foods—reflecting an increase in landings of 75 percent in 1964. Nevertheless, fishing efforts still are largely coastal in nature and, in most respects, are not as efficient as land-based food industries.

Despite these large landings and the fact that 71 percent of the world's surface is covered by the oceans, only about 1 to 2 percent of the world's total food supply is procured from the oceans, for man is not oriented toward the ocean environment. He generally considers the oceans merely as bodies of water bordering the coasts, essential to his defense, and useful only for transport of bulky cargoes.

He must become accustomed to thinking and making decisions in terms of a full understanding of conditions pertaining within the oceanic universe. Recognition of this need is implicit in growing support for substantial oceanographic and ocean engineering programs as a key to understanding and utilizing ocean wealth for our welfare.

Almost two thirds of the people of the world live in developing nations. In many of these countries, the per capita diets are substandard in terms of quantity and nutritional value. As a result, every second a child dies of hunger or from the effects of malnutrition. Similarly, in certain regions of the world, up to fifty percent of the children die of the effects of malnutrition before they become six years old.

By and large, the nutrient most often lacking in deficient diets of the developing nations is good-quality animal protein. The Food and Agriculture Organization of the United Nations has estimated that the world's 1970 deficit of animal protein will be about 6 billion kilograms. Marasmus and kwashiorkor are the principal protein-deficiency diseases—characterized by retardation in growth, intelligence, maturation, and by heavy mortalities.

Additional supplies of fish could yield an inexpensive yet nutritionally complete animal protein, which has been demonstrated to be of great therapeutic value in testing of protein-deficiency diseases.

It has taken all the years of human existence for the world's population to reach 3 billion. It will take less than thirty-five more years to add the next 3 billion if present growth rates continue.

Thus, while the problem of inadequate world food supplies is not new, it has taken on a new and more serious perspective for the near future and underlies the need for full utilization of our marine and freshwater food resources.

PRODUCTION VARIES

The world's oceans are not uniformly productive, either in numbers or species of fishes. Oceanographic conditions, when acting upon a particular species, tend to localize that species in well-defined areas.

Our present understanding of the oceanic universe, imperfect as it is, has enabled the world's fishing industry, spurred by a growing worldwide need for protein, to increase its catch from approximately 8 million tons in 1908 to about 56 million tons in 1964. It is our task during the next decade to—

(*a*) expand our understanding of the marine environment;
(*b*) increase our capacity to manage its living resources;
(*c*) reduce costs of fishing operations;
(*d*) facilitate extension of such operations to all the world's oceans;
(*e*) maximize the wise utilization of the ocean's food resources.

Constraining effects of environmental conditions and of physiological characteristics on fishes enable us to classify the world's fish resources broadly in terms of their habitats. We also will discuss, within this same context, beneficial returns to be anticipated from the various oceanographic and oceanic engineering activities.

Demersal (groundfish) species inhabit the bottoms of the continental shelves and slopes. Such fisheries are characterized by schooling cods and flounders that have supported the great traditional fisheries of the past.

Because the northern hemisphere contains 78 percent of the total area of the world's continental shelves and—at the same time—evidences water temperatures conducive to development of such species of fish, it is clearly evident why nations of this hemisphere have been, until very recently, the world's leaders in production of fish.

Significant increases in landings of groundfishes, however, must result from extensive efforts in locating, defining, and developing totally new fishing grounds; from further exploitation of known but relatively unutilized fishing banks; or from actual cultivation or farming of intensively harvested grounds. Several nations now are exploring the Patagonian, West African, Indonesian, Indian, and Australian continental shelves for groundfish stocks.

Important needs in demersal fisheries center on economics of harvesting fish. We must reduce costs in terms of time and effort required if we are to compete with other local industries for labor and capital. Such productivity increases will result only from a whole system approach to the problem of fish harvesting.

We must introduce greater automation of vessel and fishing gear and develop advanced specialized gear designed to exploit the behavioral characteristics of each fish species being harvested. We must improve on capabilities for long-distance search detection and species discrimination. We require the means to aggregate, to herd fish stocks, and to induce schooling of fishes.

PROFITS TO INCREASE

Through ocean engineering programs now being developed and implemented, the next five years will see application of modern land-based technology to the oceans and a significant increase in the profitability of fishing.

In ten years or less, most continental shelf areas of the world will be well on the way to full development and will be effectively and efficiently contributing, on a sustained basis, to the world's food supplies.

Pelagic (surface or near-surface) fishes include the highly prized, ocean-ranging tuna and swordfish as well as the single most abundant form of fish—the herring and herringlike fishes. The latter fishes (including anchovy) form the basis of the world's booming fish reduction industry and have been of such value as to be universally recognized as components of specialized, traditional diets.

Nevertheless, pelagic fishes today represent an enormous, relatively untapped, potential as a source of additional food from the sea. These resources await only development of commercially feasible harvesting and processing techniques in the fishing industry.

Five years hence, the world need for fish meal and for protein foods for human consumption will have stimulated such developments as has happened in Peru and Chile, and the world herring resources will be tending toward full utilization.

In ten years, with the development of other less costly protein substitutes for animal feeding, these herring resources will be used solely as human food.

Bathypelagic (midwater) fishes only now are being exploited to any marked degree, essentially only herring and hake. New sonar techniques permit detection of these fishes and the adjusting of depth and plane of operation of new midwater harvesting gear to coincide with the position of the fish schools.

These innovations have opened the great potentials of midwater fisheries to mankind. For example, it is anticipated that Pacific hake, a hitherto wholly latent midwater resource, alone eventually may sustain an annual harvest of about 500 million tons.

Fishes inhabiting the world's coral belt, and the bristlemouth and lantern fishes found in the "deep scattering layer," constitute totally untouched but enormous worldwide midwater resources. With the exception of the Pacific hake, we are largely discussing denizens of the open oceans and deep waters.

Special gear and techniques, to be developed through the ocean engineering program, will be necessary to aggregate and to harvest selectively these stocks economically. Ten years of intensive effort may see us on the threshold of commercial feasibility.

Estuarine fishes and shellfishes are those that, at some portion of their life histories, are found in shallow or brackish water. This class includes mollusks (oysters, mussels, and clams) of the tidal areas, lobsters, and the many species of shrimp.

Needless to say, these delicacies are in great demand and are being sought in all of the world's oceans. Such marine food resources are among those most amenable to artificial cultivation.

MANAGED RESOURCES

Recent developments in the "man-in-the-sea" concept—i.e., Sealab and similar programs—promise us the opportunity to explore, cultivate, harvest, and manage marine resources without disruption of the environment through employment of pressure-acclimated, trained divers operating from submerged pressurized habitats for relatively long periods of time. If current investigations are supported and expanded suitably, we might anticipate extensive commercial fish-culture operations by 1980.

Anadromous fishes are those marine fishes that return to fresh waters for spawning. Anadromous fishes, excepting such prized species as shad and salmon, are relatively unexploited in the United States. Five years hence, with development and marketing of fish-protein concentrate, a means of fully utilizing these fishes should be available.

The potential of fresh- and brackish-water fishes as sources of food has not been realized to any marked degree, except in a few isolated places where artificial pond culture is being practiced.

Productivity of areas, when properly managed, exceeds that of both the land and the ocean. Yields as high as 4,000 kilograms per acre-year have been realized.

UNLIMITED POTENTIAL

When we consider that fresh waters of the world include not only natural lakes, ponds, rivers, and artificially constructed waterways, but also river estuaries, closed lagoons, bays of the seas (brackish water areas), and paddy fields submerged from three to eight months per year, the potential contribution of these waters in terms of increased food for man is obvious.

The world's fresh and brackish water areas are estimated to cover about 12 billion acres. Cultivated rice fields alone total 240 million acres and represent an ideal opportunity for multiple-use of water through fish farming. A commonly accepted average fish-production figure for largely unmanaged freshwater areas is 216 kilograms per acre per year.

Using only these average production figures, annual potentials for fish production from just the 240 million acres of cultivated rice paddies can be estimated at 52 billion kilograms—demonstrating the contribution that freshwater areas could make to increasing supplies of food from the sea. In contrast to these potentials, during 1964 only 5.8 billion kilograms of fish were harvested from all the world's freshwater areas.

It is the consensus of marine biologists that the oceans can sustain an annual harvest of 250 million tons of fish. Others estimate that over twice this potential annual production is possible. For our purposes, it is enough to know that a "floor" for top annual production exists that exceeds present production by a factor of five.

Similarly, we are told that the three important, different trophic levels of commercial fish species bear a relationship to each other, in terms of relative mass of 1:10:100. Thus, the lowest trophic level above the planktonic—represented by anchovies, herrings, and herringlike fishes—contributes 100 times as much weight to the world biomass as the third-level carnivores—swordfishes, tunas, etc.

Accordingly, great increases in the world fish catch anticipated for the near future will be achieved largely through exploitation of fishes of lower trophic levels.

It is a grim irony and yet, paradoxically, a source of hope for the world that the greatest untapped abundances of coastal fish resources are in waters adjacent to those countries where protein malnutrition is found in its most extensive and intensive forms.

WHY ECONOMIC WASTE?

With such enormous untapped resources and the acknowledged world need for animal protein, why has the world not utilized these fishes now going to economic waste?

The reasons are many. Some are rooted in ignorance or in social or religious customs; others in governmental policies that favor dollar exchange and industrialization over agricultural and fisheries development and, in certain cases, in the lack of capital and skilled manpower.

Three major reasons, however, must be singled out for special mention:

1. Our utter lack of know-how as to means whereby the total of these resources may be harvested wisely, efficiently, and on a sustainable commercial basis.
2. Lack of suitable methods of preservation whereby, in developing countries, distribution of fish from coastal areas to relatively inaccessible inland regions might be accomplished satisfactorily.
3. Inability to guarantee the ultimate consumer a product that evidences the very best flavor, succulence, and general appetite appeal.

The first major problem—efficient harvesting—may well be solved through enormous interest in and support for oceanology, which has developed in recent years.

The second problem may be resolved through increased support for early and widespread industrial adoption of work now underway throughout the world, but particularly in the United States, on the development of the three basic forms of fish-protein concentrates.

Solution of the third problem awaits only the application of necessary scientific and engineering skills working within constraints of a commercial economy.

A NUCLEAR SUBMARINE TO FOLLOW THE FISH

From "Progress in 1964–65" at the Bureau of Commercial Fisheries Biological Laboratory, Honolulu, United States Department of the Interior:

On June 17, 1965, Secretary of the Interior Stewart L. Udall announced that a study sponsored by the Bureau of Commercial Fisheries shows that it is feasible to build a specially designed nuclear-powered submarine for fishery and oceanography research.

The study was conducted by Electric Boat Division of General Dynamics Corporation, Groton, Connecticut, the pioneer submarine designer and builder that developed the *Nautilus, Skipjack, George Washington,* and other submarines.

Much of the preliminary research on this project was conducted at the Honolulu Laboratory by Donald W. Strasburg. It has become increasingly apparent to the Laboratory that neither the tuna resource nor the oceanic environment can be fully understood on the basis of observations from surface vessels. A submarine would make a better platform for tuna research. The known behavior and distribution of tunas indicated that such a vehicle should have a 20-knot speed, a 1,000-foot operation depth, and a submerged endurance of six weeks. Provisions for direct viewing of fish, continuous environmental sampling, and quiet operation are also essential.

With these criteria, Electric Boat has made preliminary designs for a submarine that would be 163.5 feet long (a few feet longer than the *Townsend Cromwell,* a surface research vessel), have a maximum submerged speed of 20 knots, a surface speed of 11 knots, an operating depth of 1,000 feet. The craft would carry seven scientists in addition to the crew of twenty-four. The vehicle would be unique in almost all respects. There would be an 8-foot observation sphere in the bow with five windows for direct observation. The scientific laboratories would equal or excel those of surface craft. Equipment would include: water sampler capable of delivering fifteen water samples simultaneously, hull-mounted instruments for recording temperature, salinity, and depth; a continuous-transmission, frequency-modulated sonar; two inverted echo sounders. Seven television cameras would be mounted on the hull. In the stern laboratory would be placed a tube from which trawls, plankton nets, fishing lines, bottom samplers, and other instruments could be launched while the craft is submerged.

The object of the submarine is to place the scientist in the environment which he is studying. With it, he would be less dependent on weather (most oceanographic operations are necessarily conducted in equable climes, although the fish are less radically affected). The submarine could study such oceanic features as thermoclines, fronts, currents, turbulence, and waves, where precise control and the ability to hover or maneuver in three dimensions are needed to define the features of the environment or determine the relations among variables. A neutrally buoyant submarine could accompany a particular water mass and measure its changing physical and biological properties. There is little, in fact, in observational oceanography that the submarine could not undertake, and further uses will undoubtedly present themselves when the craft is available for operation.

NEXT? CITIES IN ROCK BENEATH THE SEA FLOOR

A NAVY scientist envisions one possible future development. By John R. McCabe in the November 25, 1966, *Rocketeer,* the newspaper of the Naval Ordnance Test Station, China Lake, California:

The Concept Calls for constructing spacious, self-supporting facilities *under* the bottom of the sea. The Rock Site concept is now being studied at the Naval Ordance Test Station, China Lake, California, under the leadership of Dr. Carl Austin, of the Research Department.

Dr. Austin explains that a Rock Site installation would consist of a room or series of rooms excavated within the bedrock beneath the sea floor, and points out that such installations have already existed for decades, established by the mining industry to reach offshore mineral deposits. He offers, to show the practicality of the Rock Site concept, the example of a long-established iron mining operation off the eastern coast of Canada, with 7 ½ square miles of permanent floor space beneath the sea floor. Connected by a main access tunnel to the land, it includes a complete machine shop among its facilities.

He points out that this method of inhabiting the bottom of the sea differs greatly in permanence and working environment from the two other major concepts. One of these, the saturation-diving technique, is being pursued in the Sealab studies. The other shares with Rock Site the goal of achieving a one-atmosphere working space in the deep sea, but calls for the use of bottom-sitting structures, either fully prefabricated or assembled on the bottom.

"An installation with several square miles of useful floor beneath eleven hundred feet of rock," says Dr. Austin, pointing to the example of the Canadian mine, "could be a major community with full family and recreational living facilities as comfortable as those in any city building.

"Located along the Mid-Atlantic Ridge or on selected seamounts (undersea plateaus) elsewhere, the potential for research from this type of site becomes large, since the site, though immobile, is also independent of surface weather conditions," he adds. . . .

The industrial implications of a successful Rock Site installation, he says, would be far-reaching and of great national importance by providing permanent petroleum drilling sites not only on the deep continental shelf but in areas beneath both intermittent and permanent ice cover. These same types of drilling sites could serve for the production of geothermal steam and brine, enabling in the near future the exploitation of deposits such as those now suspected in the floor of the Red Sea.

For hard-minerals productions, Rock Site installations would enable undersea mining to be conducted beneath a considerable depth of water and great distances offshore. By the use of observation towers plus scrapers and dewatering locks, Rock Site mining installations would enable the mining of sea-floor nodules and offshore placer deposits without the constant hazards of wind and wave damage in surface-ship-type operations.

Rock Site, he proposes, could convert any coastline to a deep-water port facility capable of handling petroleum products and mineral slurries to and from surface ships by means of hoses, with present technology; and if submersible cargo vessels eventually result, other, less easily transportable, cargoes could be handled as well.

Rock Site installations, according to Dr. Austin, would make ideal offshore nuclear-power-plant sites using convective seawater cooling, and could provide the working space and power needed for undersea booster pumping plants for pipeline systems paralleling a coastline.

Dr. Austin emphasizes that such undersea mining can be done using tools and techniques already in wide use by industry, including tunnel-boring machines. . . .

Comparisons with other sea-base methods bring out many advantages of the Rock Site concept, in Dr. Austin's reckoning. Comparing Rock Site with surface-base methods such as the use of barges and platforms, he says that:

1. Weather and waves are not a hazard.
2. All equipment is accessible to ordinary technicians and laborers.
3. The working volume or space can be expanded cheaply to meet future operational needs, once the original installation is made.
4. The Rock Site installations can be placed at great depth beneath the sea floor; their openings can be numerous and scattered; and access to the installation is absolutely controlled by the base occupants. If desired, reactor waste heat can be internally stored or dissipated into the earth by means of fluid injection into deep, permeable zones in order to prevent an undesirable heating of the surrounding water. With near the sea-floor installations, some heat will be needed to maintain a comfortable installation, since rocks near the sea floor will probably be at or near the deep-ocean temperature of only a degree or two centigrade.
5. Surface hazards such as accidental ship-caused damage and floating hazards are avoided.

With respect to bottom-squatting structures, he says, Rock Site installations show the following advantages:

1. Water mass "weather" is not a problem for Rock Site installations, but people working on the sea floor will have to contend with currents, shear on structures, and numerous other water "weather" problems.

2. The working volume is "thick-skinned," and can be quite large, avoiding the tendency for "thin-skinned" structures to suffer catastrophic flooding and high leakage rates given even minor structural damage. A leak developing through several hundred feet of rock can be grouted from within (injected with a cementing material) by means of drill holes; a leak developing through an inch or two of steel is apt to be hard to control, especially from inside.
3. Damage from accidental ship activities is far less.
4. All facilities and equipment except the outside of the lock-tube door are accessible at all times to ordinary technicians and laborers.
5. Damage from drift ice and ice-flow groundings is avoided.
6. Structures within the sea floor can easily be made large and comfortable enough to permit the quartering of crews and their families for extended periods of time, and can be made large enough to serve as supply and repair depots for large submersibles.

According to Dr. Austin's Rock Site studies, the undersea installations could be started from shore sites, as with present-day mining operations, or from ship-mounted drilling rigs. The ships could be either surface vessels or submersibles, he foresees.

Varying with the weather conditions or depths or other conditions found at a Rock Site location, entrance to installations isolated from the land could be accomplished in two ways, he proposes.

The site could be connected to a surface entrance hatch by an "air umbilical" tube, or locks mounted on the sea floor could be provided for submersibles, or both could be used. The air umbilical access tube could also be hinged at the sea floor, to swing downward, out of the way of storms and ice.

Dr. Austin points out that at present, the best examples of mine floodings and of mine operations within zones of high water pressures are to be found on land, with one of the most noteworthy under the desert in central Nevada. . . .

"Furthermore, the Rock Site concept competes with no existing Navy projects," he adds, "rather it complements many. In particular, Rock-Site-type installations can provide the working spaces from which saturated diving and submersible technology can be exploited to their fullest, freed at last from the problems of surface support and rough weather."

WHALE FARMS AND SEABED HOTELS

By Lee Edson in the winter, 1967, Petroleum Today, *Robert W. Stock, editor. Published by the American Petroleum Institute:*

Just the other day, after nerve-racking months of college interviews and admission forms, high-school senior Hank Wilson got the good news: Next fall he'll be a freshman at Deep Sea Institute, one of the nation's first sea-grant colleges.

Hank will major in aquaculture, with courses in algae raising, sea-animal husbandry, and fish herding, as well as mineral recovery, saltwater conversion, and sea-floor mining. In addition to his classroom sessions, he'll spend much of his time working at the institute's "ranch"—the campus on the sea bottom a mile offshore. He will arrive there by diving bell and shuttle between glass-bubble laboratories and experimental farms on a submarinelike sea train. He is looking forward to working summers at the underwater oil refinery nearby.

You don't know Hank Wilson—but he may turn out to be your grandson. At the moment his curriculum is entirely visionary, but its foundations are being laid by those in the forefront of today's revolution in oceanography.

It is one of the ironies of man's history that though the oceans cover 70 percent of the globe and contain 80 percent of the world's animal life, man has relatively little knowledge of their mysterious and hostile depths. In some ways he knows more about the moon.

Reasons for this ignorance are not difficult to find. Violent storms have made man an uneasy ocean visitor. When he has descended beneath the water's surface, he has discovered even more forbidding obstacles. Darkness has kept him virtually blindfolded; unbearable pressures and the limitations of his breathing apparatus have kept his underwater trips short and labored. And as if this were not enough, he has been assaulted by extreme cold and unfriendly sea denizens.

Yet if modern technology has put the moon within man's reach, why not the ocean depths? In years past the answer was simply that there was no pressing need to overcome the water barrier; land resources sufficed. Today, as civilization becomes increasingly complex, as population figures skyrocket, this is no longer true. To enjoy the comforts of the "good life," perhaps even just to live, man must turn to the ocean. One oil company executive puts it this way: "It is frustrating to think of impoverished people walking in the surf while the untapped wealth of the waters washes through their toes."

Perhaps the most important form of underwater wealth is food—and most particularly, protein, the nourishment in shortest supply in the world's developing nations. Man already hauls in from the sea 45 million tons of fish each year, but scientists believe this quantity could be increased fivefold without harming the overall supply. Seaweed is grown and eaten in some parts of Europe and Asia, but the ocean's immense supplies of vegetation (estimated at 4,000 tons per square mile) are virtually untapped.

Ocean plants and animals are also proving to be sources of exciting new medical discoveries. Marine pharmacologists have only begun their studies, yet they have already extracted from sea creatures chemicals that kill pain, inhibit the growth of tumors, fight viruses, and stimulate the heart.

The ocean has been described by one scientist as "a grandiose chemical plant." Within its borders substances are constantly being created, transported, transformed. The "wealth of the waters" includes a treasure trove of minerals.

There are millions of tons of silver, billions of tons of gold, valleys of diamonds. There are huge deposits of phosphorite, used in fertilizers, and of sulfur, also used in fertilizers as well as in tires and pesticides and explosives. There are literally "carpets" of minerals, including some areas where potato-sized nodules of manganese, a metal used in making steel, cover the ocean floor. There are untouched supplies of copper and uranium. There are great reservoirs of petroleum, barely scratched and yet already providing 16 percent of the free world's supply.

Offshore petroleum resources represent the most important current source of oceanic energy, but there are others. In some areas of the world, notably France, the tides are being harnessed to generate electricity. Elsewhere scientists are seeking to draw energy from the variations in temperature at different levels of the ocean. There are some who foresee the day when usable amounts of power may be obtained from the energy in the waves themselves. And there are scientists who envision the time when deuterium may be extracted from the ocean to produce incredible amounts of nuclear energy.

In the modern era the first man to seek to study the seas scientifically was Sir Charles Wyville Thomson, known as the Father of Oceanography. In 1872 he set sail on a four-year trip around the world [on the *Challenger; see* page 195], in the course of which he visited every ocean except the Arctic, studying currents, plumbing depths, dredging the ocean floor for marine flora and fauna.

But Sir Charles's equipment was crude. In recent years, thanks to advances in electronic and materials technology, man has obtained a firsthand look at hitherto hidden parts of the ocean, descending hundreds and even thousands of feet in elaborate diving bells and vessels. He has been able to move considerable distances through the depths and along the bottom and to apply electronic eyes and ears to probe farther and deeper into the ocean than ever before. He has gained a new understanding of the depths and a new appreciation of their wonders.

The section of the ocean adjacent to land is known as the continental shelf. It is an underwater continuation of the continent, dipping gradually toward an abrupt slope that leads to the deep ocean floor. The sun's rays penetrate to most parts of the shelf, making possible the photosynthesis necessary to plant life. When the sun sets and many of the large marine predators retreat to lower depths, smaller animals move toward the surface to partake of a plankton dinner. The wastes they leave are converted into chemical compounds that are used by tiny plants in the plankton population, thus completing the marvelous natural cycle of oceanic life.

The continental shelf may be a narrow strip or it may stretch out from the shore for 800 miles. Sometimes it is made up solely of gently sloping plains, but it may also be cut by canals or deep gorges, and it may consist of rolling hills or rugged granite mountains.

Out beyond the shelf stretches a seascape grander than anything on shore. There are globe-circling mountain chains taller than those on land and gorges that dwarf the Grand Canyon. Here, at depths between 2 and 4½ miles, all is darkness, and the frigid blackness is inhabited by eerie sea creatures that live under pressures no unprotected man could withstand.

The Swiss scientist Jacques Piccard and U.S. Navy Lieutenant Don Walsh hold the depth record; in 1960 the bathyscaphe *Trieste* descended to the bottom of the Marianas Trench, seven miles below the surface of the Pacific Ocean. But in the years since then most underwater exploration efforts have been conducted in shallower sites and have been devoted to learning how man can exist and work in the ocean environment.

One of the most dramatic and useful descents was accomplished in September, 1965, off the coast of La Jolla, California. Astronaut Scott Carpenter spent 29 days and 14 hours in and around the steel cylinder known as Sealab II at a depth of 205 feet. The experiment provided a dramatic insight into the difficulties and possibilities of underwater living.

Carpenter and the other Sealab explorers discovered that over a period of days their bodies became accustomed to the environment of the depths. They learned to adjust to the humid atmosphere of the submersible and to breathe the strange helium-oxygen mixture that sustained them. Even though headaches and ear infections were frequent—and on one occasion Carpenter was stung by a scorpion fish—the men returned safely from their long travail. They showed that man can perform many kinds of tasks on the sea bottom, from repairing a hull to using a suction gun to pick up substances from the sea floor. One of the heroes of the expedition was Tuffy, a trained porpoise, who carried safety lines to swimmers in simulated emergency situations.

Much of the research now going forward in oceanography is sponsored by the United States Government. There are programs to improve fish husbandry, particularly of shrimp (the top dollar United States seafood product) and menhaden (the largest fish product by volume). There are studies investigating the origin of icebergs and the mechanism of storms. Government scientists are pushing the construction of modern fishing and submersible craft. To understand the mysterious migrations of fish, they are studying the possibility of establishing grids of instrumented buoys that would transmit information about ocean temperatures to land-bound computers by way of communications satellites.

Perhaps the greatest concentration of government research efforts is in the military area, for the ocean depths may be the battleground of the future. This premise has given rise, for example, to programs to develop improved means of communicating and "seeing" underwater. A kind of natural built-in sonar enables dolphins to distinguish at a distance of five feet between two balls that differ in diameter by a quarter of an inch. The Navy is intensely interested in how the dolphin accomplishes this feat.

The Navy is also paying increasing attention to other kinds of oceanic phenomena. Submarines may be able to confound sonar detection by hiding behind the "deep scattering layer," the name given to a recently discovered cloud of sea life lying in the depths. The Navy is sponsoring studies to find out more about it. Navy scientists are also exploring the swift-moving underwater currents (comparable to the jet stream in the high atmosphere) which can affect undersea military movement.

But the bulk of the funds spent for ocean research and development today comes not from government but from industry. The potential for profit has provided a powerful incentive for companies to invest in underwater know-how.

Industrial efforts cover a wide gamut. Companies are busy developing materials and vessels that can withstand deep-sea pressures; one firm is experimenting with diving spheres made of glass, which, strangely enough, become stronger as the pressure increases. Other companies are seeking to make seafood products more palatable: Green algae exposed to fluorescent light lose their objectionable taste and can be ground into somewhat flavorful flour.

The leading industrial pioneer in oceanography, both in terms of experience and investment, is the oil industry. Petroleum research and development expenditures make up fully a third of the total spent each year by offshore industry. Since the first drilling rigs went to sea in the 1940's, oil companies have invested more than $3.5 billion in exploration for and development of petroleum resources—and less than half that sum has thus far been recovered. . . .

To encourage progress in exploring the ocean depths, the U.S. Congress has enacted legislation that will make possible increased government support of oceanographic research. Private industry would continue its traditional role of developing the sea's resources. Exactly what forms this progress will take is of course uncertain, but marine scientists have made some educated guesses.

They envision underwater communities where workers will live in floating glass bubbles or in domed homes attached to the sea floor. There will be vast farms where specially selected marine vegetation is cultivated and valuable sea animals, such as whales, are bred for market. (The animals will be penned in by recorded sounds of their natural enemies.) Farmers will learn their trade at sea-grant schools, comparable to the land-grant colleges that have played so important a role in modern agricultural development.

Minerals will not only be mined but also processed under water. Drilling for oil will be accomplished by means of a self-contained, watertight rig set on the ocean floor; and any oil produced will be processed in adjacent refineries-under-glass.

Scientists even picture a day when vacationers will move out from shorefront cottages to homes and hotels in the sea. There, in comfort and perfect safety, they will be able to view at firsthand the wonders of that watery world that so mystified and intrigued Hank Wilson's grandparents back in 1967.

INDEX

abyss, 14–15, 139, 140
abyssal hills, 140
  plains, size of, 139
acorn worm, giant, 225–227
  tracks, description of, 226
Acropolis, 180
Adak Canyon, 79
Adamo, Louis, 302
Adams, Rear Admiral K.T., 79
Agassiz, Louis, 164, 200
Aguadro, Lt. Comdr. Charles, 258
airlift, 44, 256
air-scrubbing, 44
Aku (Hawaiian for skipjack tuna), 216 ff.
Alaria (kelp), 205
Aleutian Islands, 78, 79
Aleutian Trench, 78, 79
Alexander the Great, 192
Alinat, Commandant Jean, 9
Aluminaut, 14, 63, 305
Alvin, 14, 63, 174
amberjacks, 34
American Association for the Advancement of Science, 226
American Fisheries Society, 151
American Geophysical Union, 114
American Museum of Natural History, 120, 170
American Petroleum Institute, 327
anchovy, 217, 317
Anderson, David, 209–213
Andrews, Roy Chapman, 170
angelfish, pygmy, 245–246
  description of, 245
animal(s), biggest in sea, 149–171
  newly found, 241–250
  oldest, *see Lingula, Neopilina*
  unknown, in sea, 215, 241–250
Anoplopoma fimbria (sablefish), 94
Antarctic, 117, 143, 221–225
  fish graveyard, 221–225
Antarctic Geological Facility, 117
aquaculture, 327–333
aqualung, 5–8, 12, 13, 19
aquanauts, 10, 41, 42, 44, 45
Aquarium Museum in The Flatts Village, Bermuda, The, 260
archaeology, undersea, 7, 63, 304
  undersea city, *see* Port Royal
Archimède, 14–15
arrow worms, 91
Ashbrook, Frank G., 165
Asherah, 63, 304, 305
Associated Press, 187, 310
ASW (Anti-Submarine Warfare) submarines, 281–285
Athens, 180
Atlantic Ocean basin, 179
Atlantis, legend of, 173–181
  lost, 124, 173–181
Atomic Energy Commission, 285
Atz, James W., 273
Austin, Dr. Carl, 323–327

Australia, *see* Great Barrier Reef
Azores, 140

Bacon, Sir Francis, 126
Baer, Dr. Ledolph, 302
Banawsky, A. J., 258
Barents Sea, 243
barnacle (s) , 193–194
  soup, 194
barracudas, 34, 212
Barth, Robert, 42
basalt, 132
Bascom, Willard, 156–160
Bastian, Dr. Jarvis, 109, 110
bathymetric maps, 78
Bathynomus doederleini (isopod) , 168
Bathynomus giganteus (isopod) , 168
bathyscaphe, 12, 14
  dive over 6 miles, 64–67
  see also Archimède; FNRS III; Trieste
Beagle, 197
Beckmann analyzer, 27, 29, 33
Beebe, William, 207–208
Bell, Lester, 261
Bender, Dr. James A., 223
bends, 9, 10
Bennett, J. G., 175
Bergensfjord, 292
Bermuda aquarium, 246
Bermuda Islands, 80–85
Biggerstaff, Mrs. Margaret, 186–188, 252
bioacoustics, 186
biological clock, 187, 188
bioluminescence, 92
Bishop Lighthouse, Isles of Scilly, 298
Blake Plateau, 239
Blakeslee, Alton L., 187
Boeing Company, 154–155
Bond, Capt. George F., 9, 10, 44
Bourne, Donald W., 225–227
Bowden, Ralph, 170
Bowdish, Harley, 155
Bowers Ridge, 78, 79
brachiopod, 248
breathing gas, *see* Helium
Breland, Osmund P., 165
bristlemouth, 317
British Petroleum Company, 53 ff.
brittle stars, 94, 96
Bronx Zoo, 207
Brosseau, Cecil, 277
Brown, Dan, 158
Brown, Dr. Frank A., 186–188
Bryozoa, 207–208
bubbles, oldest in world, 224
Buckley, 82
Buckner, Howard, 42
buildings on sea floor, 19 ff., 21–22, 40–45
  see also SPID
Bunton, Bill, 43, 44
buoy, monster, 307, 308
  recording, 15
  sponbuoy, 15
Bureau of Commercial Fisheries, 227, 236, 313
Bureau of Commercial Fisheries, Biological Laboratory, Honolulu, 189, 216 ff., 321
Bureau of Commercial Fisheries, Biological Laboratory, Woods Hole, 200
Bureau of Sport Fisheries and Wildlife, 236
Butler, Charles, 313–321
butterflies, 8 inches across, 210

cable, submarine, 76–77
Caltex Group, 53
Calypso, 7, 11, 19
camera, Calpyso-Phot, 35
  deep sea, 48
  Lamont, 247
  monster, 157, 158
  movie, 11, 95, 190
  underwater, 11, 72
cancer, bone, 204
Cannon, Berry, 42
canyons, undersea, 85–88, 137
Cape Hatteras, 70, 83, 85, 237–239
Cape of Good Hope, 74
caravel, 62
carbon-14, 71–72, 119, 120
  see also radiocarbon dating
Carcharodon carcharias, 169
Cardone, Vincent, 302
Carlisle, D. B., 243
Caroline Islands, 118–120
Carpenter, Comdr. M. Scott, 10, 40–43, 251, 331
Carr, Jerome B., 128–130
Carson, Rachel L., 89, 197, 204–205
Case, Phil, 245–246
Catalina Basin, 90
Catalina Island, 206

Centropyge argi, 246
cephalocarida, 242 ff.
cephalopod, 263
Cercopithecus callitrichus, 178
cetacean, 102, 103
Chain, 176
Challenger, 195–199, 199–201, 225, 227, 329
Challenger II, 198
Challenger Deep, 64, 65, 90
Challenger Expedition, 48, 195–199, 199–201, 225, 227, 329
Chang, Miss Ming Shun, 302
Chang, Randolph K. C., 192
Chapman, Sydney, 230
Charles H. Gilbert, 190, 192
chelonian, 167
Chelonibia, 193
cherub fish, *see* Angelfish, pygmy
Chicago Natural History Museum, 246
chitons, 248, 250
cirripeds, 193
cities in rock beneath sea floor, 323–327
city, sunken, Atlantis, 124, 173–181
  Port Royal, 254–259
civilization, sunken (Atlantis), 174–181
clam, giant, 169–170, 212
  5 or 6 feet long, 210
  grip of, 170
Clark, Tom, 42
Clarke, Dr. Robert, 162
clown fish 211–212
CO_2 scrubber, 26, 28, 29, 30
Coast and Geodetic Survey, 236
Coates, Christopher, 276
cobalt, 48, 51
Coffman, Billie, 41
Coggeshall, Charles, 43
college campus on bottom of sea, first, 21–22
Collins, W. L., 258
Colman, John S., 205
Columbia University, 74–77, 80–82, 114, 116, 136, 146, 201, 225 ff., 236, 246, 247, 249
Columbus, Christopher, 62
comb jellies, 91
Communications Research Institute, 108
compass points to South Pole, 115–116
Conda, Kenneth, 42
Congo River, 76–77
Conshelf I, 9
Conshelf II, 10
Conshelf III, 5, 10–11
Continental (oil company), 54
continental debris, 143
continental drift, 122–125, 126–127, 131, 133 ff., 147
continental shelf, 8, 11, 17, 19, 135, 209–210, 316, 330
  Argentine, 136
  importance of, 20–21, 41
  minerals, 8
  size, 8, 41
  widest, 135
continental slope, 12, 135
Cooper, Bryan, 52–59
copepods, 91
copper, 48, 51
coral, 197, 209–213
  Antarctic, 221, 223
  brain, 211
  colors, 211
  heads, 211
  polyp, 209–213
  on seamount, 74, 75
  reef, 141
  staghorn, 211
  table, 211
  see also Great Barrier Reef
coral-based islands, 141
cores, 44, 76, 88, 117, 145
  ice, 222 ff.
  importance of, 115
  sediment, 136
coring, 44, 145
  description of, 49
Cornell University, 120
"corners" of earth, 73
Corning Glass Works, 310, 311
Cornish, Edward, 62–63
Cornwall, Ira, 193–194
Coronula diadema, 194
Coronula reginae, 194
Cousteau, Jacques-Yves, 5–15, 18, 19, 20, 64, 274, 275
Cousteau, Simone, 18
Cowen, Robert C., 232–233
crab (s), 41
  fiddler, 186–188
  giant, 168
  noise of, 186
  spider, 166
  turn darker at low tide, 186–188

Craven, Dr. John, 44
Crawford, 239
Crete, 174 ff.
Crickett II, 161
Crompton, John, 166
Cromwell Current, description of, 231 ff.
Cromwell, Oliver, 254
Cromwell, Townsend, 231, 232
crust, of earth, 132, 133
new, under midocean ridges, 134
cubmarine, 21, 22
Curray, Dr. Joseph R., 118–120
Current, Cromwell, 230 ff.
current (s) , deep, 95, 96, 140
at depths, 230 ff., 332
fastest measured, 234
measurement of, 94–96
on sea floor, 95, 96
see also Gulf Stream
CURV (Cable-Controlled Underwater Research Vehicle) , 63

Dace, U.S.S. (ASW submarine) , 281–285
description of, 282
Darwin, Charles, 141, 197
dating, carbon-14, 71–72
ionium-uranium, 120
radiocarbon, 119, 136
Dean, Alfred, 167
Debenham, Frank, 221–223
Deck Decompression Chamber, 36
decompression, 8, 9, 20, 41, 111
Deep Cabin, 20
deep scattering layer, 86, 87, 89–93, 96, 318, 332
Deep Submergence Program, 281, 311 ff.
Deep Submergence Rescue Vehicle, 312, 313
Deepstar 4000, 5, 14
Dempsey, Dennis, 164
Dempsey, Joseph, 164
depth, gauge, correction of, 65
problems of, 328
recorder, 72, 75
Derringer, Don, 49, 50
desaturation, 36 ff.
Deuterostomata, 244
DGSS-555 Dolphin, 281
diamonds, offshore, 21, 63, 156
diatoms, 143
Dickson, Dr. Jim (Topside) , 23, 24, 30, 37, 39
Dietz, Dr. Robert S., 123–125, 131
Discovery II, 243
dive, deep excursion, 41, 43
longest deep, 10, 22–39
over six miles down, 330
saturation, 9, 10, 41, 323, 327
divers, deep, 8
diving saucer, 5, 10, 12, 18, 20, 64
description of, 11
Dolphin, DGSS-555, 281
dolphin (fish) , 193
Donaldson, John, 155
Dowling, George B., 42
Drach, Pierre, 7
Draper, L., 299–300
dredging, 145
rock, 145
drugs from sea, 204, 328
dugongs, 213
Duke University, 85, 86, 201, 236
Duke University Marine Laboratory, 70–72, 86, 239
D'Urville, Dumont, 298
Du Toit, A. L., 134

Earth, crust of, 132, 133
four "corners" of, 73
levels of, 132, 133, 138
polarity of, 115–117
shape of, 73
Earth sciences, 201
earthquakes, 137
Eastward, 71–72, 85, 86, 88, 239
Eaton, Wilbur, 41
Echo I, 82, 83, 85
Echo II, 82, 83, 85
echo sounder, 12, 79, 91, 145
Eckels, 73
Edgerton, Harold, 176
Edson, Lee, 327–333
eels, 235
moray, 274
Egstrom, Glen, 206
Eisenhower, Dwight D., 66
Elasipoda holothurbidea, 94
Eltanin, USNS, 117, 226
Eniwetok Atoll, 141–142
enteropneust, 225–227
erosion in oceans, 131
ESSA (Environmental Science Services Administration) , 78, 123, 236, 239

euphausids, 92
Ewing, John I., 81, 146
Ewing, Dr. Maurice, 75–76, 80–82, 130–148, 247, 273
Explorer, 79, 238, 239

Falco, Albert, 10
false bottom, 91
see also deep scattering layer
Farrell, W. T., 258
Fenton, George, 50, 51
Ferris, Capt. Noel P., 120
Fersten, Harvey, 161
fireflies, 210
fish, anadromous, 318
barnacles on, 194
farming, 21, 319
graveyard, Antarctic, 221–225
largest, 169
lateral line, 7, 150
noise, 184, 185, 191
smallest, 171
that walk on land, *see* mudskipper
Fish, Marie Poland, 184–186
fishing, deep sea, 8
predicted, 216 ff.
flatfish, over 6 miles down, 65–66
Flechsig, Arthur, 42
floodlights on bottom, 26, 67, 91, 92, 94
Florida Atlantic University, 21–22
Florida State University, 107, 116, 117, 247
flying fish, 50
foam, polyurethane, 43, 63
Food and Agriculture Organization, of the United Nations, 314
food, for men on bottom, 30, 35, 41
from sea, 313–321
Forbes, Edward, 197
forests, undersea, 204 ff.
Fort James, 257 ff.
Navy divers explore, 258
Fouqué, Ferdinand André, 177
French Undersea Research Center, 9, 11, 64

Gagnan, Emile, 5
Galanopoulos, Prof. A. G., 175–177, 180
Gaskell, Dr. T. F., 52–59
gas wells, offshore, 20
Great Britain, 52–59
Gaul, Albro, 275–276
General Dynamics, 286 ff., 304 ff., 307, 308, 321
geodesy, 73
geophysics, aim of, 131
George Washington, 290
Gerard, Robert D., 74, 75
Gigantocypris agassizi, 168
glass, 13, 310, 311
Glass, Bill, 114
Glassell, Alfred C., Jr., 167
globigerina ooze, 142
Glomar IV, 54
Gloucester Technology Laboratory, 314
goby (smallest fish in world) , 171
Gondwanaland, 123 ff.
Goodell, Dr. H. Grant, 116–117
Gooding, Reginald M., 192
Gow, Anthony J., 222–225
granite, 132
Gray, Capt. William B., 100–102, 245
Great Barrier Reef, 208–213
animals of, 210–213
colors, 211
size of, 209
Great Britain, 52–59, 196 ff.
grenadiers, 157
Griffin, Ted, 156
Grigg, Rick, 43
Grimble, Sir Arthur, 266–271
Gronbuki, Ivan, 292
grouper, 31, 32, 34, 35, 212
Grundy, Lt. C. D., 258
Guam, 138, 198
Gulf of California, 207–208
Gulf Oil, 54
Gulf Stream, 21, 71, 86, 229–239
course of, 237
current beneath, 235
eddies, 237
eels ride, 235
fastest current measured, 234
importance of, 233
meanders, 237
pulse, 233, 235
size of flow, 239
twists and bends, 235, 237
gulls, 213
guyots, 141

Haines, Bob, 51
hake, 317
Hardy, Sir Alister, 163, 230
Harnett, Charles, 252–253
Harvard University, 200
Hass, Hans, 7, 209

Hatteras, Cape, *see* Cape Hatteras
Hatteras Abyssal Plain, 86
Hatteras Submarine Canyon, 85–88
Hawaiian Islands, 140, 216–221
Hawley, Rear Adm. Jean A., 79
Hays, Dr. J. D., 116, 117
H-bomb, sunken, 63
heavenly bodies, collisions of, 114–116
Hedgpeth, Joel W., 199
Heezen, Bruce C., 175, 176, 225–227
Heindsmann, T. E., 154–155
helium breathing, 22, 23, 25, 44, 331
  voice distortion, 23, 32, 34
Hendrickson, George, 222, 225
Henifin, Lt. Comdr, E. E., 313
herring, 317
Hey, Glen, 42
Hodgson, Duncan M., 164
Holland, 287, 290, 304
Holston, John A., 313–321
Hopkins Biological Station of Stanford University, 200
Horizon, 49, 120
Horton, Ed, 158
Hosmer, Mrs. Jean, 302
hotels in sea, 333
Hubbs, Dr. Carl, 157
Huber, George, 272
humuhumunukunukuapuaa, 193
hydras, giant, 168
hydraulic hand, 11, 305
hydrography, 201
Hydro-Lab, 21–22
hydronauts, 311 ff.
hydrophone ear, 82

ice cores, 222 ff.
Idyll, C. P., 61, 168, 183, 230–232
Imbrie, Dr. John, 247–249
Ingalls Shipbuilding Division of Litton Industries, 282
Inoue, Tokujiro, 302
Institute for Oceanography (ESSA), 78, 236
Institute of Marine Resources of the University of California, 51
instruments, oceanographic, 198
internal waves, 95, 122
International Game Fish Association, 167
iodine, 204
ionium-uranium dating, 120
iron, 48, 51
Isaacs, John, 157, 158, 159
isopods, deep sea, 168
  giant, 168
isothermic suit, 27
Iszak, Dr. Imre, 73
Ivanov, Prof. A. V., 243–244

James, Dr. Richard W., 301
Japan, fishing fleet, 220
jellyfish, giant, 164–165
  over 6 miles down, 67
Jenkins, Wally, 42, 43
jewel fish, 31
Johler, Fred, 42
Johns Hopkins University Applied Physics Laboratory, 72–73
Johnson, Lyndon B., 249–250

kangaroo fish, 212
Karo, Rear Admiral H. Arnold, 83
Keller, Hannes, 8
Kellogg, Dr. W. N., 107, 108
kelp, 204–208
  animals in, 205, 207, 208
  elk, 206
  giant, 204–207
  horsetail, 205
  importance of, 204
  on seamount, 74
Kelvin Seamount group, 141
Kennedy, John F., 279
Kewalo facility, 189
kingfish, 212
Kitching, J. A., 205
Kitty Hawk, U.S.S., 279
Klingel, G. C., 272, 273
Knauss, Dr. John A., 65, 231, 232
Knight, Brooks, 249–250
krill, 163
Kyma, 239

laboratory, first seaside, 200
LaFond, Dr. Eugene, 90–96
laminarias, 204, 205
Lamont Geological Observatory, 74, 80–82, 114, 116, 127–128, 130, 201, 225 ff., 236, 247
land, formation of, 210, 211
Landrin, Armand, 166
Lane, Frank W., 162, 275
Lang, Dr. Thomas G., 105
lantern fish, 318

Laurasia, 123
Leningrad University, 243
Lerner Marine Laboratory, Bimini, Bahamas, 236
levels, two most common earth, 132, 133, 138
Libby, Willard F., 119
life, in depths, 197 ff.
on sea bottom, 14, 31
light, beneath sea (natural), 6, 8, 26, 34
stiletto, 20
lighthouses, 298, 299
Lilly, Dr. John C., 108–109
lime, on seamount, 74
Lindbergh, Anne Morrow, 22
Lindbergh, Charles A., 22
Lindbergh, Jon, 10, 22–39
Lingula, 248
Link, Edwin A., 9, 23, 24, 29, 32, 35, 225, 256, 259, 303
Link, Marion Clayton, 23, 255, 256, 259
Litton Industries, 282
living in sea, 5, 9–11, 17–45, 333
lobsters, 318
Lockheed Aircraft Company, 312
Lockheed-California Company, 301, 302
Long, Capt. E. John, 130, 199–201
Loring, E., 178
Los Angeles, movement toward San Francisco, 125
lutite (red clay), 143
Lyman, Dr. John, 65
Lyons, John, 43

McCabe, John R., 323–327
McDade, Matt C., 233
McDonald, Admiral, Chief of Naval Operations, 45
MacGinitie, George E., 274
MacGinitie, Nellie, 274
McLean, William B., 311
McMurdo Sound, 221
mackerel, king, 34
Spanish, 212
Magdalena river, 76
Magnuson, John J., 189, 192
Magnuson, Senator Warren G., 3, 69
mahimahi, 193
manatees, 213
barnacles on, 194
manganese, 48, 51
dioxide, 51
see also nodules
Man-in-the-Sea experiment, 40–45, 111, 318
manned undersea stations, 11, 19
manta ray, 166
mantle of earth, 132
Marggraff, Lt. (J.G.) Frederick C., 296
Marianas Trench, 6, 14, 64–67, 90, 138, 198, 330
Maribo II, 155
Marine Biological Association of San Diego, 200
Marine Biological Association of United Kingdom, 200
Marine Biological Laboratory of Woods Hole, 200
Marine Biology Facility, Naval Missile Center, Point Mugu, California, 109–110
marine geology, 130–148
aim of, 131–132
Marineland, St. Augustine, Florida, 203, 271
Mariner IV photos, 125
Mark-48 torpedo, 281
Marlin, 167, 169
Marr, John C., 220–221
Marshall Islands, 118, 120
Massachusetts Institute of Technology, 236, 285
Maury, Matthew Fontaine, 229
Mavor, J. W., Jr., 174–181
Maxwell, Walter, 167
measurement of currents, 94–96
mechanical arm, 11, 305
medusa, 91
Meeka, Bill, 43
Meisky, Lavern, 43
Mellis, 175
Melson, Captain L. B., 45
menhaden, 331
Menzies, Dr. Robert J., 71, 72, 86–88, 247
Miami Sequarium, 100–101, 244–246
Michelangelo, 300–301
microcontinents, missing, 122–125
microtektites, 114–115
Mid-Atlantic Ridge, 179, 324
Midlam, Mrs. Diana, 118
mid-ocean ridges, 138, 142
Military Sea Transporation Service, 117

Milne-Edwards Trench, 247
Mindanao Trench, 138, 198
minerals, 8, 47–52, 329
mining, sample, 44
  undersea, 324
Minoan civilization, 175 ff.
Minots Ledge, Massachusetts, Lighthouse, 299
Mistichthys luzonnensis, 171
mollusks, 318
monkey, fossil, 178
Monoplacophora, 250
monsters, ocean, 149–171
Morgan, Gov. Henry, 255
moths, 210
mountain range (s), submerged, 78
  undersea, 12
mountain ridges, undersea, 77
mountains, rocks of, from sea, 133
  undersea, 77–79
Mowbray, Louis, 246
mudskipper, 212
Murray Canyon, 79
Murray, Sir John, 195
Murry, Earl, 42
Museum of Comparative Zoology at Harvard, 200
Museum of Natural History, Smithsonian Institution, 167
mysteries, 113–148

Nahant, 23, 25, 26, 31, 38
Naples, seaside laboratory, 200
narcosis, nitrogen, 8, 33
Nares, George, 198
National Geographic Society, 64, 140, 235, 256, 281
National Institute of Oceanography of Great Britain, 299
National Science Foundation, 65, 116, 117, 120, 150, 221 ff.
Nautilus, 287
Naval Oceanographic Office, 84, 236, 301, 302
Naval Ordnance Test Station, China Lake, 100, 311, 323
Naval Ordnance Test Station, Pasadena, 105
Naval submarines, 279–290
Naval Weapons Plant, 65
Navy Electronics Laboratory, 43, 64, 90, 91
  oceanographic research tower, 91, 95
Navy Hydrographic Office, 235
Navy Mine Defense Laboratory, 42
Navy Missile Center, Point Mugu, 43
Navy's Deep Submergence Program, 281, 311 ff.
Navy's Man-in-the-Sea Program, 40–45, 111, 318
nehu, 217
nenue (fish), 193
Nenue (raft), 192, 193
Neopilina, 246–250
  description of, 247–248, 250
  first seen, 249
Neopilina galathea, 250
New York Aquarium at Coney Island, 273, 276
New York University, 236, 239, 301, 302
New York Zoological Society, 207
Newhouse, Lt. Edgar L., III, 81–82
Newman, Murray, 277
Newman, Dr. William A., 120
Newton, John G., 86–87
Newton, Dr. Robert R., 73
Nichols, Haven, 78
nickel, 48, 51
Ninkovich, 175
Nitze, Paul H., 45
noddies, 213
nodules, manganese, 21, 48, 51, 142, 324
  amount of, 51
  value of, 52
Norris, Dr. Kenneth S., 105, 108, 272–275
North Sea, 52–59
Northwestern University, 186–187
Nowell, C. E., 258
NR-1, 281
nuclear power stations on sea floor, 324

ocean, area of, 314
  basin, 137
  data station, 307, 308
  floor of, 147
  future of, 303–333
Ocean Science and Engineering, Inc., 156
Ocean Systems, Inc., 22
Ocean Weather Ships, 299–300
Oceanauts, 11, 15, 17–21
  first, 10
Oceaneer, 156–160

oceanography, history of, 196–201
oceanology, 201
octopus, 266–270, 271–277
  intelligence of, 276–277
  monster, 276
  size of, 210, 272
  suckers, 275
  uses tool, 275–276
Octopus vulgaris, 272
Office Français de Recherches Sous-marines, 9, 11, 64
Office of Naval Research, 105, 151, 154, 184, 226, 236, 307, 308
oil, offshore, 7, 20, 52, 63
oil industry, 332
O'Keefe, 73
ophiuroids (brittle stars) , 94
ostracod, giant, 168
oysters, 188

P & O Lines, 209
Pace, Earl, 155
Pacific Marine Station, California, 199
pangaea, 123
Parker, Dr. Bruce, 206–7
parrot fish, 212
Pathfinder, 79
Peck, D. E., 258
Peila, Mario, 155
Peirce, 239
Pelagophycus giganteus, 206
pelicans, 213
Penikese Island, 200
Perry, John H., Jr., 17, 21
Perry, Richard B., 78
Perry Submarine Builders, Inc., 21, 22
Peterson, Mendel, 254–259, 260
petrels, 213
Petrovich, G. V., 286
Philippine Islands, 138, 198
Philippine Trench, 14
photography, underwater, 7, 34–35, 145
phytoplankton, 92
Piccard, Jacques, 64–67, 90, 330
Pierson, Dr. Willard, Jr., 301–302
Pilkey, Dr. Orrin, 71–72
Pillars of Hercules, 178
Pioneer, 79
plains, sea bottom, 12–13, 139
  size of, 13
plankton, 14, 33, 34, 41, 91
Plato, 174 ff.
Platylepas, 194
Pleistocene glaciation, 136
Pogonophora, 241–244
  description of, 242–244
Point Defiance Aquarium, Tacoma, Washington, 277
polarity of earth, 115–117
polyp, coral, 209–213
porpoise, 40, 43, 97–112, 153, 155, 194, 331
  attack sharks, 104
  barnacles on, 194
  brain of, 109
  food of, 101
  hydrodynamics, 95, 105, 111
  language, 100, 105, 109, 110
  mother's treatment of dead baby, 102
  noise of, 186
  save human lives, 104
  sonar, 99, 105, 107, 108, 111, 331–332
  speed of, 106, 107
  white, 100
  withstand pressure, 110–111
Port Royal, Jamaica, 253–259
Port Sudan, 19
Poulianos, Professor, 178
Powell, Bill, 100
pressure, water, 25, 66, 67, 283

Raborn, Vice Adm. William Francis, Jr., 286
radiocarbon dating, 119, 136
radiolarians, 143
radio telephone, 11
Ramapo, 292–299, 300
"rapture of the deep," 8
ratfish, 165
ray, manta, 166
Reaves, John, 42
Rechnitzer, Dr. Andreas B., 67
Reef, Great Barrier, 210 ff.
reefs, table, 141
Reference File of Biological Sounds, 184–185
Revelle, Roger, 230
Reynolds International, 305
Rhineodon typus, 169
Ridgway, Dr. Sam H., 40, 98–100
Riedel, Bill, 49, 51
Ripley, Robert, 209
Rivero, Dr. Luis Howell, 162
Rockefeller public service award, 311
Rock Site, 323–327

Rosaldo, 19
Rosenblatt, Dick, 158
Ross, Wally, 43
Rougemont, Louis de, 213
Rowland, Robert, 222, 225
Royal Society, 198
rudder fish, 193
Ruzic, Neil P., 313

sablefish, 94, 157
salmon, 227, 318.
salvage at great depth, 43, 63
"Samfrau" geosyncline, 134
San Andreas Fault, 125
San Clemente Islands, 206
San Diego Trough, 90
San Francisco, 125
Sanders, Dr. H., 242
Santa Cruz Island, 206
sardinellas, 19
sardines, 31, 33, 34
Sargasso Sea, 233, 234
  hot water tank for Europe, 234
satellites, 15, 72, 73, 82, 83, 85, 125
  to measure waves, 301–302
saturation diving, 9, 10, 41, 323, 327
sauries, 50
Schmid, Dr. Hellmut, 83
Schmitt, Waldo L., 193–194
scorpion fish, 331
Scott Expedition, second, 221
Scripps family, 200
Scripps Canyon, 41, 43, 44
Scripps' Hydraulic Facility, 121
Scripps Institution for Biological Research, 200
Scripps Institution of Oceanography, 7, 40, 42, 43, 48, 49, 65, 118, 120, 158, 200, 230, 231, 232
scuba, 7, 8, 91, 206
sea, around islands, 120–122
  beasts, 160–171
  bottom, brown and gray mud, 93
    diatomaceous ooze, 64–65, 67
    grayish, 24
    snuff-colored ooze, 64
  inconstancy of, 95
  level, changes in, 118–120, 135
  monster, 156–160
  spring in the, 6
  tracks on bottom of, 225–227
  working beneath the, 5, 20, 41 ff.
sea anemone, 211, 212
sea cows, noise of, 186
sea cucumbers, 94, 96
Sea Diver, 9, 25, 38, 256
sea eagles, 213
Sea Gem, 53, 54, 57
Sea Hunter, 22
sea lions, noise of, 186
Sea of Okhotsk, 243
sea pens, giant, 168
sea slugs, 212
sea snakes, 194, 210, 212
"sea snow," 90, 92
sea urchins, 168, 212
seabed hotels, 327–333
Seal, elephant, 165
Sealab, 323
Sealab I, 10, 18
Sealab II, 10, 18, 40–45, 111, 331
Sealab III, 111
seamount group, 140
seamounts, 74–76, 77–79, 140, 324
Seaver, Don, 70–72, 85–88
Seckel, Gunter, 218
Sediment (s) , 14, 76, 77, 133, 139, 142, 144–147
  distributions, 146
  importance of, 144
  pelagic, 142
  terrigenous, 142, 144
  thickness, 146–147
Sedimentation, rate of, 144–145
seeing underwater. 6
seismic-refraction, 145
Seismological Society of America, 128
sergeant fish, 212
shad, 318
shark (s) , 101, 149, 150–153
  basking, 169
  detect sounds, 150–153
  ears, 153
  food of, 151
  Greenland, 157–158
  hammerhead, 159
  lateral line, 153
  tiger, 26, 167
  whale, 169, 170, 171
  white, 161–162, 167, 169
shear pattern, 129 ff.
Sheats, Robert, 43, 44
Shell/Esso Group, 53
shellfish, clamlike, 222, 223
Shepard, Dr. Francis P., 120

shrimp, 31, 33, 34, 92, 318
noise, 186
over 6 miles down, 67
top dollar U.S. seafood product, 331
Signal (oil company), 54
siliceous ooze, 143
silverfish, thousands of, 32
siphonophores, 91
Skidmore, J. D., 42
Smith, Al, 49
Smithsonian Astrophysical Observatory, 73
Smithsonian Institution, 164, 254, 256
snails, 248
snakes, sea, *see* sea snakes
Snider, A., 134
SOFAR (Sound Fixing and Ranging), 80–82
Sollas, W. J., 144
sonar, 66, 70, 72, 75, 85, 87, 191, 192, 282, 284, 317, 332
porpoise, *see* porpoise, sonar
sonar operator, problems of, 155
Sonnenburg, Lt. Robert, 41, 43
Sound channels, undersea, 79–82
sound waves, 146
South Africa, 74
Spanish treasure fleet, 252–253, 253–259
Sperry Piedmont Company, 312
Sperry Rand Research Center, 128, 129
SPID (Submersible Portable Inflatable Dwelling), 24, 26, 27, 34, 37
Spilhaus, Athelstan, 64
sponbuoy, 15
sponges, 31
glass, 221, 223
Springer, Stuart, 246
Sputnik, 73
squid, 50
giant, 162–163, 262–266, 276
SSBN (Submarine Ballistic Nuclear), 287
Stanford University, 200
Star II, 305
Star III, 305
starfish, 212, 274
a foot across, 210
Starfish House, 20
steel, high-grade, 13
Hy-80, 288, 305
Stenuit, Robert, 9, 10, 22–39
Stephan, Capt. Charles R., 22
Stewart, Dr. Harris B., Jr., 48–52, 236 ff.
Stock, Robert W., 327
Stolephorus purpureus, 217
Stomatolepas, 194
Stommel, Henry, 234, 235
Stormy Petrel, 239
Straits of Florida, 253
Straits of Gibraltar, 178
Strasburg, Donald W., 321
Stranghan, Robert P. L., 170–171
sturgeon, 169
submarine, aluminum, 305
base on sea floor, 18, 20
deep-diving, 5, 11–15, 17, 61–63
officers and men trained, 311 ff.
future, 281
glass, 310–311
life in, 289
midget, 11, 62–63
naval, 279–290
nuclear, 281–285, 287, 290
to follow the fish, 321 ff.
oceanographic, 191–192
oceanographic, 15
Polaris missile, 286–290
parts of, 287
research, 191–192, 304–306, 394 ff.
rescue, 63
trains, 64
U.S. Navy's first, 287, 304
U.S. Navy's first Polaris, 290
see also Dace, U.S.S.; George Washington; Nautilus; Will Rogers
"submarine jungles," 204
Submarine Squadron Three, 311 ff.
Submarine Support Facility, Ballast Point, San Diego, 311 ff.
submobiles, 64
Subroc (Submarine Rocket), 285
sulphur, offshore, 21
superbathyscaphe, 14–15
supercontinent, 122 ff.
Surveyor, 79
swordfish, 317

table reefs, 141
Tarawa, Gilbert Islands, 266
Taylor, Lt. Comdr. Eugene, 83
Teague, Jim, 102–112
tektites, 114–115
telephone, 20, 66
radio, 11

television, 20, 23, 31, 91, 94
terns, 213
teutologist, 271
Texas A. & M. University, 40, 99, 201
Thera, 174 ff.
Thomas, Ray, 153–156
Thomson, Sir Charles Wyville, 198, 329
Thule, 157
Tick, Dr. Leo J., 302
Tidal Institute (England), 201
Tillamook Rock Lighthouse, 299
tin, 63
titanium, 13
Tolbert, William, Jr., 42
Tonga Trench, 14
Total (oil company), 54
Townsend Cromwell, 191, 322
tracks on bottom of sea, 225–227
treasure, sunken, 63, 251–259
Treasure, Tucker, 260
trenches, 13, 14, 132, 137
  area of, 14
  deep, connected with earth's mountain-building, 137
  location of, 14
trevally, 212
Trident, 239
Trieste, 6, 13, 14, 15, 64–67, 90, 92, 93, 94, 95, 96, 330
Trieste II, 312–313
trigger fish, 193
Tubicinella major (rarest of whale barnacles), 194
Tucker, Teddy, 260
Tuckfield, Cyril, 41
tuna, 188–191, 212, 231, 317
  bigeye, 220
  bluefin, 164, 169
  skipjack, 190, 191, 216–221
  speed of, 189–191
  yellowfin, 190, 191, 220
turbidity currents, 76–77, 87, 137, 139, 144
turtle, hawksbill, 212
  leathery (leatherback), 167–168
  loggerhead, 212
  sea, barnacles on, 193, 194
turtle-riding as sport, 212–213
Tweedie, M. W. F., 168
twilight zone, 8, 11

Uchida, Richard N., 217
Udall, Stewart L., 321
Uffen, R. J., 116
undersea canyons, 85–88, 137
  forests, 204
U.S. Antarctic Research Program, 117, 221 ff.
U.S. Army Cold Regions Research and Engineering Laboratory, 223
U.S. Coast and Geodetic Survey, 48, 78, 79, 83, 84, 85, 235, 236, 238, 239
U.S. Coast Guard, 236, 239
U.S. Fish and Wildlife Service, 231
U.S. Geological Survey, 120
U.S. Naval Academy, 285
U.S. Naval Institute, 130
U.S. Naval Missile Center, Point Mugu, 98 ff.
University of California at Los Angeles, 206, 272, 274, 275
University of California, San Diego, 118, 120
University of Cambridge, 225 ff.
University of Miami, 150–153, 201, 236, 239
University of Miami's Institute of Marine Sciences, 151
University of Miami Marine Laboratory, 201, 235
University of Pennsylvania Museum, 63, 304
University of Rhode Island, 184, 236, 239
University of Washington, 200
upwelling of deep water, 143
"Ur continent," 134

Van Dorn, Dr. William G., 120–122
Vancouver Public Aquarium, Canada, 272, 273, 274, 277
Vema, 74, 76, 80–81, 136, 144, 226, 247–249
Vening Meinesz, F. A., 129, 135
Verne, Jules, 19, 173, 262–266
Vitiaz, 243
volcanoes, undersea, 12, 137, 140
Vosburgh, Frederick G., 282

Walford, Lionel A., 113, 215
Walsh, Comdr. John A., 282 ff.
Walsh, Lt. Don, 64–67, 90, 330
Waters, Rear Adm. Odale D. (Muddy), Jr., 47, 261

Watkins, Dr. Norman D., 116–117
wave (s) , 290–302
  caused by wind, 301
  highest measured by instruments, 299–300
  highest seen, 292 ff.
  112 feet high, 296
  satellites to measure, 301–302
  67 feet high, 296
Weather Bureau, 236
weather forecast from ocean, 306 ff.
Weather Reporter, 299–300
weather station, underwater, 42
Weeks, W. F., 225
Wegener, Alfred, 126–127, 132, 134
Wells, John Morgan, 43
Wells, Paul, 43
Wesly, Claude, 10
wet suit, 27
Weyer, Edward M., 164
Whale (s) , barnacles on, 193–194
  blue, 163–164
    description of, 163
    heart of, 164
  farms, 327–333
  killer, 101, 153–156
  Namu, 153–156
  noise of, 185, 186
  talk, 153–156
Whitemarsh, Lt. Comdr. R.P., 292–299
Wilcove, Raymond, 236–239
Wilkie, Don, 158
Will Rogers, 290
Wilson, Capt. Dan, 22–23, 29
winds, 294
Winton, Alec, 158
Wisby, Dr. Warren J., 151–153
Wood, F. G., Jr., 271, 272, 274, 276
Wood, Jane, 244–246
Woods Hole Fisheries Station, 200
Woods Hole Oceanographic Institution, 7, 81, 174, 176, 187, 200, 226, 234, 235, 236, 239, 242, 299
Woods, Dr. Loren, 246
working beneath sea, 5, 20, 41 ff.
Workman, Dr., 37
worm tubes, 93, 96
worms, 31, 197
  oligochaete, 205
  polychaete, 205
  Spirorbis, 208
Worzel, Dr. J. Lamar, 247

Yale University, 120, 201
Yuen, Heeny S. H., 190

Zaca, 208
Zarudski, E. F. K., 176
Zenkevitch, Prof. L., 242–244
zooplankton, 91

Date Due

SEP 27 1973	
APR 25 1974	
FEB 17 1975	
APR 1 1980 HAHA	
APR 29 1983	
MAR 31 1987	

Soule, Gardner Soule
Under the Sea;